D080827 3

सारा

Paris

london.

Neef 2015-2016.

Fahrie matrielle

de la

En journal

Les plus jolies
fautes de français
de nos grands écrivains

Anne Boquel & Étienne Kern

Les plus jolies
fautes de français
de nos grands écrivains

PAYOT

Retrouvez l'ensemble des parutions
des Éditions Payot & Rivages sur

payot-rivages.fr

© Éditions Payot & Rivages, Paris, 2015.

Pour Anne et Pierre

Prologue

En juin 1857, les rares amateurs de poésie à s'être procuré, pour la somme de trois francs, un nouveau recueil signé par un auteur à peu près inconnu pouvaient découvrir ces lignes en ouverture du volume :

AU POÈTE IMPECCABLE
AU PARFAIT MAGICIEN ÈS LANGUE FRANÇAISE
À MON TRÈS-CHER ET TRÈS-VÉNÉRÉ
MAÎTRE ET AMI
THÉOPHILE GAUTIER
AVEC LES SENTIMENTS
DE LA PLUS PROFONDE HUMILITÉ
JE DÉDIE
CES FLEURS MALADIVES
C. B.

Vous aurez sans doute, amis lecteurs, reconnu la dédicace des *Fleurs du Mal*, ainsi que les initiales de Charles Baudelaire. Mais vous n'aurez peut-être pas remarqué la faute de langue dissimulée dans ces quelques mots. Relisez, relisez bien. Les tirets qui suivent l'adverbe « très », peut-être ? Non pas, ils étaient de mise à l'époque. C'est plus haut, au tout début, que se cache la faute en question : « *ès langue française* ». Résultat d'une contraction entre « en » et « les », la préposition « ès » ne peut s'employer qu'avec un terme au pluriel…

Baudelaire ne s'est rendu compte de son erreur qu'en recevant les volumes imprimés ; quand on connaît son amour de la perfection, on imagine sans peine son désespoir. Il n'eut finalement d'autre choix, face à la catastrophe, que de corriger à la main les exemplaires qu'il distribuait autour de lui, en remplaçant « *ès langue française* » par « ès langues françaises », avant d'opter, lors de la réédition de l'œuvre en 1861, pour un plus satisfaisant « ès lettres françaises ».

On ne sait rien, hélas, de la réaction de Théophile Gautier. Mais on ne risque pas grand-chose à supposer que la bévue de son jeune confrère a dû le faire sourire. Gide l'a écrit : « Les fautes des autres, c'est toujours réjouissant. » La formule n'est pas très charitable, il est

10

vrai, mais elle n'en est pas moins juste : qui n'a jamais éprouvé de l'amusement en découvrant dans un imprimé quelconque – livre, journal, écrit officiel – l'une ou l'autre de ces « grossissimes fautes de français » que Baudelaire lui-même ne se privait pas de pointer chez les autres ? Il existe un comique orthographique comme il est au théâtre un comique de gestes ou de situation.

N'allons pas croire, pourtant, que le ressort de ce comique d'un genre particulier soit la mesquinerie, la malveillance ou l'orgueil. Le rire, on le sait depuis Freud, naît de l'angoisse. Et quoi de plus angoissant, pour l'ancien écolier qui sommeille en chacun de nous, que les règles innombrables, implacables, absurdes parfois, qui régissent notre langue ? Une ligne à écrire, un mot à rédiger, quelques phrases à rendre publiques, et les voici, tapies en embuscade, qui nous considèrent d'un œil mauvais : fautera ? fautera pas ? Si les « fautes des autres » suscitent le rire, c'est toujours un rire double : joie d'avoir su repérer l'erreur, et conscience secrète que nous aurions pu la faire.

Conjurer ce vieux démon, dédramatiser le faux pas et fournir, au passage, une occasion plaisante d'aiguiser sa grammaire : tels sont les objectifs de ce petit livre. Apprenez donc, amis lecteurs, que la faute de français est la chose du monde la mieux partagée. Pour vous en convaincre, nous sommes allés glaner, dans les lettres, les manuscrits et les chefs-d'œuvre de nos grands écrivains, quelques-uns des plus beaux, des plus énormes, des plus irrésistibles méfaits commis contre la syntaxe et l'orthographe – ou plutôt, pour écrire comme Stendhal, contre « l'*ortographe* ».

Pour autant, ce florilège n'a rien d'iconoclaste. Il voudrait, tout au contraire, faire partager l'émotion qu'on ressent à pénétrer dans l'atelier de l'écrivain, là où les mots se forgent, se choisissent, se raturent ; faire comprendre les affres de l'homme ou de la femme qui lutte contre la langue ; faire entendre, derrière le crissement de la plume, un cœur qui bat. En un mot, il n'a d'autre but que celui-ci : que les amoureux des lettres redoublent d'admiration pour les écrivains qui leur sont chers.

Car, disons-le tout net, il est des cas, plus nombreux qu'on ne pense, où la faute est admirable. Elle l'est – même grossière, même injustifiable – comme la faiblesse d'un héros dont on sait qu'il fait route vers de nouveaux exploits ; elle l'est, surtout, parce que nul ne saurait dire où s'arrête la faute – par rapport à quelle norme ? – et où commence le style. C'est peut-être bien, pour reprendre une formule que l'on prête à Montherlant, « à l'audace de leurs fautes de grammaire que l'on reconnaît les grands écrivains ».

Nota bene – Ce n'est qu'au XIXᵉ siècle que se fixe l'orthographe française telle que nous la connaissons. Nous n'avons pas tenu compte, ici, des graphies qui passeraient aujourd'hui pour d'épouvantables fautes d'orthographe mais qui relèvent en réalité de l'état de la langue à une époque donnée *(hazard, j'avois, long-tems…)*.

Règle n° 1
Commencer
par le commencement

Nathalie Sarraute est encore une petite fille quand elle entreprend de suivre la voie maternelle : devenir romancière. Dans son autobiographie, Enfance, *elle raconte comment elle s'est lancée, dès son plus jeune âge, dans la rédaction d'un roman. Voici que sa mère, recevant au salon un « monsieur », la prie avec insistance de montrer ses premiers travaux au visiteur. La fillette obéissante monte dans sa chambre et va chercher un cahier recouvert de toile cirée noire. Le monsieur feuillette le précieux manuscrit, d'un air d'abord étonné, puis mécontent, et rend une sentence définitive : « Avant de se mettre à écrire un roman, il faut apprendre l'orthographe… »*

La faute d'orthographe est le péché originel qui fait naître l'amoureux des lettres à sa future condition. Adam et Ève pèchent contre le Créateur ; l'écrivain

en herbe contre les lois du langage : à la première faute,
c'en est fini du paradis de l'enfance où cohabitaient
délicieusement le son et le sens. L'étendue de la malé-
diction se découvre : il ne suffit pas d'écrire, il faut
écrire juste.

Mais le fruit défendu conserve un charme
irrésistible...

Gustave Flaubert n'a, paraît-il, appris à lire qu'à l'âge de neuf ans. Il faut supposer qu'il a fait des progrès rapides, car il n'a pas encore dix ans quand il prend sa plus belle plume pour proposer une collaboration littéraire à un camarade de classe : « Cher Ernest, je te prie de me répondre et me dire si tu veux *nous associer* pour écrire des *histoire*, je t'en prie *dit-moi le, parceque ci* tu veux bien nous associer je *t'enveirai* des *cathiers* que j'ai commencé à écrire, et je te *prirait* de me les renvoyer, si tu veux écrire *quelques* chose dedans tu me *fras* beaucoup de *plaisirs*. [...] Je ne t'en écris pas plus long j'ai du devoir qui me presse. Je finis de t'écrire en *t'en brassant*. » (Lettre à Ernest Chevalier)

Jean-Paul Sartre évoque, dans *Les Mots*, sa première expérience de l'orthographe. Âgé de neuf ou dix ans, il vient d'entrer en classe de huitième au lycée Montaigne. Sa première dictée est si désespérante qu'on convoque en urgence son grand-père, éminent professeur d'allemand. De retour au foyer, le patriarche excédé jette sur la table une copie où s'étale, surchargée de ratures, cette phrase : « *Le lapen çovache ême le ten.* » Colère homérique du vieil homme, tandis que sa fille, la mère du garçon, ne peut réprimer un fou rire. Quelque temps plus tard, la famille inscrit Sartre dans un autre lycée.

À qui trouverait l'anecdote trop belle pour être vraie, on peut fournir, comme gage d'authenticité, ce billet adressé par le petit Jean-Paul à un célèbre dramaturge : « Cher Monsieur Courteline, Grand-père m'a dit qu'on vous a donné une grande décoration cela me *fai* bien plaisir *quart* je *rit* bien en lisant *Théodore* [...]. Votre futur ami. »

Proust avait précédé Sartre et suivi Flaubert sur le chemin qui mène les jeunes enfants à la rédaction d'épîtres incertaines ; le voici qui, âgé de sept ans, s'adresse à son grand-père : « Pardonne moi de mon péché car j'ai *moin* mangé qu'*a* l'ordinaire j'ai pleuré pendant un *cardeur apré* cela *j'étais* en *senglot*. » (Lettre à Nathé Weil)

« Racontez les tribulations d'un chapeau haut de forme » : tel est le sujet auquel l'abbé Launay, professeur au Mans, soumet en 1914 sa classe de collégiens. Parmi eux, Antoine de Saint-Exupéry, quatorze ans. Le futur aviateur imagine que le chapeau en question passe de main en main avant de finir sa carrière en Afrique. Dans la copie, c'est le couvre-chef qui parle : « Je *naquit* dans une grande usine de *chapeaus*. [...] Pendant plusieurs jours, je *subit* toutes sortes de supplices : on me découpait, on me tendait, on me vernissait. Enfin un soir je fus envoyé avec mes frères chez le plus grand *chapellier* de Paris. [...] J'écris ces lignes sur le déclin de mes jours ; *esperant* qu'elles parviendront aux *français*, je leur *dit* que [...] j'*espere* bien *etre venere* à titre de relique pour avoir orné le *crane* de mon illustre possesseur Bam-Boum II roi du Niger. »

La rédaction récolta un 12/20, assorti de ce commentaire : « Bien. Trop de fautes d'ortho-graphe. Style parfois lourd. »

« Mon frère, il faut bien que je t'écrive aussi, car il faut avouer que j'ai été bien *parraisseux*. » Charles Baudelaire a onze ans quand il envoie ces mots à son frère Alphonse. Il était en effet bien temps de se mettre au travail !

Règle n° 2
Ne pas se fier
à la prononciation

Alexandre Dumas s'enorgueillissait d'avoir à son service une cuisinière capable d'écrire son prénom sans la moindre lettre juste — prénommée Sophie, elle signait « Çaufy ». Voilà qui, comme Flaubert aurait pu le dire, était « hénaurme » ! Mais qui jettera la pierre à « Çaufy » ? Pourquoi diable le son {o}, pour ne prendre que cet exemple, se note-t-il parfois comme dans « halo », parfois comme dans « chaud », sans même parler de « château », de « pot » ou de « tantôt » ?

Tout est là : au fondement de la faute d'orthographe, il y a le fossé entre l'écriture et la prononciation. De ce divorce, les écrivains sont, comme nous tous, les victimes. Ils n'ont pas les excuses de la touchante cuisinière, mais nul ne saurait les blâmer de s'être mépris sur l'orthographe de certains mots. Peut-être même faut-il leur en savoir gré : bien des manuscrits

*ont de quoi faire rosir de plaisir et de soulagement tout
lecteur un tant soit peu complexé par les difficultés de
notre langue.*

La pauvre Sophie était née trop tard dans un
monde trop vieux ; un siècle plus tôt, à une
époque où l'orthographe était encore très libre,
nul ne se serait étonné de la manière dont elle
signait. En tout cas, Voltaire n'aurait pas eu
de leçons à lui donner : il écrit fréquemment
« *filosofie* » ou « *relligion* », et quand il évoque
son meilleur ennemi, Rousseau, il lui arrive de
parler de « l'*orloger* de Genève ». Dans une lettre
du 24 décembre 1757, adressée à un certain
Bernard, on lit ces mots savoureux : « Mon cher
philosofe […], je m'imagine que le *termomètre*
de votre *apartement* est comme le mien, tout près
de l'eau bouillante. »

❧

S'il en est un qui risque de bouillir, c'est bien
le maître d'école qui aurait dans sa classe les
auteurs des phrases suivantes :

Cette timidité qui *fesait* mon malheur diminue.
(Baudelaire, lettre à sa mère)

Je ne suis *décendu* du Janicule que lorsque la légère brume du soir est venue… (Stendhal, manuscrit de *Vie de Henry Brulard*)

Trois ans *plutard*, elle était sourde ; et elle parlait très haut, même à l'église. (Flaubert, manuscrit d'*Un cœur simple*)

· Enfin je vais connaître les environs de Vienne et on va remanger de la *saussisse*. (Céline, lettre à Cillie Ambor)

Parmi les spécialités de Céline, il y avait aussi l'omission des accents – ses manuscrits n'en comportent que fort peu. Il s'agit bien sûr d'inadvertances, mais il vaut mieux être écrivain que collégien pour se les permettre : « L'amour c'est l'infini mis *a* la portée des caniches », écrit le romancier dans le texte original du *Voyage au bout de la nuit*.

La pratique des cartes postales ne date pas d'hier. En 1917, Cocteau envoie ces mots à Apollinaire : « Pense *a* vous couché sur le sable. »

※

Des accents, Paul Éluard aurait plutôt tendance à trop en mettre, comme dans cette lettre
à Gala : « Depuis que je suis revenu, je me levais
à 4 heures de l'après-midi. *Çà* m'a fait du bien. »
Il confond ici le pronom démonstratif « ça » et
l'adverbe de lieu « çà ».

※

L'apostrophe, encore plus discrète que
l'accent, est, elle aussi, bien souvent négligée
par les écrivains pressés. L'absence de ce petit
trait de plume entraîne parfois des effets saisis-
sants : « Je t'ai dit cela pour que tu ne *tétonnes*
plus quand je refuse de t'entendre faire des
projets pour moi. » (Sand, manuscrit du
Marquis de Villemer)

※

Du reste, George Sand l'affirme dans *Histoire
de ma vie*, elle n'a jamais su l'orthographe. À son
fils Maurice, qu'elle essaie de convaincre d'aller
visiter un musée, elle écrit joliment : « Il y a une

quantité de belles statues, que tu reconnaîtrais à présent que tu comprends un peu la *mithologie*. » Mais on ne peut qu'être frappé de l'humilité avec laquelle, déjà sexagénaire, elle noircit deux pages d'un carnet conservé à la Bibliothèque nationale de France :

Fautes que je fais :
egrèner *{sic}* non égrainer
termes bornes, limites
thermes bains
exorbitant non exhorbitant
baraque non barraque
carrosse non carosse
dorlotter non dorelotter etc.

Elle savait qu'on n'a jamais fini d'apprendre.

Hemingway l'a dit, Paris est une fête. C'est peut-être la raison de l'incroyable lapsus orthographique de Jules Verne, dans cette lettre où il décrit à ses parents la situation dans la capitale après le coup d'État de 1851 : « Les maisons sont criblées de *bal* ! »

Jules Verne était, du reste, le premier à s'amuser de son étourderie : « Grand Dieu ! j'ai laissé échapper une faute d'orthographe dans ma dernière lettre ; je suis perdu pour l'Académie ! » (Lettre à Jules Claretie)

❦

C'est encore une belle confusion que commet Claudel dans cette didascalie qui pose le décor de l'une des scènes de son chef-d'œuvre : « Le soir. Toute une caravane prête à partir. Mules, bagages, armes, chevaux *scellés*, etc. » (manuscrit du *Soulier de satin*)

❦

Guillaume Apollinaire disait : « Je classe les gens en trois catégories. Ceux qui écrivent Apollinaire avec deux p et un l. Ceux qui l'écrivent avec un p et un l. Ceux qui l'écrivent avec deux p et deux l. » À vous de ranger dans la catégorie qui convient les auteurs des phrases suivantes :

Dans dix ans, j'aurai la plus belle *clientelle* de Paris. (Balzac, *Un début dans la vie*)

Ma *cravatte* violette, celle de l'oncle Lucien, [...] a fait une violente impression... (Giraudoux, lettre à ses parents)

J'ai été *constament* occupé par des amours malheureuses. (Stendhal, *Vie de Henry Brulard*)

Baudelaire, lui, a la prudence de botter en touche. « Faut-il écrire fourmilière ou *fourmillière* ? » Telle est la question qu'il se pose sur un jeu d'épreuves des *Fleurs du Mal*, en marge de ces deux vers du « Crépuscule du soir » :

La Prostitution s'allume dans les rues ;
Comme une fourmilière elle ouvre ses issues

Les lecteurs du *Rouge et le Noir* se souviennent que l'ambitieux Julien Sorel devient le secrétaire de monsieur de La Mole. À peine engagé, il se voit confier de menus travaux d'écriture :

Une heure après, le marquis entra, regarda les copies et remarqua avec étonnement que Julien écrivait cela avec deux ll, cella. [...] Le marquis, fort découragé, lui dit avec douceur :

— Vous n'êtes pas sûr de votre orthographe ?

S'il y en a un qui n'était pas sûr de son orthographe, c'était bien Stendhal. Lorsque, tout jeune homme, il occupait un poste de secrétaire au ministère de la Guerre, il fallait faire relire ses lettres. Avec « *cella* », c'est même l'une de ses propres fautes qu'il prête à son personnage !

Fils d'instituteur, Alain-Fournier était fort sourcilleux en matière d'orthographe. En 1911, alors que sa sœur et son beau-frère, Isabelle et Jacques Rivière, viennent de lui donner des nouvelles de leur bébé, il pointe une faute dans leur lettre et répond avec humour : « Et à ce propos je rappelle à Jacques Rivière que les verbes en eler et en eter doublent la consonne finale lorsqu'elle est suivie d'un e muet (téter : elle *tette {sic}*). (Un jeune professeur non marié, mais dont la situation ne laisse pas d'être intéressante, donnerait leçons de français, etc., etc.). »

Le sel de cette histoire est qu'Alain-Fournier se trompe et qu'il convient bel et bien d'écrire « elle tète » !

Règle n° 3
Accorder l'adjectif

On ne lit plus guère, de nos jours, l'ouvrage qui a rendu Balzac célèbre en son temps : Physiologie du mariage. *C'est un livre fort plaisant, mais quelque peu déroutant, à l'image de son interminable sous-titre :* Méditations de philosophie éclectique sur le bonheur et le malheur conjugal. *À sa parution, en 1829, on crie au scandale. Un critique plus féroce que les autres fait remarquer que Balzac ne porte pas seulement atteinte à la morale, mais aussi à la grammaire : « Il eût fallu mettre : conjugaux puisque l'épithète qualificative se rapporte également au bonheur et au malheur des gens mariés. Mais qu'est-ce qu'un solécisme de plus ou de moins pour M. de Balzac ? »*

Il est vrai que, pour sa défense, Balzac aurait pu répondre qu'il restait fidèle à un principe hérité

29

du latin et bien attesté dans la littérature classique : la « règle de proximité » voulait que, quand l'adjectif se rapporte à plusieurs noms, il s'accorde avec le plus proche. Racine pouvait, dans *Athalie*, écrire ces deux vers en toute sérénité :

> Surtout j'ai cru devoir aux larmes, aux prières
> Consacrer ces trois jours et ces trois nuits *entières*.

Mais l'argument n'aurait sûrement pas suffi à apaiser le sourcilleux critique : au XIXe siècle, cette règle était depuis longtemps tombée en désuétude. Du reste, en fait de négligences, Balzac n'en est pas à son coup d'essai, et il récidivera en 1833 dans *Le Médecin de campagne* : « *Telles* étaient la décoration et le mobilier de cette pauvre demeure. »

Les manuscrits de Proust sont une source infinie d'émerveillements. Les brouillons du premier livre de *La Recherche* réservent plusieurs surprises aux curieux : *primo*, la « madeleine de Proust » a d'abord été une biscotte ; *secundo*, le romancier faisait, comme tout le monde, des fautes d'accord. Voici deux passages qu'on ne trouvera plus, du moins sous cette forme, dans le texte définitif :

> Que le goût d'une biscotte *trempé* dans du thé le fasse seulement tressaillir en nous, nous sentons au plaisir qui nous inonde comme le passé réel [...] diffère de celui que l'intelligence nous rappelait froidement.
>
> Mais ce plaisir mystérieux est là ce charme qui nous rend *indifférent* les motifs utilitaires que nous aurions d'y renoncer.

❧

Quand il se rapporte à des formules comme « le plus » ou « le moins », l'adjectif « possible » demeure invariable. Jean Giono écrit pourtant : « Il voulait lui donner le plus de choses *possibles*. » *(Le Moulin de Pologne)*

❧

Les méandres de la versification font parfois une victime : la règle de l'accord. Dans l'édition originale des *Fleurs du Mal* (1857), on peut lire :

Ma pauvre muse, hélas ! qu'as-tu donc ce matin ?
Tes yeux creux sont peuplés de visions nocturnes,

Et je vois tour à tour *réfléchis* sur ton teint
La folie et l'horreur, froides et taciturnes.

(« La Muse malade »)

« Folie » et « horreur » étant féminins, il faudrait, en bonne logique, que l'adjectif attribut du complément d'objet direct soit « réfléchies ». Mais Baudelaire pouvait plaider non coupable, car la graphie qu'il adopte, pour être grammaticalement aberrante, se justifie selon les lois de la prosodie et relève à ce titre de la licence poétique : en vertu de principes forgés à la Renaissance, les puristes estiment que, dans le décompte des syllabes, il faut prendre en considération jusqu'aux « e » qui ne se prononcent pas. En clair, le féminin « réfléchies » a beau ne pas se distinguer, à l'oreille, de « réfléchis », il aurait compté pour quatre syllabes, et le bel alexandrin aurait été dénaturé. Quoi qu'il en soit, Baudelaire n'était pas satisfait de cette entorse à la grammaire ; dans une réédition des *Fleurs du Mal*, il propose une variante plus prudente :

Et je vois tour à tour s'étaler sur ton teint
La folie et l'horreur, froides et taciturnes.

Alors qu'il prend quelques notes sur son prochain roman – *Germinal* – dans un carnet de travail, Zola se montre bien distrait : « C'est la scène où les Grégoire se trouvent en face des *ouvrier*, de l'émeute. Leurs sensations, la logique qui les conduit. Et ce qu'ils penseront ensuite. C'est une scène *capital*, dont le contrecoup se trouve à la fin. » Actionnaires et ouvriers ont sans doute éveillé chez l'écrivain l'idée du « capital » !

Mais, dès qu'il s'agit d'accorder l'adjectif à un nom, encore faut-il savoir si ce dernier est masculin ou féminin ! « Effluve », par exemple, est invariablement donné pour masculin par les dictionnaires. On trouve pourtant « les *futures* effluves du sang » chez Chateaubriand, ou encore, dans un poème de Verlaine :

> D'ailleurs, le salut
> Viendra d'un Messie
> Dont tu ne sens plus
> Depuis bien des lieues
> Les effluves *bleues*
> Sous tes bras perclus.

Et que faire des noms qui ont deux genres ? Certains d'entre eux, comme « après-midi », sont conciliants : nous sommes libres de les considérer comme masculins ou féminins. Mais « délice » et « amour », masculins au singulier, changent de genre au pluriel : en toute rigueur, « le grand amour » s'oppose aux « amours mortes ». Balzac s'y perd ; tout en évoquant dans *La Femme de trente ans* « des amours *morts-nés* » (double faute, il faudrait « mort-nées »), il écrit ces lignes – magnifiques – à Ève Hanska : « Saurez-vous seulement combien il m'a fallu de force pour vous écrire ceci, sans vous rien dire qui vous peignît la vivacité de *cette unique amour, conservée* comme mon seul trésor, ma seule espérance ? »

Règle n° 4
Accorder le déterminant

Dans ses Souvenirs littéraires, *Maxime Du Camp évoque en ces termes les longues heures passées à corriger* L'Éducation sentimentale *avec son ami Gustave Flaubert : « Il avait beau regimber, s'irriter, {…} me traiter de pion et de grammairien détraqué, il s'attendrissait, avait les larmes aux yeux et éclatait de rire quand je lui disais : "Au nom de ta gloire, respecte la règle des possessifs !" »*

Et s'il n'y avait que les possessifs ! Les déterminants – définis, indéfinis, démonstratifs, interrogatifs… – sont aussi nombreux que difficiles à manipuler.

« Chaque », déterminant indéfini, ne s'emploie normalement qu'au singulier. On trouve pourtant chez Lamartine : « Et qui des sons discords que *rendent chaques* sens » *(La Mort*

35

de Socrate). On note dans le même temps une faute d'accord du verbe.

« Tout » n'est pas commode. Dans des expressions comme « à toute heure » ou « tous les hommes », nous avons affaire à un déterminant qui, à ce titre, s'accorde avec le nom. Mais quand, pour simplifier, « tout » a un sens proche de « pleinement », c'est un adverbe : « ils sont tout heureux ». Dans le manuscrit de *Lorenzaccio*, Musset fait dire à l'un de ses personnages : « mes entrailles sont *toutes* émues », ce qui signifie, littéralement, que la totalité de ses entrailles sont émues. Le texte définitif corrige cette inadvertance en tournant le passage différemment : « mes entrailles sont émues trop vivement ».

Mais attention, l'adverbe « tout » n'est pas toujours invariable ! Il s'accorde devant un mot féminin commençant par une consonne (« elle est toute contente »), ce que Balzac oublie lorsqu'il écrit, dans *Eugénie Grandet* : « Mon neveu le président, pour lui éviter les tracas d'une affaire *tout* judiciaire, lui offre de partir sur-le-champ pour Paris afin de transiger avec les créanciers et les satisfaire convenablement. »

Le cas particulier de l'accord du déterminant numéral a de quoi donner des sueurs froides. D'une manière générale, à l'exception de « un » (« on n'a qu'une vie »), le numéral cardinal ne s'accorde pas avec le nom auquel il se rapporte : « trente », par exemple, s'écrira toujours de la même manière. Mais les choses se corsent avec « vingt » et « cent ». Lorsqu'ils appartiennent à une forme complexe, ils demeurent invariables si le nombre procède par addition (« vingt-trois », « cent quatre ») ; s'ils sont précédés par un multiplicateur, ils prennent un « s » quand – et seulement quand – ils constituent le dernier élément du déterminant. On écrira donc « quatre-vingts » ou « huit cents » (mais « quatre-vingt-trois » ou « huit cent deux »). À ces difficultés s'ajoute l'usage du trait d'union quand le nombre est inférieur à cent et qu'il n'y a pas de « et ». Arthur Rimbaud s'y perd un peu. En 1887, à une époque où il a déjà renoncé à la poésie pour se faire marchand d'armes, il écrit : « Ma chère maman, j'ai reçu les cinq *cent franc* au Consulat au Caire. Je vous remercie bien […]. »

❧

Quelques années plus tôt, dans le manuscrit de « Villes » *(Illuminations)*, Rimbaud mettait un « s » là où il n'en fallait pas, et *vice versa* : « Quelques divans de velours rouge : on sert des boissons polaires dont le prix varie de huit *cent* à huit mille roupies. […] Le faubourg aussi élégant qu'une belle rue de Paris est favorisé d'un air de lumière. L'élément démocratique compte *quelques cents* âmes. »

❧

On remarquera, dans l'exemple précédent, que le poète confond le déterminant « quelque » (qui s'accorde, comme dans « quelques personnes ») avec l'adverbe, qui est invariable et signifie « environ ». Il est vrai que « quelque » est redoutable. Dans *Zazie dans le métro*, Queneau commet la faute inverse : « Elle se déplaçait le long du mur avec la plus grande aisance et n'avait plus qu'un petit saut de trois mètres et *quelque* pour terminer son itinéraire. » Dans ce cas-là, il convient d'écrire « et quelques » : il ne s'agit pas de l'adverbe, mais bel et bien du déterminant, employé ici avec un substantif sous-entendu (« et quelques centimètres »).

Deux tournures servant à exprimer la concession sont souvent confondues : « quelque… que » et « quel… que ». Dans le premier cas, l'élément détaché est un adverbe et demeure invariable (« quelque anciens que soient ces bâtiments ») ; dans le second cas, nous sommes confrontés à un déterminant interrogatif en fonction d'attribut qui, en tant que tel, doit s'accorder avec le sujet (« quelle que soit ta taille »). Baudelaire se trompe dans cette lettre adressée à sa mère : « *Quelque* soit la destinée qui s'empare de moi, si, après avoir préparé la liste de mes dettes, je disparaissais brusquement, si tu vivais encore, il faudrait faire quelque chose pour soulager cette vieille beauté transformée en infirme. »

George Sand ne s'est pas trompée de forme, quant à elle, mais elle a oublié l'accord, dans cette touchante lettre qu'elle envoie à son amie Zoé Leroy : « J'aime à penser qu'il y a beaucoup de rapport dans notre manière de sentir, *quel* que soit la différence extérieure de nos humeurs et de nos caractères. »

Quand on emploie une formule comme « espèce de », il convient d'accorder le déterminant au féminin, quel que soit le genre du nom introduit par la préposition « de ». On dira donc « cette [et non *cet*] espèce d'énergumène ». L'erreur, très courante, se trouve chez Aragon : « Adrien couchait avec la femme d'un des plus farouches francs-maçons de la ville, le marchand de meubles Reboul, *un* espèce de colosse noir, à moustaches [...]. » *(Les Beaux Quartiers)*

Règle n° 5
Accorder le verbe

Nos ancêtres ne connaissaient pas leur chance : au XVIIe siècle, les règles de l'accord du verbe étaient beaucoup plus souples que de nos jours. C'était un héritage de la syntaxe latine. Rien n'empêchait, par exemple, de maintenir un verbe au singulier après une énumération, et nul n'aurait blâmé Corneille d'avoir écrit dans Polyeucte : « Sa bonté, son pouvoir, sa justice est immense. » C'est au cours du XVIIIe siècle que se sont fixés les grands principes qui nous sont familiers. Mais, pour être élémentaires, ces derniers sont souvent mis à mal !

« Nous t'affirmons, méthode ! Nous n'oublions pas que tu *a* glorifié hier chacun de nos âges. » (Rimbaud, manuscrit de « Matinée d'ivresse », *Les Illuminations*)

41

« Une dernière fois je vide mon esprit de toute autre chose, je le mets en face du souvenir du goût de la biscotte, et je sens tressaillir tout au fond de moi quelque chose qui se déplace et *voudrais* monter jusqu'à ma conscience. » (Proust, brouillon de *Du côté de chez Swann*)

Dans cette lettre à Gaston Gallimard, Proust oublie que le sujet du verbe est un groupe nominal pluriel : « Si les proportions un peu vastes qu'a prises la *Recherche du Temps perdu* vous *donnait* quelque regret d'en avoir entrepris la publication, ne craignez pas de me froisser ni de me nuire. » Que les « proportions un peu vastes » de *La Recherche* n'aient pas mérité un pluriel, voilà qui est particulièrement savoureux !

« Ta pension de retraite, et le peu que j'ai, en mon nom, nous *suffira*. » (Balzac, *La Cousine Bette*)

🐌

« Allons adieu, vous une de mes consolations secrètes, vous vers qui *vole* mon âme et ma pensée. » (Balzac, lettre à Mme Hanska)

C'est l'un des plus célèbres poèmes de Victor Hugo : dans « Le Mendiant » *(Les Contemplations)*, le poète ouvre sa porte à un pauvre homme, l'invite à venir se sécher au coin du feu et médite en regardant son manteau troué « qui semblait un ciel noir étoilé ». Aveuglé sans doute par l'éclat des étoiles, Hugo ne s'avise pas qu'il commet une faute d'accord :

Et, pendant qu'il séchait ce haillon désolé
D'où *ruisselait* la pluie et l'eau des fondrières,
Je songeais que cet homme était plein de prières […]

Dans les vers qui suivent, Lamartine va plus loin, puisque la faute d'accord se double d'un étonnant flottement syntaxique :

Un jeune montagnard, près d'une jeune fille,
Sur la même racine *étaient assis tous deux.* (*Jocelyn*)

De la même manière, Maupassant, peut-être piégé par l'inversion du sujet, fait comme si ce dernier était au pluriel : « Nous allions nous mettre à table devant le grand feu de la haute cheminée où *rôtissaient* un râble de lièvre flanqué de deux perdrix qui sentaient bon. » (« Un Réveillon », *Mademoiselle Fifi*)

Il arrive souvent que l'auteur se souvienne des derniers mots écrits plutôt que du sujet exprimé : « Il passait pour être un bon administrateur, il fut souvent question de le nommer

maire d'Alençon ; mais le souvenir de ses tripo-
tages dans les gouvernements républicains lui
nuisirent, il ne fut jamais reçu à la Préfecture. »
(Balzac, *La Vieille Fille*)

❧

« Ma chère mère, une de tes dernières lettres
contenaient des promesses et des offres que pour
rien au monde je n'accepterais. » (Baudelaire,
lettre à sa mère)

❧

Dans le manuscrit d'*Aurélien*, Aragon a écrit :
« L'entrée de ces gens l'*avaient* mis à la porte. »
Dans le texte publié, on lit finalement :
« L'entrée de ces gens l'avait mis à la rue. »

❧

Quand le pronom relatif « qui » est sujet, le
verbe se met au même nombre et à la même personne que l'antécédent du pronom ; il convient
ainsi de dire « toi qui es » et non « toi qui *est* ».

On lit pourtant dans une lettre de Baudelaire à sa mère : « C'est toi qui *occupe* ma pensée, toujours, toute la journée. »

« J'ai bien du mal, avec mes différents emplois en plus de ma littérature. Je dois tout mener de front. C'est infernal. Souvent j'en ai assez. Mais il faut. Ma mère qui vieillit. Ma fille qui grandit… Et moi qui ne *rajeunit* pas. » (Céline, lettre à Cillie Ambor)

« C'est en son absence que la mère a acheté la concession. Terrible aventure, mais pour nous les enfants qui *restaient*, moins terrible que n'aurait été la présence de l'assassin des enfants de la nuit, de la nuit du chasseur. » (Duras, *L'Amant*)

Redouter en particulier l'accord du participe

S'il est une pièce qu'on devrait jouer plus souvent dans les théâtres et les établissements scolaires, c'est bien La Grammaire *d'Eugène Labiche (1867). Ce vaudeville savoureux a pour héros un gros bourgeois campagnard, Caboussat. Ce dernier, fort considéré dans sa région, rêve d'ascension sociale. Hélas, un obstacle se dresse devant son ambition : « Je ne sais pas l'orthographe ! Les participes surtout, on ne sait par quel bout les prendre... Tantôt ils s'accordent, tantôt ils ne s'accordent pas... quels fichus caractères ! »*

Caboussat n'est pas le seul à faire les frais de la mauvaise humeur des participes...

C'est une loi intangible : le participe passé employé avec l'auxiliaire « être » s'accorde en genre et en nombre avec le sujet. Baudelaire l'oublie le temps d'une lettre : « Il y a quelques jours, Malassis me dit que Jeanne est *venu* le prier de lui acheter des livres. »

Si pareilles inattentions sont rares, de nombreux écrivains sont en délicatesse avec l'accord du participe passé conjugué avec « avoir ». Rappelons qu'il se fait avec le complément d'objet direct si ce dernier est placé avant le verbe – et seulement avant, n'en déplaise à Rimbaud, qui écrit à sa famille : « Il me semble que j'avais *postée* dernièrement une lettre pour vous. »

« Les angoisses que tu as *eu*, mon Ève, je les ai bien cruellement ressenties, car ta lettre m'arrive seulement aujourd'hui. » (Balzac, lettre à Mme Hanska)

« Quels petits malheurs n'avaient pas *causé* les femmes ce jour-là ! » (Giraudoux, *Siegfried et le Limousin*)

On lit dans « Gaieté » *(Petits Châteaux de Bohême)* de Nerval :

Tu me guéris pendant l'été
De la soif qu'un vin plus vanté
M'avait *laissé* depuis la veille […]

Mais Nerval a l'excuse de la prosodie, comme dans l'exemple de Baudelaire cité plus haut : avec « laissée », le vers aurait compté neuf syllabes, contre huit pour les autres.

Licence poétique ou inadvertance ? Toujours est-il que, dans les premières éditions d'*Alcools*, on trouve, à deux pages d'intervalle, deux fautes d'accord, corrigées depuis. Dans « Les Cloches », Apollinaire écrit :

Toutes les cloches à la ronde
Nous ont *vu* du haut des clochers
Et le disent à tout le monde.

Dans le poème suivant, « La Loreley », la sorcière s'exprime ainsi :

Je suis lasse de vivre et mes yeux sont maudits
Ceux qui m'ont *regardé* évêque en ont péri.

🐦

La règle se complique encore un peu dans le cas de la proposition infinitive. Lorsque le participe passé conjugué avec « avoir » est suivi d'un infinitif, il s'accorde avec le complément d'objet direct antéposé si ce dernier accomplit l'action exprimée par l'infinitif. On dira ainsi « les enfants que j'ai vus jouer » (ce sont les enfants qui jouent), mais « la pièce que j'ai vu jouer ». Dans une triste lettre de Balzac à Mme Hanska, on lit : « Le café m'a attaqué l'estomac ; j'ai vu tomber mes cheveux et je les ai *vu* blanchir. »

🐦

Mais en fait d'accord du participe, le mieux est parfois l'ennemi du bien : « Pendant que j'adressais à Albertine des reproches que je n'aurais pas *dus*, elle avait l'air de sucer avec délices un sucre d'orge. » Dans cette phrase de Proust, « reproches » n'est pas complément d'objet direct du participe, mais d'un infinitif sous-entendu (adresser) : il faudrait « dû ».

Plus difficiles encore à respecter, les règles d'accord des verbes pronominaux. Lorsque le pronom « se » est complément d'objet direct du verbe, le participe passé s'accorde avec le sujet ; en revanche, lorsque « se » est complément d'objet indirect, le participe ne s'accorde pas. Si Baudelaire oublie le « s » dans « nous nous sommes donc *promené* dans toutes les salles » (lettre à son beau-père), Balzac utilise un « e » surnuméraire dans *Le Cabinet des Antiques* : « Ainsi, accablée sous le poids de dettes énormes, la duchesse s'était *ordonnée* à elle-même [...] de ne songer à cette avalanche de soucis qu'en un seul moment et pour prendre un parti définitif. »

Attention, cependant, car il y a des exceptions. Le participe passé des verbes « se rire », « se plaire », « se complaire » et « se déplaire » est toujours invariable. Or, on trouve chez Balzac, dans *Le Contrat de mariage* : « Madame Evangélista, forcée par les affaires de son mari d'habiter Bordeaux, s'y était *déplue*. »

Une fois ces règles parfaitement maîtrisées, reste le plus évident, mais pas toujours le plus simple : ne pas malmener l'orthographe du participe passé en question, et éviter de le confondre avec un infinitif ! Dans une esquisse préparatoire de *Germinal*, Zola jette ces mots sans se relire : « il est *poursuivit* par quelques-uns » et « il a *dépenser* un million ».

Respecter l'emploi des modes et des temps

*On n'est jamais mieux servi que par soi-même. Fort de ce principe, André Gide publie en 1942 un volume d'*Interviews imaginaires. *Il s'y pose à lui-même une question sur un sujet qu'il trouve « réjouissant » : « les fautes des autres ». Trop heureux, sans doute, d'être interrogé sur ce point, Gide saisit l'occasion pour assener un coup de griffe à Proust : ce dernier confondrait souvent le passé simple de l'indicatif et l'imparfait du subjonctif.*

Pour étayer ses propos, Gide reproduit, non sans gourmandise, un certain nombre de phrases fautives qu'il a relevées dans son édition de Sodome et Gomorrhe *: « M. de Charlus ne s'inquiétait pas que Mme Verdurin* fut *debout » ; « j'avais peur qu'elle ne* prit *froid » ; « dès qu'il* fût *entré à pas de loup dans le vestibule ». Proust — ou son typographe — oublie l'accent quand il en faut un, et en met un là où* *il ne devrait pas y en avoir (c'est-à-dire au passé simple) ! Pire encore, il recourt à un passé antérieur en lieu et place d'un conditionnel passé : « J'eus été celui pour qui l'on se cache de tout » (il fallait « j'aurais été » ou « j'eusse été »).*

Ce n'est pas un mystère : pour être l'une des sources de la beauté et de la subtilité de notre langue, l'enchevêtrement tortueux des modes et des temps est aussi l'une de ses plus grandes difficultés.

Il n'est pas toujours nécessaire d'aller aussi loin que l'utilisation du subjonctif et du conditionnel pour malmener les conjugaisons. Nos auteurs ont souvent maille à partir avec l'impératif. Ils oublient ainsi que les verbes du premier groupe et un certain nombre de verbes du troisième groupe ne prennent pas de « s » à la deuxième personne du présent de l'impératif : « Ne t'*effraies* pas tant, prends patience aussi, *soignes*-toi, prends courage. » (Rimbaud, lettre à sa sœur)

❧

« *Vas* donc à Paris, et, je t'en supplie en grâce, prends bien garde aux voitures. » (Baudelaire, lettre à sa mère)

« *Songes* à mon bonheur si j'illustrais le nom Balzac ! » (Balzac, lettre à sa sœur)

Dans une autre lettre à sa sœur, Balzac, non content d'accumuler les impératifs douteux, va jusqu'à forger un monstre quand il s'agit d'employer – dans une phrase au demeurant superbe – un simple présent de l'indicatif : « Quelle forte tête il faut ! Et l'*ais*-je comme il faut, la mienne toute fêlée, meurtrie de maux de dents affreux ? Plains-moi ! *envies*-moi ! *penses* à moi ! »

L'imparfait de l'indicatif a parfois une valeur conditionnelle, comme dans les subordonnées hypothétiques (« s'il venait, je serais content ») ou dans une formule comme « n'était... » : « N'était sa couleur, ce champignon pourrait passer pour un bolet. » Dans cette phrase étrange, Marguerite Duras semble confondre cette dernière tournure avec « ne serait-ce que » et recourt abusivement au conditionnel : « *Ne serait-ce* la soie de sa chemise, le daim, la ceinture, on pourrait le prendre pour un type du centre. » *(La Douleur)*

Dans *Le Bal du comte d'Orgel*, Radiguet imagine que son héroïne, Mahaut, terrifiée par ses propres sentiments pour François de Séryeuse, fait un choix radical pour ne pas céder à l'adultère : écrire à la digne mère du jeune homme pour tout lui révéler de sa passion. Dans une première esquisse de son œuvre, le romancier prête ces mots à Mahaut : « Je suis seule coupable. S'il en était autrement, vous comprenez bien que ce n'est pas à vous que je *demanderai* de me sauver. » Le futur de l'indicatif est mis pour le conditionnel.

La confusion classique entre l'indicatif et le subjonctif tient souvent à très peu de chose, un « i » ou un « e » oublié : « Voulez-vous que nous nous *voyons* au chemin de fer dimanche soir ? » (Baudelaire, lettre à Poulet-Malassis) ; « Il est possible que j'*ai* un conte publié par la *Nouvelle Revue française.* » (Saint-Exupéry, lettre à sa mère)

Quel lycéen ne s'est jamais vu rappeler par ses professeurs que la conjonction de subordination « bien que » est suivie du subjonctif ? Les réfractaires se réjouiront d'apprendre que beaucoup de grands auteurs n'hésitent pas à recourir au conditionnel, voire à l'indicatif : « Bien que ses péchés *auraient pu* sans déshonneur pour elle, ni inconvénient pour le monde, se répandre à tous les coins du diocèse, M. le curé jugea convenable de ne plus recevoir sa confession que dans la sacristie. » (Flaubert, *Trois Contes*)

« Bien que nous *fûmes*, mon bon maître et moi, très attentifs à cacher notre surprise, M. d'Astarac la devina [...]. » (Anatole France, *La Rôtisserie de la reine Pédauque*)

Tous les puristes le confirmeront : « après que » doit se construire avec l'indicatif, dans la mesure où le fait évoqué est considéré comme ayant déjà eu lieu ; le subjonctif, mode qui s'applique au fait envisagé, n'est pas de mise. Mais depuis quelques décennies, on a de plus en plus tendance à employer le subjonctif, par analogie avec « avant que » : « Autrefois — longtemps même après qu'elle m'*ait* quitté — j'ai pensé pour Anny. Maintenant je ne pense plus pour personne. » (Sartre, *La Nausée*)

« Il est distrait au volant de son auto et laisse souvent ses flèches de direction levées, même après qu'il *ait* effectué son tournant. » (Camus, *La Peste*)

En fait de subjonctif, gare aux excès de zèle : « Après que *j'eusse eu fini*, nous fûmes invités, Zilcken et moi, à une soirée chez les

Haverman. » *(Quinze jours en Hollande)* Verlaine est allé chercher un improbable subjonctif plus-que-parfait surcomposé alors qu'un passé antérieur de l'indicatif (« après que j'eus fini ») aurait plus justement exprimé l'antériorité de la subordonnée par rapport à la principale.

❧

Dans les toutes premières éditions de *Du côté de chez Swann* (Grasset), on pouvait lire : « J'allais, sans en avoir l'air, dire qu'on *apporte* les sirops. » La phrase devient, quand l'ouvrage est réédité par Gallimard : « J'allais, sans en avoir l'air, dire qu'on apportât les sirops. » Il y avait en effet un problème de concordance des temps : avec une principale au passé, il convient en toute rigueur d'utiliser un imparfait du subjonctif et non un subjonctif présent pour exprimer la simultanéité ou la postériorité.

❧

Si l'imparfait et, *a fortiori*, le plus-que-parfait du subjonctif tombent aujourd'hui en désuétude, ils ne faisaient déjà plus l'unanimité au

XIXᵉ siècle. La concordance des temps irritait particulièrement Flaubert. Un soir qu'il avait – jusque fort tard – travaillé avec Du Camp à peaufiner un manuscrit, il prend congé de son ami de méchante humeur. Sans y prêter attention, Du Camp va se coucher. Deux heures plus tard, en pleine nuit, il est réveillé par des coups de pied portés contre la porte. Effaré, il se lève et va ouvrir, pour trouver Flaubert qui lui crie, avant de dégringoler les escaliers : « Oui, vieux pédagogue, l'accord des temps est une ineptie, j'ai le droit de dire : Je voudrais que la grammaire *soit* à tous les diables et non pas *fût*, entends-tu ? »

La parution d'*À la recherche du temps perdu* ne fut pas un long fleuve tranquille. Le 10 décembre 1913, Paul Souday, l'un des critiques les plus redoutés à l'époque, s'en prit à Proust en pointant notamment plusieurs emplois fautifs du subjonctif dans le premier tome de l'œuvre. Le savant puriste n'avait pas peur de passer pour un grincheux : « Visiblement, les jeunes ne savent plus du tout le français. La langue se décompose, se mue en un patois informe et glisse à la barbarie. Il serait temps de réagir. »

Ces imprécations ont, avec le recul, quelque chose de franchement comique ! Elles sont moins savoureuses, pourtant, que la réponse que Proust rédigea dès le lendemain. Avec une politesse exquise et une ironie redoutable, le romancier, loin de manifester le moindre courroux, attire l'attention de Souday sur une coquille dans son propre article et lui signale qu'il a prêté à Horace une citation latine qui revenait à Ovide…

Terminons par cette superbe lettre de Bernard-Marie Koltès à son ami François Regnault. Le dramaturge soumet malicieusement au philosophe un problème grammatical auquel le confronte une phrase de *Dans la solitude des champs de coton* (1986) :

> Car j'ai d'abord torturé Grevisse, sans qu'il n'avoue rien ; puis autour de moi, interrogé tout ce que Pigalle compte d'anciens professeurs devenus bistros, d'instituteurs reconvertis, de garçons cultivés tombés dans la débauche, et de débauchés beaux parleurs ; et toutes, je dis bien : toutes les

terminaisons de verbes m'ont été successivement proposées. Au point que petit à petit, je me suis mis à douter non seulement de la terminaison, mais du verbe entier, puis du sujet du verbe, puis de la phrase, puis des phrases qui l'entourent avec un silence complice, puis des champs, du coton et de la solitude.

Alors te voilà sommé de trancher entre l'indicatif et le subjonctif, le passé et le présent ; je te remets une phrase fatiguée d'être tripotée par n'importe qui, égarée, inquiète de ne plus rien comprendre, dégoûtée de vivre [...].

a) Compléter selon les pointillés :

« C'est pourquoi sans vous connaître je vous ai, dès le premier mot, traité correctement, dès le premier pas que j'ai fait vers vous, un pas correct, humble et respectueux, sans savoir si quoi que ce soit chez vous mérit... le respect, sans rien connaître de vous qui puisse me faire savoir si la comparaison de nos deux états autoris... que je fusse humble et vous arrogant. »

b) « quoi que ce soit » et « fusse » sont-ils corrects ?

c) Ton jugement sera celui de Dieu.

Koltès mettra finalement un imparfait de l'indicatif à la place des pointillés.

Passer les formes verbales
à la loupe

En mars 1939, alors que Terre des hommes *connaît un grand succès, Saint-Exupéry reçoit un télégramme de sa sœur. Elle attire son attention sur une phrase de l'œuvre :* « Il se fit un silence et pendant ce silence quelque chose siffla légèrement sur le parquet, bruissa sous la table, puis se tut. » *Coup de tonnerre pour Saint-Ex, qui se rend compte, effaré, qu'il aurait fallu écrire* « quelque chose bruit » *(si tant est qu'il existe, le passé simple de* « bruire » *suit le modèle de* « finir »*). Un ami présent ce jour-là, Georges Pélissier, raconte la scène :* « Je voulus le consoler, m'armai d'érudition et lui montrai que puisque la formation irrégulière de l'imparfait : bruissait, était entrée de nos jours dans la langue française, un écrivain de sa classe pouvait se permettre d'écrire bruissa, si voisin de bruissait, et qui enrichissait le français d'un*

temps de verbe commode. Rien n'y fit. Il demeurait
inconsolable. »

Peut-être les erreurs de ses confrères en la matière,
erreurs que la grammaire appelle « barbarismes »,
l'auraient-elles rasséréné…

Conjuguer le verbe « pleuvoir » relève de la gageure, mais on s'accorde à considérer qu'au futur il faut écrire « il pleuvra ». Quand Baudelaire fit paraître « Le Cygne » pour la première fois, on pouvait lire ce vers : « Eau, quand *pleuveras*-tu ? Quand tonneras-tu, foudre ? » Dans sa réédition des *Fleurs du Mal*, en 1861, le poète corrige la faute : « Eau, quand donc pleuvrastu ? Quand tonneras-tu, foudre ? »

Le passé composé a beau être d'un usage courant, il pose souvent le problème du choix de l'auxiliaire : « La femme des brigands, ne sachant rien de ce qu'ils *avaient* convenu de faire pendant la nuit, accueillit la bossue et la mit en haut, sans lumière. » Dans cette phrase du *Médecin de campagne*, Balzac oublie que « convenir » ne s'emploie qu'avec « être ».

« Descendre » se conjugue avec « avoir »
quand il est transitif, avec « être » quand il n'a
pas de complément d'objet direct. On dira « j'ai
descendu l'escalier » mais « je suis descendu ».
Dans une lettre à un ami, Flaubert écrit cependant : « Nous *sommes descendus* la Saône en bateau
à vapeur jusqu'à Lyon et, de Lyon, le Rhône
jusqu'à Avignon. »

Vous vous demandez si Romulus fonda Rome
ou s'il la fondit et vous hésitez entre « il fut »
et « il fût » ? Rassurez-vous, les victimes du
passé simple sont nombreuses. Dans *À rebours*,
Huysmans écrit : « ils *requérirent* la séparation
de corps », là où « requirent » aurait suffi.

Mais attention, ce qui vaut pour « requérir »
ne vaut pas pour « luire », n'en déplaise à Saint-
Exupéry, encore lui : dans une expression comme
« les lampes à arc, toutes à la fois, *luirent* »
(*Courrier Sud*), c'est « luisirent » qui, en l'occurrence, est requis !

Quant au verbe « distraire », autant renoncer à lui prêter un passé simple ; au XVIIIᵉ siècle, on trouvait bien çà et là « il distrayit », mais il y a de quoi rester dubitatif devant cette phrase de Duras (*Les Petits Chevaux de Tarquinia*) : « Une fois les poissons ramenés dans la barque, il s'en *distraya*. »

Jacques de Lacretelle raconte que Radiguet « s'amusa tout le premier, non sans en rougir », d'avoir laissé passer un barbarisme dans *Le Diable au corps* : « Je ne *concluai* pas de son silence que mes baisers lui fissent plaisir. » Il faut croire que, dès qu'il s'agit de conclure en amour, la grammaire n'a plus cours, car Marivaux faisait la même faute dans un contexte similaire : « J'ouvris alors les yeux sur ma bonne fortune, et je *concluai* sur le champ qu'il fallait qu'elle eût du penchant pour moi, puisqu'elle n'arrêtait pas des discours aussi tendres que les miens. » (*Le Paysan parvenu*)

Même lorsqu'il trébuche sur l'imparfait du subjonctif, Alexandre Dumas ne perd pas son panache : « Je suis enchanté, mademoiselle ; mais je voudrais bien qu'ils ne *fuyassent* point de notre côté », écrit-il là où « fuissent » s'imposait. (*La Chasse au chastre*)

Quant aux frères GONCOURT, on ne sait pas trop d'où leur vient cette forme étrange, mise pour « rassît » : « Il fallait que mademoiselle la *rasseyât* de force et lui ordonnât de rester tranquille » (*Germinie Lacerteux*). Il est vrai que le verbe « asseoir » et ses dérivés sont infernaux : dans un brouillon de *Germinal*, Zola écrit « le père *s'asseoit* à son tour et mange sa soupe » alors qu'il faudrait « s'assoit » ou « s'assied ».

En matière de subjonctif, la palme de l'audace revient à Victor Hugo. Dans un poème intitulé « Dieu », il commet, pour les besoins de la rime, une faute seigneuriale : « Jusqu'à ce qu'il s'en aille en cendre et se *dissoude*. » Tous ceux qui s'attendaient à « dissolve » repasseront !

Il y a de quoi hésiter sur l'imparfait du verbe « vêtir » (« je vêtais »), et il faudrait être bien sévère pour reprocher au même Hugo d'avoir écrit, dans *Les Misérables*, qu'un personnage toujours vêtu de noir – Marius, jeune homme fier et ténébreux – « se *vêtissait* de nuit ».

« Quelle joie de voir une pervenche *poindant* sous la neige ! » (Balzac, *L'Interdiction*). Rappelons que « poignant » sert normalement de participe présent à « poindre ».

Dans les tournures interrogatives, il est tout à fait possible, au présent de l'indicatif, de postposer le « je » après certains verbes courants (« vais-je », « suis-je », « ai-je ») ou, à condition d'ajouter un accent aigu, après les verbes du premier groupe : « chanté-je ? » ou « me trompé-je » sont corrects. Mais il n'en va pas de même pour les autres verbes. Quand Giraudoux fait dire « Que *voulé*-je d'elle ? » à un personnage de *Judith* ou quand Balzac écrit, dans *La Peau de chagrin*, « aussi *metté*-je toujours quelques chiffons rouges dans ma parure », ils n'échappent pas davantage au barbarisme que Dumas dans sa pièce *Don Juan de Marana* : « Pourquoi cette voix me fait-elle tressaillir jusqu'au fond des entrailles ? pourquoi me *senté*-je malgré moi tout prêt à lui obéir ? »

Comment employer un verbe au conditionnel quand la forme verbale en question n'est pas attestée ? Il suffit de l'inventer, comme Marguerite Yourcenar dans *Mémoires d'Hadrien*, où l'on trouve « elle *giserait* à jamais dans cette caisse hermétiquement close ».

Règle nº 9
Choisir le mot juste

« *Chacun a ses faiblesses. Littré en avait pour sa bonne. Un jour qu'il la lutinait, Madame Littré poussa la porte et s'écria : "Ah, monsieur, je suis surprise !" Et le regretté Littré, se rajustant, lui répondit : "Non, madame, vous êtes étonnée. C'est nous qui sommes surpris [1]."* »

Bien choisir ses mots n'est pas si facile qu'on pourrait le croire, et l'erreur, en cette matière, produit souvent des effets cocasses.

Dans son poème « La Flûte », Vigny écrit d'abord : « Comme pour le *martyr* s'apprêtait un apôtre », confondant ainsi les substantifs « martyr » et « martyre » (le premier étant

_____

1. Alain Duchesne et Thierry Leguay, *La Nuance*, Paris, Larousse, 1994.

celui qui subit le second). Le vers sera par la suite corrigé en « Comme se préparait au *martyre* un apôtre ».

« Il ne put enfin la prendre dans ses bras que parce qu'elle était à demi évanouie et qu'elle ne *recouvrit* ses sens que sur la première marche » (Mauriac, *Les Chemins de la mer*). « Recouvrit » est le passé simple de « recouvrir » ! Il fallait « recouvra ».

Dans *Les Rayons et les Ombres*, Hugo, emporté par un élan panthéiste, met « s'épanche » pour « s'étanche » :

Nous sommes la nature et la source éternelle
Où toute soif *s'épanche*, où se lave toute aile.

72

« Il trouva l'église désertée par les habitants qui, malgré leur dévotion, étaient allés voir sur le port l'*embarcation* des troupes » (Balzac, *La Duchesse de Langeais*). Il faudrait « embarquement ».

Les impropriétés peuvent relever de la confusion grammaticale entre deux tournures. Il arrive ainsi fréquemment qu'on emploie « ceci » ou « voici » (termes d'annonce) pour « cela » ou « voilà » (termes de reprise) et *vice versa*, comme dans cet exemple du *Rouge et le Noir* : « Je vais être destitué. *Ceci* m'afflige. »

« Cosette, *prête à* défaillir, ne poussa pas un cri. » Hugo ne voulait-il pas plutôt dire que l'héroïne des *Misérables* était « près de défaillir » ?

« À force de patauger dans les choses *soi-disant* sérieuses, on arrive au crime », écrit Flaubert. Il aurait fallu « choses prétendument sérieuses », car « soi-disant » ne s'emploie, en toute rigueur, qu'à propos des personnes (susceptibles de « dire »).

De nos jours, du moins dans la langue orale, l'expression « de suite », synonyme de « successivement », tend à remplacer « tout de suite ». On peut le déplorer. Mais la confusion n'est pas récente. Dans un texte de jeunesse, *Novembre*, Flaubert écrit : « Elle se leva *de suite*, alla chercher ses ciseaux et me coupa, derrière la tête, une mèche de cheveux. »

En 1855, Baudelaire, qui est encore un quasi inconnu dans le monde des lettres, adresse une lettre flagorneuse à George Sand pour lui demander d'user de son influence en faveur de sa maîtresse, la comédienne Marie Daubrun, qui peine alors à trouver des rôles. La romancière répondit fort obligeamment : « Je vais écrire *de suite*. » En haut du billet qu'il vient de recevoir, le poète note sans indulgence, ni, il faut bien le dire, élégance : « Remarquez la faute de français : *de suite* pour *tout de suite*. »

Le néologisme est l'une des prérogatives des écrivains : forger des mots nouveaux est leur droit, sinon leur rôle. Mais il arrive que leurs créations ne soient pas frappées du sceau de la nécessité. À partir de l'adjectif « vil », on a, dès le Moyen Âge, tiré le substantif « vilenie », qu'on a tendance à malmener de nos jours en le prononçant, voire en l'écrivant « vilénie ». En ancien français, on parlait aussi de « vileté », et ce terme, semble-t-il, ne s'employait qu'au singulier. Or, on lit dans les *Mémoires d'outre-tombe*, à propos des crimes de Napoléon : « Qui voudrait défendre la cause du faible contre le fort, si le courage, exposé à la vengeance des *viletés* du présent, devait encore attendre le blâme des lâchetés de l'avenir ? »

Comme le comte de Marcellus en faisait le reproche à Chateaubriand, celui-ci répondit : « Que voulez-vous ? à des actes presque inouïs,

tant ils sont serviles, il faut des expressions inso-
lites. » Mais dans *Clio*, Charles Péguy ira plus
loin encore en parlant de « *vilitude* » !

❧

La tendance balzacienne à l'invention verbale
excitait la verve ironique de ses contemporains.
Un journal satirique, *Le Charivari*, publie ces
lignes en 1837 : « Le sire de Balzac écrit et parle
un grand nombre de langues avec une pureté et
une facilité qui fait l'étonnement de tous ceux
qui ne connaissent pas les langues. Nous
citerons, entre autres l'Indostan, le Tartare, le
Mantchou, et surtout le Charabias. Quant au
Charabias, de l'aveu de tout le monde, il le pos-
sède à fond, et il l'emploie avec un rare bonheur,
témoin *La Vieille Fille*, *Le Lys*… »

❧

« La *compatissance* et la tendresse d'une jeune
fille possèdent une influence vraiment magné-
tique. » (Balzac, *Eugénie Grandet*)

76

« Quoique très nerveux et *impressible*, Charles IX ne tressaillit point. » (Balzac, *Sur Catherine de Médicis*)

« Il causait avec l'*inexpériente* Fanny, la fille du banquier. » (Balzac, *L'Auberge rouge*)

« Il fit, en frappant la langue contre le palais, un bruit *désapprobatif* qui peut se traduire par : titt, titt, titt. » (Balzac, *Les Comédiens sans le savoir*)

Un jour que le comédien Louis Monrose, répétant son rôle dans *Marion Delorme*, avait osé reprocher à Victor Hugo l'emploi d'un mot selon toute apparence inventé par l'auteur, ce dernier répliqua :

> — Vous ne trouvez pas ce mot français, monsieur Monrose ?
> — Non, Monsieur...
> — Eh bien ! il le deviendra !...

Éviter pléonasmes
et redondances

« *Toute cette procession cheminait dans l'allée qui s'enfonce à travers la verdure des arbres verts.* » (Manette Salomon) : *la répétition est certes un trait de style chez les frères Goncourt, mais elle va parfois, comme c'est le cas ici, jusqu'au pléonasme. Le mot, emprunté au grec, signifie étymologiquement « surabondance », « excès » ; de fait, en littérature, le trop-plein est souvent l'ennemi du beau — mais peut s'avérer fort réjouissant.*

« L'une des gloires de Molière est d'avoir admirablement peint, *d'un seul côté seulement*, ces natures de femmes dans la plus grande figure qu'il ait taillée en plein marbre : Célimène ! » (Balzac, *Le Cabinet des Antiques*)

« C'est ce que je demande, s'écria-t-elle, en se *levant debout*. » (Stendhal, *Le Rouge et le Noir*)

« Le père Goriot regarda *tristement* son ouvrage *d'un air triste*, des larmes sortirent de ses yeux [...]. » (Balzac, *Le Père Goriot*)

« Ouverture du puits de *l'infini sans borne* [...] » (Hugo, « Le Satyre », *La Légende des siècles*)

« La pieuse fille n'avait pu être *canonisée sainte*, faute de protections. » (Hugo, *Notre-Dame de Paris*)

À vouloir trop marquer les articulations de la phrase, on en oublie parfois qu'un mot de liaison suffit. Chateaubriand écrit dans *Génie du christianisme* : « *car en effet* il n'y a que deux états dans la vie : le célibat et le mariage », tandis qu'on trouve dans « Suicides » de Maupassant : « Quand [ces papiers] seront en cendres, écrasez-les encore en une poussière invisible… *ou sinon* vous êtes perdu. »

Certains pléonasmes, moins flagrants, tiennent à l'étymologie. Quand Balzac écrit que « les savants prétendaient qu'il avait trouvé la *panacée universelle* » (*Maître Cornélius*), il oublie qu'une « panacée » est « universelle » par définition : ce terme tiré du grec ancien désigne un remède (*akos*) valable pour toutes les maladies (le préfixe « pan » exprime la totalité, comme dans « panorama » ou « pangermanisme »).

« Delestang, correctement boutonné dans sa redingote, était *assis* avec dignité *sur son séant*, le corps ni trop en avant ni trop en arrière » (Zola, *Son excellence Eugène Rougon*). Être « assis sur son séant » est redondant car les mots « séant » et « asseoir » ont la même origine.

« Gavroche n'était tombé que pour se redresser ; il resta *assis sur son séant*, un long filet de sang rayait son visage, il éleva ses deux bras en l'air, regarda du côté d'où était venu le coup, et se mit à chanter. » (Hugo, *Les Misérables*)

Il existe aussi des pléonasmes grammaticaux, qui tiennent à la tournure de phrase employée. Dans le célèbre « Art poétique » de Verlaine, on lit ainsi : « Prends l'éloquence et tords-*lui son* cou. » On voit bien que le poète a fait passer l'expressivité avant la correction, mais un puriste aurait pu lui reprocher de n'avoir pas choisi entre deux constructions : « tords-lui le cou » et « tords son cou ».

∼∾

Boileau écrit : « C'est à vous, mon esprit, *à qui* je veux parler. » La répétition de la préposition « à » permet au poète d'atteindre ses douze syllabes, mais elle est en réalité superflue. Si vous vous attendiez à « c'est à vous, mon esprit, que je veux parler », vous n'êtes pas les seuls, car Chateaubriand lui-même pointe la faute de son illustre devancier dans un passage des *Mémoires d'outre-tombe* :

> Mon maître d'écriture, M. Després, [...] n'était pas plus content de moi que mes parents ; il me faisait copier éternellement, d'après un exemple de sa façon, ces deux vers que j'ai pris en horreur, non à cause de la faute de langue qui s'y trouve :
>
> *C'est à vous, mon esprit, à qui je veux parler :*
> *Vous avez des défauts que je ne puis celer.*
>
> Il accompagnait ses réprimandes de coups de poing qu'il me donnait dans le cou, en m'appelant *tête d'achôcre* ; voulait-il dire *achore* ? Je ne sais pas ce que c'est qu'une tête d'*achôcre*, mais je la tiens pour effroyable.

Précisons qu'en patois normand, un « achôcre » est un propre à rien, un maladroit, tandis qu'en français d'époque « achore » est l'équivalent d'« ulcère ». Dans les deux cas, la réprimande avait de quoi terrifier le petit garçon !

Règle n° 11
Ne pas torturer la syntaxe

Un jour, Victor Hugo fit poliment remarquer à Lamartine qu'il avait laissé passer quelques incorrections dans l'un de ses poèmes. L'auteur du « Lac » répondit avec l'aplomb qui le caractérisait : « Mon principe est cependant qu'il faut en faire en vers, sans cela la grammaire écrase la poésie. La grammaire n'a pas été faite pour nous. »

Il faut reconnaître cette qualité à Lamartine : il restait fidèle à ses principes, comme en témoigne ce passage du « Poète mourant » (Nouvelles Méditations poétiques) :

Ah ! qu'il pleure celui dont les mains acharnées
S'attachant, comme un lierre, aux débris des années,
Voit avec l'avenir s'écrouler son espoir !

En fait d'espoir, autant renoncer à celui de donner un sens satisfaisant à cette phrase : elle s'est écroulée dès le « dont » du premier vers ! Mais Lamartine n'est pas le seul, tant s'en faut, à malmener de temps à autre la syntaxe…

« C'est comme un poids dont il faut que je me débarrasse sur quiconque, homme ou animal, *qui* passe devant moi » (Koltès, *Dans la solitude des champs de coton*). « Quiconque » est déjà un pronom relatif ; le « qui » est donc inutile !

Proust, quant à lui, met « dont » à la place d'un pronom relatif plus complexe, comme « avec lequel » : « Elle avait eu l'étonnement, l'embarras et la honte de quelqu'un qui a devant lui à table un instrument nouvellement inventé dont il ne sait pas l'usage et *dont* il n'ose pas commencer à manger. » *(Sodome et Gomorrhe)*

Quand « dont » équivaut à un complément du nom, on ne peut pas, en principe, l'associer à un déterminant possessif. On ne dirait pas, par exemple, « l'écrivain dont j'ai lu *ses* livres », mais bien « l'écrivain dont j'ai lu les livres ». Dans *Jean Santeuil*, Proust écrit pourtant : « Mais à Paris tous ceux *dont* un sombre chagrin ne fermait pas *leur* âme à la gaîté du soleil en ressentaient la bienfaisante influence. »

❦

Dans des notes de travail, Zola jette les bases de ce qui sera l'une des scènes les plus fortes de *Germinal* : « Si j'avais un surveillant, couchant avec toutes et qui se tuerait de lui-même, et *auxquelles* les femmes arracheraient ensuite les parties génitales. » On aurait pu mettre « à qui » ou « dont », mais sûrement pas cet improbable « *auxquelles* » !

❦

À d'autres moments, on a l'impression que plusieurs tournures se disputent les faveurs de l'écrivain, et qu'il ne parvient pas à choisir celle qui lui plaît le plus. Balzac écrit dans *La Rabouilleuse* : « Il le montra naturellement à sa mère qui ne put reconnaître son frère, *tant il ressemblait si peu* à ce qu'il était quand elle l'avait quitté. »

« Nos discussions portaient surtout *au sujet de* l'éducation de nos enfants. » (Gide, *Robert*)

Flaubert confond deux expressions dans *Madame Bovary* : « La mère Lefrançois, qui, passant par un guichet sa tête en bonnet de coton, le chargeait de commissions et lui donnait des explications à troubler *un tout autre homme*. » Il faudrait soit « tout autre homme » soit « un autre homme », « un tout autre homme » signifiant « un homme tout différent ».

La construction des verbes met en jeu le choix de la bonne préposition : « On le voyait au passage entrer ou sortir *de* son cabinet », écrit Pagnol *(Le Temps des secrets)*. « Entrer dans son cabinet ou en sortir » aurait été plus correct.

« Pallier », quoiqu'on l'oublie souvent, est un verbe transitif ; son complément n'a pas besoin d'être introduit par une préposition. On trouve pourtant chez Gide : « Les événements lamentables que je vous ai dits [...] sont la condamnation du divorce et de tout ce que l'homme a inventé pour essayer de *pallier aux* conséquences de ses fautes » *(Isabelle)*. De même, chez Camus : « Dans toutes les armées du monde, on *pallie* généralement *au* manque de matériel par des hommes. » (Première édition de *La Peste*)

On se « souvient de quelque chose », mais on se « rappelle quelque chose », sans préposition : comme dans le cas précédent, on a affaire à un verbe transitif. Flaubert écrit pourtant à sa nièce : « Remercie de ma part Mme Robert qui a bien voulu se rappeler *de* moi. » Claudel commet la même erreur : « Moi, quand il m'arrive de me rappeler *de* mon âme, c'est ainsi que je la verrais. » *(La Rose et le rosaire)*

S'il est une chose qu'on ne se rappelle pas souvent, c'est que le participe détaché en tête de phrase renvoie nécessairement au sujet de la proposition principale. En principe, on ne peut dire, comme Gide dans *L'Immoraliste*, « *sitôt sortis* de Sousse et de l'abri de ses collines, le vent commença de souffler ».

« *Une fois par terre*, leurs tilburys vont vous passer sur le corps. » (Stendhal, *Le Rouge et le Noir*)

On ne se méfie jamais assez de la négation. Baudelaire se laisse piéger par la liaison : « J'attends une lettre de toi avec bien de l'impatience ; il me semble que voici bien longtemps que je n'en *n'*ai pas reçu. » (Lettre à sa mère)

❧

L'admiration qu'on voue à Flaubert n'a d'égale que l'acharnement de ses détracteurs à contester la justesse et l'élégance de son style. Au début du XXᵉ siècle, une violente querelle, lancée par un article intitulé « Flaubert savait-il écrire ? », a déchaîné les passions, et certains sont allés, avec une étonnante mauvaise foi, jusqu'à dresser des sottisiers flaubertiens. Toujours est-il qu'on peut s'étonner que les formules suivantes, extraites de *Madame Bovary*, aient passé avec succès la fameuse épreuve du « gueuloir » :

> C'était le curé de son village *qui lui avait commencé le latin* […].
> Enfin son mari, sachant qu'elle aimait à se promener en voiture, trouva un boc d'occasion, qui, *ayant une fois des lanternes neuves* […], ressembla presque à un tilbury.

La dorure du baromètre, sur *qui* frappait un rayon de soleil, étalait des feux dans la glace [...].

Par moments ils *s*'échangeaient une parole.

⁊

Madame de Sévigné s'enquiert de la santé du poète Ménage, qui lui répond : « Je suis enrhumé, Madame. » Ce à quoi elle réplique : « Je *la* suis aussi ». Or, les règles en la matière sont les suivantes : pour représenter un nom précédé de l'article défini, on emploie le pronom « le », « la », « les », en accordant avec le nom : « je passe ici pour votre maîtresse [...] mais je ne la suis point » (Hugo) ; en revanche, pour représenter un adjectif (ou un nom construit sans déterminant), on emploie le pronom neutre « le » : Romain Rolland parle ainsi d'« une femme compatissante et qui ose le paraître ».

Répondant à Madame de Sévigné, Ménage fait donc justement remarquer qu'il faudrait dire « je le suis », mais l'illustre épistolière n'est pas d'accord : « Vous direz comme il vous plaira, mais, pour moi, je croirais avoir de la barbe si je disais autrement. »

De l'importance de se relire

« Tout le mal n'est que dans ces cinq lettres B, R, U, L, A, R, D, qui forment mon nom » : est-il possible que Stendhal, déjà fort brouillé avec l'orthographe, ait eu quelques difficultés en arithmétique ? Qu'on se rassure ! Cette jolie bourde n'est qu'un lapsus : en écrivant « Brulard », Stendhal songe en fait à « Beyle », son véritable patronyme, confirmant par là le caractère autobiographique de la Vie de Henry Brulard.

Il n'est pas rare que les écrivains laissent ainsi passer quelques perles dont l'éclat rehausse celui des plus grands chefs-d'œuvre…

« Le bruit du galop de son cheval, qui retentit sur le pavé de la pelouse, diminua rapidement. » (Balzac, *Une ténébreuse affaire*)

« [Robert] faisait demander s'il pouvait entrer chez elle et là, moitié tristesse réelle, moitié énervement de cette vie, moitié simulation chaque jour plus audacieuse, sanglotait, s'inondait d'eau froide, parlait de sa mort prochaine [...]. » (Proust, *Le Temps retrouvé*)

❧

« Le gentilhomme tira sa bourse, et jetant deux louis sur le tapis, non sans humeur :

— Quarante francs, juste comme de l'or, dit-il. Et diantre ! il est onze heures.

— Il est onze heures, répéta le personnage muet en regardant le peintre. » (Balzac, *La Bourse*)

❧

« On n'entend d'autre bruit, dans cet isolement,

Que quelques voix d'enfants, ou quelque bêlement

De génisse ou de chèvre au ravin descendues. » (Lamartine, *Jocelyn*)

« [La femme de chambre] lui cria deux mots à voix basse. » (Balzac, *La Muse du département*)

❧

« Ah ! dit Don Manoël en portugais. » (Dumas, *Le Collier de la reine*)

❧

« Quel plaisir d'arriver couvert de neige dans une chambre éclairée par des parfums ! » (Balzac, *La Peau de chagrin*)

❧

« De nouveau, elle leva un bras qui ne semblait pas faire partie de son corps : un reptile hésitant dont la main eût été la tête. » (François Mauriac, *Les Anges noirs*)

« La Delaware coule parallèlement à la rue qui suit son bord occidental. » (Chateaubriand, *Mémoires d'outre-tombe*)

« Je foule aux pieds ce trône, et je règne en des lieux
Où mon front avili n'osa lever les yeux. » (Voltaire, *L'Orphelin de la Chine*)

« Puis, c'était un capitaine, le bras gauche arraché, le flanc droit percé jusqu'à la cuisse, étalé sur le ventre, qui se traînait sur les coudes. » (Zola, *La Débâcle*)

« On avait marché onze heures, ce qui, avec les deux heures de repos laissées en quatre fois aux chevaux pour manger l'avoine et souffler, faisait quatorze. » (Maupassant, *Boule de Suif*)

« Nous sommes amoureux à vingt ans (passez-moi les différences), et nous cessons de l'être à cinquante. Pendant ces vingt années, combien de fois le besoin [de l'amour] se ferait-il sentir si nous n'étions pas provoqués [...] par l'habitude que nous avons de vivre en présence, non pas d'une femme, mais des femmes ? » (Balzac, *Physiologie du mariage*)

« Une rage inexprimable rendit le capitaine plus blanc que ses voiles. D'un seul bond, il sauta sur le timonier, et l'atteignit si furieusement de son poignard qu'il le manqua. » (Balzac, *La Femme de trente ans*)

« La Pologne et la France ont toujours été frères. » (Balzac, *Le Médecin de campagne*)

Pour autant, l'art de ne pas se relire a peut-être aussi ses vertus. C'est la leçon qu'on pourra tirer de ce savoureux récit, emprunté aux *Récréations littéraires* de Cizeron-Rival (1765) et portant sur quatre vers d'une tragédie de Corneille, *Tite et Bérénice* :

> Faut-il mourir, madame ? et, si proche du terme.
> Votre illustre inconstance est-elle encor si ferme
> Que les restes d'un feu que j'avais cru si fort
> Puissent dans quatre jours se promettre ma mort ?

« Baron, ce célèbre acteur, devait faire le rôle de Domitian dans cette même tragédie, et comme il étudiait son rôle, l'obscurité des vers rapportés ci-dessus lui fit quelque peine, et il en alla demander l'explication à Molière chez qui il demeurait. Molière, après les avoir lus, lui dit qu'il ne les entendait pas non plus ; mais attendez, dit-il à Baron, M. Corneille doit venir souper avec nous aujourd'hui, et vous lui direz qu'il vous les explique. Dès que Corneille arriva, le jeune Baron [...] le pria de lui expliquer ces quatre vers, disant à Corneille qu'il ne les entendait pas. Corneille, après les avoir examinés quelque temps, dit : "Je ne les entends pas trop bien non plus ; mais récitez-les toujours, tel qui ne les entendra pas les admirera." »

RÈGLE n° 13
Bien choisir ses relecteurs

« *Non, non, tu n'as pas le droit d'être incorrect, sous prétexte de style, et je ne puis te dire combien je rage de te voir te payer de tels motifs pour ne pas te purger de toutes ces crottes. Aie donc du courage, chameau, et sarcle ton champ ; il n'en sera que plus beau quand tu auras retiré les mauvaises herbes.* »

On ne peut qu'admirer le sens de la métaphore dont fait preuve le sévère Du Camp à l'égard de son ami Flaubert, qui vient de protester contre quelques remarques un peu vives à propos de L'Éducation sentimentale.

Qu'elle soit faite par des proches, des éditeurs ou d'autres écrivains, la relecture est une expérience aussi mortifiante pour l'auteur que désopilante pour le lecteur…

Il faut dire que Du Camp ne s'embarrassait pas de précautions oratoires, comme en témoigne cette liste de corrections proposées pour *L'Éducation sentimentale* :

Page 71, ligne 18, *Une heure sonna lentement* – ça c'est farce – comment veux-tu qu'un coup sonne lentement ? deux ou trois, à la bonne heure.

Page 100, ligne 30, *Plus vaste qu'il n'était* – non ; qu'il *ne* l'était. [...]

Page 120, ligne 10, *Le fixer* n'est pas français – on fixe les yeux sur – ôte cela, tu vas regimber, mais c'est inadmissible.

Page 163, ligne 4, *J'y ai besoin* – est du charabias. [...]

Page 165, ligne 27, Tu te fous trop de la grammaire. [...]

Page 257, ligne 5, Non, pas prêts à s'embrasser (c'est-à-dire préparés à), mais près de s'embrasser, c'est-à-dire sur le point de.

Mme de Kostrowitzky, mère d'Apollinaire, avait l'habitude de réprimander son fils : « Surveille-toi dans tes lettres : c'est honteux pour un garçon ayant fait ses classes de faire tout le temps des fautes d'*ortographes*. Je comprends que ce ne sont que des fautes d'*inattentions*, mais si tu écris ainsi à d'autres personnes *ils* commenteront tes lettres plus sévèrement et c'est honteux. »

Apollinaire avait manifestement de qui tenir…

« J'ai lu ton livre. [...] D'aucuns passages m'ont paru admirables, d'autres... je m'abstiens de t'en parler. [...] Ton style n'est pas toujours clair : les fautes d'orthographe fourmillent. » (Louis-Prosper Claudel, à propos de *Tête d'or*)

Mme de Vigny ne plaisantait pas avec la grammaire. Il existe un exemplaire du premier recueil de son fils, *Poèmes* (1822), sèchement annoté par ses soins. Les vers suivants sont retoqués :

Un navire insurgé tout à coup sort de l'ombre.
Un étendard de sang claque à ses légers mâts,
D'armes et de guerriers un éclatant amas
Surchargent ses trois ponts ; [...]

Mme de Vigny a biffé « nt » et écrit en marge : « C'est un *éclatant amas* qui est le nominatif de la phrase. Le verbe doit être au singulier. » Plus loin, dans « Doublez à nos vaisseaux la splendeur des étoiles » *(Héléna)*, elle remplace « à » par « pour » et commente : « Le mot *pour* est plus français et plus clair que *à*. »

❧

Début 1920, Proust, épuisé et malade, s'attache temporairement les services d'un jeune homme plein d'avenir, André Breton, pour s'épargner la tâche de corriger *Le Côté de Guermantes* avant la remise à l'éditeur. Quelques mois plus tard, le premier jeu d'épreuves arrive au domicile de Proust. C'est un cauchemar ! Breton n'a, de toute évidence, pas mis beaucoup de cœur à l'ouvrage… Les fautes sont pléthoriques, les incohérences flagrantes, le texte défiguré (« Bergotte » est devenu « Bergson »…). Il est trop tard, hélas, pour réparer le mal. Proust rédige un *erratum* de vingt-trois pages et adresse cette lettre à Gaston Gallimard : « Vous voyez un homme au désespoir. Hier, en rentrant, je me suis mis à lire *Le Côté de Guermantes* ; sauf dans certaines parties, les fautes sont tellement nombreuses et rendent les phrases si inintelligibles, que devant mon déshonneur j'ai compris Vatel se perçant de son épée. »

༄

« Le jour où le jeune écrivain corrige sa première épreuve, il est fier comme un écolier qui vient de gagner sa première vérole. » (Baudelaire, *Mon cœur mis à nu*)

༄

Robert Merle a toujours été redevable à sa correctrice, Madeleine, du tact qu'elle mettait à lui signaler ses erreurs : « Elle m'appelle au téléphone et me dit : "Robert, dans tel passage, est-ce un effet de style ?" Alors je relis et je lui réponds : "Non, non, ça n'en est pas un." "Alors c'est une faute de français !" me répond-elle ! Si j'étais ministre de l'Éducation, je lui donnerais tout de suite un cours à la Sorbonne ! »

Règle n° 14
Garder un œil
sur l'imprimeur

*Quel est le pire cauchemar de l'écrivain ? La page
blanche ? La critique assassine dans un grand quoti-
dien ? Non, la faute d'impression ! Quoi de plus déso-
lant, après tant d'efforts, que de voir son œuvre
dénaturée par des typographes, ou plutôt, pour
reprendre le jargon de l'édition, des « protes » ? Dans
son* Journal, *André Gide rapporte l'anecdote suivante
à propos de J.-H. Rosny, coauteur, avec son frère, de*
La Guerre du feu *(1909) : « On raconte que Rosny,
exaspéré par les erreurs typographiques que les protes
faisaient ou laissaient passer, écrivit un article ven-
geur intitulé "Mes coquilles". Quand Rosny le lendemain ouvrit le journal, il lut avec stupeur, en gros
caractères, cet étrange titre : "*MES COUILLES*". Un
prote, négligent ou malicieux, avait laissé tomber
le q... J'écris ceci pour me consoler. »*

Les fautes les plus fréquentes tiennent à l'ajout intempestif d'un mot ou d'un caractère. « Ses mains étaient de celles qui sont sales après *les* avoir été lavées. » (Balzac, *Une fille d'Ève*, édition Furne, 1842)

« Madame Jules était là, naïvement posée, comme la femme la moins artificieuse du monde, douce, pleine d'une sérénité *majestueuseuse*. » (Balzac, *Ferragus*, édition Furne, 1843)

« – Monsieur est du journal, dit Finot en remerciant Étienne et lui jetant le fin regard de *l'exploitateur*. » (Balzac, *Illusions perdues*, édition Furne, 1843)

« Mais chaque spectateur cherchait en soi l'enfant *miracuculeux*. » (Apollinaire, « Un fantôme de nuées », *Calligrammes*, Mercure de France, 1918)

❧

Mais il peut aussi s'agir de ce qu'on appelle en jargon d'imprimerie un « bourdon », c'est-à-dire de l'oubli d'un ou de plusieurs éléments (lettre, mot, paragraphe...), dont l'effet se révèle parfois comique : « Julie se leva, se jeta dans les *bas* d'Arthur. » (Balzac, *La Femme de trente ans*, édition Furne, 1842)

❧

Il arrive que la faute prenne des dimensions plus importantes, comme lorsqu'il y a substitution d'un mot à un autre : « Elle n'est point folle, répondit *silencieusement* le commissaire de police » (*La Cousine Bette*, édition Michel Lévy, 1871). En fait, Balzac avait écrit : « Elle n'est point folle, répondit sentencieusement le commissaire de police. »

« Après tout, on s'est vu trois épouser des bergères ! » (*Un ménage de garçon*, édition Furne, 1843). Inutile d'essayer de comprendre ; sur le manuscrit de Balzac, on lit : « On a vu des rois épouser des bergères. »

« Je sortis et j'entrai dans une brasserie où j'absorbai deux tasses de café et quatre ou cinq petits *vers* pour me donner du courage. » (Maupassant, « La Patronne », dans la revue *La Lanterne* en 1889)

Dans *La Petite Roque*, le même Maupassant imagine qu'un prêtre entreprend de consoler la mère d'une fillette qui vient d'être assassinée. Il écrit : « La douleur de la mère s'atténuait sous la parole sucrée de l'ecclésiastique. »

Dans certaines éditions de la nouvelle, on trouve ce cas étonnant de fausse coquille qui relève en fait de la censure : « La douleur de la mère s'atténuait sous la parole *sacrée* de l'ecclésiastique. »

❧

Dans son *Essai sur la typographie* (1855), l'imprimeur Ambroise Firmin-Didot raconte qu'un jour, en visitant les presses, il est arrivé juste à temps pour éviter l'irréparable dans une réédition d'*Iphigénie* de Racine. Là où Achille déclare : « Vous allez à l'autel, et moi j'y cours, madame », le prote avait composé le texte comme suit : « Vous allez à l'*hôtel*, et moi j'y cours, madame. »

❧

Voici un témoignage du journaliste Charles Yriarte sur Baudelaire : « Une faute d'impression, une coquille le mettaient au désespoir [...]. Une des douleurs de sa vie était de voir ceux qui lui écrivaient et qui connaissaient peu l'œuvre et l'homme, écrire son nom avec un *e* : "Beaudelaire". »

Dans l'incroyable capharnaüm qui sert de maison à Bouvard et Pécuchet, on trouve une bien étonnante statue :

> Mais le plus beau, c'était dans l'embrasure de la fenêtre une statue de saint Pierre ! Sa main droite couverte d'un gant serrait la clef du Paradis, de couleur vert pomme. Sa chasuble que des fleurs de lys agrémentaient était bleu-ciel, & sa tiare très jaune pointue comme une pagode.

C'est là, du moins, ce qu'écrit Flaubert dans le manuscrit de *Bouvard et Pécuchet*… Car dans la première édition du roman – édition posthume (Lemerre, 1881) –, une malheureuse erreur de ponctuation crée, de toutes pièces, une perle qu'on attribue parfois, à tort, à l'écrivain :

> Sa main droite couverte d'un gant serrait la clef du Paradis. De couleur vert pomme, sa chasuble, que des fleurs de lis agrémentaient, était bleu-ciel […].

De Malherbe, on ne retient aujourd'hui que ces deux vers tirés de la « Consolation à M. Du Périer », adressée à un père pleurant la mort de sa fille :

> Et rose elle a vécu ce que vivent les roses,
> L'espace d'un matin.

On raconte parfois que le poète avait d'abord écrit « Et Rosette a vécu ce que vivent les roses », et que le raccourci heureux aurait été le fait d'un typographe avisé… La légende est belle, mais la réalité est plus prosaïque. Malherbe avait rédigé, avant la fameuse « Consolation », une première version du poème, dédiée à un autre ami qui avait lui aussi perdu sa fille. Il se trouve que la malheureuse enfant s'appelait Rosette, et qu'elle avait inspiré ces vers :

> Mais elle était du monde où les plus belles choses
> Font le moins de séjour,
> Et ne pouvait Rosette être mieux que les roses
> Qui ne vivent qu'un seul jour.

Adaptant son texte à son nouveau destinataire, Malherbe remplaça « Rosette » par « rose », et c'est cette substitution, et non une erreur d'imprimerie, qui fut à l'origine de la belle trouvaille poétique.

En 1911, Gide convainc le jeune Alexis Leger, qui deviendra bientôt célèbre sous le nom de Saint-John Perse, de publier un poème dans la *Nouvelle Revue française*. Peu après, le poète reçoit ses épreuves, et constate avec dépit qu'il doit les corriger copieusement. Assez peu lisible, son manuscrit a manifestement posé des problèmes aux typographes : une expression comme « le Songeur aux joues sales » est devenue « la rougeur aux joues pâles » ; plus étonnant encore, « le goût de tuer » est remplacé par « le goût de sucre » ! Leger se met à l'ouvrage et s'empresse de renvoyer ses corrections à un collaborateur de la *NRF*. C'était compter sans l'indolence de ce dernier, qui, sans même prendre la peine de relever son courrier, s'est contenté de faire suivre à Gide le premier jeu d'épreuves. Quand Leger reçoit son exemplaire de la revue, il est désespéré : « Lorsque j'ai eu jeté les yeux sur cette première page de fou que l'on donnait là sous mon nom, j'ai eu envie de crier comme un enfant. Non, je n'oublierai jamais le tour que l'on m'a joué, à cette revue de cuistres où il s'est trouvé des hommes assez mal élevés pour livrer un manuscrit de plus de vingt pages sans faire état de mes épreuves, par moi corrigées, renvoyées avec soin […] dans les trois jours. » (Lettre à Jacques Rivière)

En définitive, l'idéal, pour l'écrivain, ne serait-il pas d'être à lui-même son propre typographe ? C'est en tout cas le rêve que caresse, non sans humour, Chateaubriand dans l'Avant-propos des *Mémoires d'outre-tombe* : « Ces Mémoires ont été l'objet de ma prédilection : saint Bonaventure obtint du ciel la permission de continuer les siens après sa mort ; je n'espère pas une telle faveur, mais je désirerais ressusciter à l'heure des fantômes, pour corriger au moins les épreuves. […] C'est l'impossibilité probable d'être mon prote qui m'a fait tant de fois lire et relire le manuscrit, passer et repasser la lime sur l'ouvrage. »

Sans doute ne faut-il pas souhaiter cette résurrection-là à Paul Morand – la première chose qu'il apercevrait serait, gravée sur sa pierre tombale, dans le cimetière de Trieste, cette faute d'orthographe doublée d'une impropriété d'usage : « Paul Morand de l'*Accadémie de* France » !

Savoir rire de la faute

« Être où ne pas être, c'est peut-être aussi la question. » Le potentiel ludique de la faute n'a pas échappé au magicien des lettres qu'était Jacques Prévert. Les écrivains ne sont pas seulement victimes de la faute d'orthographe, ils n'hésitent pas à y recourir volontairement – pour notre plus grand bonheur !

Il s'agit bien souvent de faire entendre la voix du peuple. On connaît les fameux « c'est la faute à Voltaire », « c'est la faute à Rousseau », mis dans la bouche de Gavroche par Victor Hugo. Rappelons-nous aussi Françoise, l'attachante cuisinière de *La Recherche* : « Je ne sais pas m'*esprimer*. » Ses maladresses, tour à tour désopilantes et touchantes, sont toujours savoureuses, comme ici dans *Le Temps retrouvé* : « Seigneur, Vierge Marie, s'écriait Françoise, ça ne leur suffit pas d'avoir *conquéri* la pauvre Belgique. Elle a assez souffert celle-là au moment de son *envahition*. » La même sévissait déjà dans *Albertine disparue* : « Comme Françoise, à mon contact, avait enrichi son vocabulaire de termes nouveaux, mais en les arrangeant à sa mode, elle disait d'Albertine qu'elle n'avait jamais connu personne d'une telle *"perfidité"*. »

Les poilus du *Feu* s'expriment dans un argot largement reconstitué par Henri Barbusse. L'un d'entre eux s'inquiète auprès du personnage-narrateur, romancier de son état : « — Dis donc, sans t'commander… Y a quéqu'chose que j'voudrais te d'mander. Voilà la chose : si tu fais parler les troufions, dans ton livre, est-ce que tu les f'ras parler comme ils parlent, ou bien est-ce que tu arrangeras ça, en lousdoc ? »

Il s'entend répondre que la transcription sera fidèle. Il rétorque alors : « T'auras de la peine au dernier moment, t'es trop poli ! »

Molière avait pris les devants. Dans ce passage des *Femmes savantes*, les pédantes Bélise et Philaminte s'opposent à leur servante Martine pour cause de solécisme :

MARTINE
Quand on se fait entendre, on parle toujours bien,
Et tous vos biaux dictons ne servent pas de rien.

PHILAMINTE
Hé bien ! ne voilà pas encore de son style ?
Ne servent pas de rien !

BÉLISE
Ô cervelle indocile !
Faut-il qu'avec les soins qu'on prend incessamment,
On ne te puisse apprendre à parler congrûment ?
De *pas* mis avec *rien* tu fais la récidive ;
Et c'est, comme on t'a dit, trop d'une négative.

MARTINE
Mon Dieu, je n'avons pas étugué comme vous,
Et je parlons tout droit comme on parle cheux nous.

PHILAMINTE
Ah ! peut-on y tenir ?

BÉLISE
Quel solécisme horrible !

PHILAMINTE
En voilà pour tuer une oreille sensible.

BÉLISE

Ton esprit, je l'avoue, est bien matériel !
Je n'est qu'un singulier ; *avons*, est pluriel.
Veux-tu toute ta vie offenser la grammaire ?

MARTINE

Qui parle d'offenser grand'mère ni grand-père ?

Avec la faute volontaire, on peut donner dans la loufoquerie pure, comme dans le poème de Verlaine intitulé « À A. Duvigneaux, trop fougueux adversaire de l'orthographe phonétique » :

É coi vréman, bon Duvignô,
Vou zôci dou ke lé zagnô
É méïeur ke le pin con manj,
Vou metr'an ce courou zétranj

Contr(e) ce tâ de brav(e) jan
O fon plus bête ke méchan
Drapan leur linguistic étic
Dan l'ortograf(e) fonétic ?

Kel ir(e) donq vou zambala
Vizavi de cé zoizola […] ?

Farouche partisan d'une simplification de l'orthographe, Raymond Queneau reprend le procédé avec délectation dans *Bâtons, chiffres et lettres* : « Il s'agit [...] de choisir quelle orthographe donner au nouveau français. La plus phonétique semblerait s'imposer ; on pourrait employer l'alphabet [...] en observant cette règle que toute lettre se prononce, et sans jamais changer de valeur, quelle que soit sa position. Mézalor, mézalor, késkon nobtyin ! [...] On lrekonê pudutou, lfransé, amésa pudutou [...]. Avrédir, sêmêm maran. Jérlu toudsuit lé kat lign sidsu, jépapu manpéché demmaré. Mézifobyindir, sé un pur kestion dabitud. On népa zabitué, sétou. Unfoua kon sra zabitué, saïra tousel. »

Règle n° 16
Oser la faute

Un jour de 1888, monsieur Gaucher, professeur de lettres au lycée Condorcet, reçut la visite d'un éminent inspecteur général de l'Instruction publique, Eugène Manuel, qui publiait, à ses heures, des recueils de poésies. Le meilleur élève de la classe, un certain Marcel Proust, fut invité à lire l'une de ses compositions. Après la lecture, Manuel s'écria : « Vous n'auriez point, parmi les derniers de votre classe, un élève écrivant plus clairement et correctement en français ? » Gaucher répondit : « Monsieur l'inspecteur général, aucun de mes élèves n'écrit en français de manuel. »

Ce mot audacieux invite à juste titre à distinguer le style et la correction grammaticale. Comme l'a écrit Claudel dans Positions et propositions, *« les grands écrivains n'ont jamais été faits pour subir la loi des grammairiens mais pour imposer la leur, et non pas seulement leur volonté, mais leur caprice ». Bien des trouvailles poétiques sont nées de ce caprice.*

« Je t'aimais inconstant ; qu'aurais-je fait fidèle ? » Comment ne pas être ébloui par ce vers que prononce Hermione dans *Andromaque* ? Dans une lettre délicieuse, Proust, toujours lui, imagine les réticences d'un éditeur de son temps – en l'occurrence, le directeur de la *Revue de Paris*, qui passait pour un puriste – face au grand Racine : « Je comprends votre pensée ; vous voulez dire "je t'aimais inconstant, qu'est-ce que cela aurait été si tu avais été fidèle". Mais c'est mal exprimé. Cela peut signifier aussi bien que c'est vous qui auriez été fidèle. Préposé à la défense de la langue française je ne puis laisser passer cela. »

❧

« Il pleure dans mon cœur comme il pleut sur la ville. » C'est bien d'une faute de langue, à savoir l'emploi impersonnel du verbe « pleurer », que ce vers de Verlaine tire son charme. Aragon l'a dit : « Où la syntaxe est violée, [...] là combien de fois le lecteur frémit. »

« Il faut aussi que tu n'ailles point / Choisir tes mots sans quelque méprise. » Dans son fameux « Art poétique », Verlaine revendique une poétique de la maladresse grammaticale et de l'impropriété lexicale, infiniment plus suggestives, selon lui, qu'une langue impeccable. Dans un poème comme « Charleroi » *(Romances sans paroles)*, il parvient, en multipliant les écarts par rapport au « bon usage », à donner une présence étonnante au paysage belge :

Quoi donc se sent ?
L'avoine siffle.
Un buisson gifle
L'œil au passant. [...]

Où sent donc quoi ?
Des gares tonnent,
Les yeux s'étonnent,
Où Charleroi ?

Parfums sinistres !
Qu'est-ce que c'est ?
Quoi bruissait
Comme des sistres ?

Les audaces poétiques de Verlaine semblent faire écho aux recherches formelles des peintres

impressionnistes : incorrections et tours inso-
lites traduisent à merveille l'éparpillement des
sensations.

᪥

S'est-on déjà avisé que le plus beau poème de
la langue française, « Le Pont Mirabeau »
d'Apollinaire, contient, dès sa première
strophe, une énorme faute d'accord ?

> Sous le pont Mirabeau coule la Seine
> Et nos amours
> Faut-il qu'il m'en souvienne
> La joie venait toujours après la peine

Certes, on peut toujours imaginer un point
après « Seine » et voir dans « nos amours »
l'antécédent du pronom « en » (ce qui équivau-
drait à quelque chose comme « et faut-il que je
me souvienne de nos amours ? »), mais n'est-il
pas plus probable que le groupe nominal « nos
amours » soit, au même titre que « la Seine »,
sujet du verbe « coule » ? Comme la faute est
belle ! Non seulement l'isolement – rimique,
rythmique, visuel et grammatical – de « et nos
amours » est lourd de sens, mais encore ce

flottement syntaxique qui nous fait hésiter entre deux constructions s'accorde à ravir avec la thématique et la mélodie de ce poème fluvial.

❧

Dans le même poème, quelques strophes plus bas, on lit cet autre miracle poétique :

Passent les jours et passent les semaines
Ni temps passé
Ni les amours reviennent
Sous le pont Mirabeau coule la Seine

En toute rigueur grammaticale, il y a là de quoi froncer les sourcils : on attendrait « Ni le temps passé / Ni les amours ne reviennent ». Mais ajoutez ces deux syllabes, et tout l'effet s'écroule !

❧

Dans la préface des *Yeux d'Elsa*, Aragon évoque le pouvoir poétique des fautes de français : « J'avais, à l'âge où l'on apprend à aimer les poèmes, été singulièrement frappé par ces vers de Rimbaud :

> Mais des chansons spirituelles
> Voltigent partout les groseilles

tels qu'ils figuraient sous le titre *Patience (d'un été…)* dans l'édition Vanier. On veut aujourd'hui (édition critique, Mercure de France) qu'ils se lisent

> Voltigent parmi les groseilles

et sans doute qu'il en est ainsi. Mais je ne puis refaire le chemin parcouru et, pour moi, tant que je vivrai, je lirai *Voltigent partout…* avec cet étrange transitif du verbe voltiger, qu'on peut me dire être une faute, et que je persiste à considérer comme une beauté. »

Le langage courant, c'est entendu depuis Mallarmé, ne peut guère désigner que la plate réalité. Si l'on veut plonger dans l'inconnu pour dire ce qui n'a de nom dans aucune langue connue, il faut d'autres mots, d'autres associations, d'autres tournures de phrase, comme l'affirmeront les poètes du XXᵉ siècle. Chez Césaire ou Senghor, cette émancipation langagière revêt en outre une dimension politique : cette langue française qu'ils attaquent de l'intérieur, c'est celle du colonisateur. « Puisque l'oppresseur est présent jusque dans la langue qu'ils parlent », explique Sartre, les poètes de la négritude « parleront cette langue pour la détruire ». Dans le *Cahier d'un retour au pays natal*, c'est en se libérant lui-même d'un carcan, celui de la grammaire, que Césaire célèbre la libération des Noirs ; les liens syntaxiques s'effacent au profit d'une logique musicale et visuelle :

> Et elle est debout la négraille [...]
>   debout
>   et
>   libre
> debout et non point pauvre folle dans sa liberté et son
> dénuement maritimes girant en la dérive parfaite
> et la voici :
> plus inattendument debout
> debout dans les cordages
> debout à la barre
> debout à la boussole
> debout à la carte
> debout sous les étoiles
>   debout
>   et
>   libre
> et le navire lustral s'avancer impavide sur les eaux
> écroulées

À la question « c'est quoi, du Duras ? », la romancière répond : « C'est laisser le mot venir quand il vient, l'attraper comme il vient, à sa place de départ ou ailleurs, quand il passe. Et vite, vite, écrire, qu'on n'oublie pas comment c'est arrivé vers soi. » Quand elle évoque, dans *L'Amant*, la mort de son frère, Duras, se tenant au plus près de son émotion, s'affranchit des règles grammaticales pour mieux traduire l'essentiel : « Le petit frère. Mort. D'abord c'est inintelligible et puis, brusquement, de partout, du fond du monde, la douleur arrive, elle m'a recouverte, elle m'a emportée, je ne reconnaissais rien, je n'ai plus existé sauf la douleur. »

Écrire avec son cœur

Au chapitre XX *du* Rouge et le Noir, *Mme de Rênal fait discrètement parvenir un billet à Julien Sorel. C'était, dit le narrateur, une lettre « écrite à la hâte, baignée de larmes et sans la moindre ortho-graphe. Ordinairement Mme de Rênal la mettait fort bien, {Julien} fut touché de ce détail ».*

Il avait de quoi être touché : les fautes sont le miroir de l'âme. Le trouble et l'émotion s'y révèlent plus sûre-ment que dans de grands discours. Les lettres que Zola adressait à son épouse étaient d'une correction impec-cable, alors que celles qu'il écrivait à Jeanne Rozerot, la mère de ses deux enfants, étaient émaillées de négli-gences. Tel est le prix de l'authenticité. Comme disait Balzac, « il n'y a pas d'orthographe pour le cœur ».

Stendhal exige de sa sœur Pauline qu'elle lui écrive plus souvent : « Une lettre par semaine !

ce qui te viendra ; point de préparation, des fautes d'orthographe ; j'en fais beaucoup et je les aime ; je vois qu'on n'a point fait de brouillon, et rien de bête comme les lettres à brouillon. »

Lui-même liait ses fautes d'orthographe à l'intensité des émotions qu'il éprouvait : « Depuis la fin de mai jusqu'au mois d'octobre ou de novembre [...], je trouvai cinq ou six mois de bonheur céleste et complet.

On ne peut pas *appercevoir* distinctement la partie du ciel trop voisine du soleil, par un effet semblable j'aurai grand'peine à faire une narration raisonnable de mon amour pour Angela Pietragrua. Comment faire un récit un peu raisonnable de tant de folies ? Par où commencer ? Comment rendre cela un peu intelligible ? Voilà déjà que j'oublie l'*ortographe*, comme il m'arrive dans les grands transports de passion, et il s'agit pourtant de choses passées il y a trente-six ans. » (Manuscrit de *Vie de Henry Brulard*)

« C'est bien vrai, mon ange, je ne t'ai jamais *aimé* comme à présent. » (Hugo, lettre à Juliette Drouet)

Si le bonheur fait oublier « l'*ortographe* » à Stendalh ou Hugo, c'est la détresse la plus noire qui anime cette lettre ardente de Rimbaud à Verlaine, lequel vient juste, après une violente querelle, de quitter Londres pour gagner la Belgique :

Londres, vendredi ap-midi.

Reviens, reviens, cher ami, seul ami, reviens. Je te jure que je serai bon. [...] Voilà deux jours que je ne cesse de pleurer. Reviens. Sois courageux, cher ami. Rien n'est perdu. Tu n'as qu'à refaire le voyage. Nous revivrons ici bien courageusement, patiemment. Ah ! je t'en supplie. [...]

Oh tu ne *m'oubliera* pas, dis ?

Non tu ne peux pas m'oublier. Moi je t'ai toujours là.

Dis, *répons* à ton ami, est-ce que nous ne devons plus vivre ensemble. Sois courageux. Réponds-moi vite. Je ne puis rester ici plus longtemps. N'écoute que ton bon cœur.

Vite, dis si je dois te rejoindre.

à toi toute la vie.

Rimbaud

La lettre est datée du 4 juillet 1873 ; quelques jours plus tard, Rimbaud reçoit enfin un télégramme de son compagnon et part le rejoindre à Bruxelles. C'est le 10 juillet que Verlaine tire deux coups de revolver sur l'auteur du « Bateau ivre ».

Baudelaire vient d'apprendre qu'à la demande de sa famille, effrayée par ses dépenses inconsidérées, un conseil de tutelle est sur le point de se tenir. Il écrit à sa mère une lettre où deux fautes et l'oubli d'un mot trahissent son agitation : « Seulement il ne sera pas question de conseil judiciaire. Si je m'*appercevais* que tu l'*a* fait à mon insu, je me sauverais immédiate-ment, et pour le coup tu ne [me] verrais plus, car j'irais demeurer chez Jeanne. »

« Ô George ! George ! écoute ; ne *penses* pas au passé ; non, non ! au nom du ciel, ne compare pas, ne réfléchis pas, je t'aime comme *on a* jamais aimé. » (Musset, lettre à George Sand)

On sait combien Marcel Proust était attaché à sa mère. Elle est mourante quand il écrit ces mots à l'une de ses correspondantes, Geneviève Straus : « Peu après notre arrivée Maman a été prise de vomissements et de vertiges et est *tombé* gravement malade. Il a fallu la ramener à Paris. Mais le retour l'a achevée. Elle est actuellement dans un état terrible. Il a fallu cela pour que je ne vous aie pas encore *remercié* de votre lettre [...]. Mais je suis si malheureux que j'ai peu de courage pour écrire. »

À son grand dam, Cocteau se brouillait souvent avec son ami Apollinaire. Ce touchant billet, daté de juin 1917, porte la trace de sa sensibilité : « Cher Apollinaire, je suis triste aussi, *parceque* j'espérais que nous nous verrions [,] que nous nous approcherions, sûrs l'un de l'autre. Chaque fois que je vous rencontre je vous suis "suspect". *Cloisons étanche* – solitude – et savoir du moment qu'un homme comme vous ne distingue pas mes couches profondes qu'il est impossible à personne de les découvrir. »

C'est sans doute chez Maupassant qu'on trouvera les fautes les plus déchirantes. Atteint de syphilis, le romancier souffrait de troubles neurologiques, notamment de graves problèmes de vue ; lors de ses crises, il n'arrivait pratiquement plus à écrire. En juin 1891, deux ans avant sa mort, il adresse à sa mère une lettre couverte de ratures dans laquelle se devinent ses efforts désespérés pour se concentrer. On déchiffre assez péniblement : « Je veux te dire que je quitte Divonne en quelques mots seulement, ma bien chère Mère, mais je ne vais pas loin et j'y reviendrai sans doute. [...] Cazalis m'a donné rendez-vous à Genève. Il m'a trouvé si bonne mine, l'air si fort, qu'il s'est écrié : "Vous êtes guéri." »

Au début du XXᵉ siècle, un médecin décrit en ces termes la lettre dont nous parlons : « Au lieu de "reviendrai", il écrit d'abord "revierai" puis "revienai" et enfin, il efface son essai maladroit pour écrire correctement "reviendrai". Dans "j'y", Maupassant n'arrive pas à placer correctement son apostrophe, qui est entourée de points traduisant l'achoppement de sa plume ; il met d'abord *touches* pour douches, *lide* pour lire

[…] ; nous remarquons encore "vous ête gueri", *idéee* pour idée, etc. Les lettres sont mal formées, l'écriture est tremblée, hésitante, roide, anguleuse, parfois ataxique. La fin de la lettre est d'une écriture enfantine. »

Laissons, pour finir, la parole à l'un de ceux que nous avons abondamment cités dans ces pages. Dans cette confidence à Mme Hanska, Balzac nous rappelle que si la faute est émouvante, c'est aussi, et tout simplement, parce qu'elle révèle quelque chose de la dure condition des gens de lettres : « Je travaille dix-huit heures par jour. Je me suis aperçu des défauts de style qui déparent *La Peau de chagrin*, je la corrige pour la rendre irréprochable ; mais après deux mois de travail, *La Peau* réimprimée, je découvre encore une centaine de fautes. Ce sont des chagrins de poète. […] De tous côtés, l'on me crie que je ne sais pas écrire, et cela est cruel quand je me le suis déjà dit et que je consacre le jour à mes nouveaux travaux, et la nuit à perfectionner les anciens. »

AUX LECTEURS

Ne plus commettre aucune faute : un rêve à réaliser, ou un jeu auquel on n'a jamais fini de jouer ? André Gide suggérait dans son *Journal* de rendre l'apprentissage de l'orthographe plus ludique en remplaçant la sacro-sainte dictée par un exercice de correction d'épreuves ; sans chercher à les piéger, on inviterait les élèves à repérer dans les textes erreurs, coquilles ou impropriétés tout en s'amusant.

Le principe est en effet bien séduisant, si séduisant que les auteurs de ce petit livre n'ont pas résisté à la tentation d'introduire une faute d'orthographe dans les pages qui précèdent – une faute, oui, mais, pas n'importe laquelle, puisque Balzac la commettait déjà en son temps. À vous, amis lecteurs, de la découvrir !

SOURCES

Ce petit ouvrage n'aurait pas pu voir le jour sans le travail des équipes de recherche qui reproduisent ou numérisent les manuscrits, publient les textes avec la plus grande fidélité possible, rendent compte des ratures, répertorient les variantes. Outre les livres cités ci-dessous, nous avons notamment eu recours à la base de données Frantext (qui permet des recherches ciblées au sein d'un très vaste corpus de textes littéraires), à l'édition critique en ligne de *La Comédie humaine* (réalisée par le Groupe international de recherches balzaciennes, la Mairie de Paris et l'université de Chicago), ainsi qu'aux manuscrits stendhaliens numérisés par la Bibliothèque municipale de Grenoble et l'université Stendhal. Nous souhaitons également dire notre dette à l'égard de l'incontournable grammaire de Maurice Grevisse et André

Goosse, *Le Bon Usage*, qui se lit avec autant de plaisir que les romans cités dans ces pages.

Les références données ci-dessous suivent l'ordre des citations au sein des différents chapitres.

Prologue

WINDELS Loïc, « La lettre volée par le diable. Lecture d'une faute de langue dans la dédicace des *Fleurs du Mal* », *Les Chantiers de la création* [en ligne], 2, 2009, http://lcc.revues.org/182.

BAUDELAIRE Charles, *Correspondance*, t. I, éd. Claude Pichois et Jean Ziegler, Gallimard, « Bibliothèque de la Pléiade », 1973, p. 255 (lettre à Champfleury, 14 janvier 1854).

GIDE André, *Interviews imaginaires*, Gallimard, 1942, p. 34.

DIAZ Brigitte, *Stendhal en sa correspondance ou « L'Histoire d'un esprit »*, Honoré Champion, 2003, p. 109 (lettre de Stendhal à sa sœur Pauline, octobre 1804).

Règle n° 1

SARRAUTE Nathalie, *Enfance*, Gallimard, « Folio », 1983, p. 83-85.

FLAUBERT Gustave, *Correspondance*, t. I, éd. Jean Bruneau, Gallimard, « Bibliothèque de la Pléiade », 1973, p. 5.

SARTRE Jean-Paul, *Les Mots*, Gallimard, « Folio »,
   1991, p. 65.

CONTAT Michel et RYBALKA Michel, *Les Écrits de
   Sartre*, Gallimard, 1970, p. 225.

PROUST Marcel, *Lettres*, éd. Françoise Leriche, Plon,
   2004, p. 61 (lettre du 2 avril 1879).

VALLIÈRES Nathalie DES, *Les Plus Beaux Manuscrits de
   Saint-Exupéry*, La Martinière, 2003, p. 36-37.

BAUDELAIRE Charles, *Correspondance*, *op. cit.*, t. I,
   p. 695 (lettre du 3 juillet 1832).

Règle n° 2

LAROUSSE Pierre, *Le Livre des permutations*, Boyer,
   1882, p. 3.

VOLTAIRE, *Lettres inédites*, Mongie, 1821, p. 40-41
   (lettre du 24 décembre 1757).

BAUDELAIRE Charles, *Correspondance*, *op. cit.*, t. II,
   p. 960 (lettre du 12 février 1866).

STENDHAL, *Vie de Henry Brulard*, t. I, éd. Gérard et
   Yvonne Rannaud, Klincksieck, 1996 (transcription diplomatique du manuscrit), p. 7.

BONACCORSO Giovanni, *Corpus Flaubertianum*, t. I :
   Un cœur simple, Les Belles Lettres, 1983, p. 553.

CÉLINE Louis-Ferdinand, *Lettres*, éd. Henri Godard et
   Jean-Paul Louis, Gallimard, « Bibliothèque de la
   Pléiade », 2009, p. 377.

CÉLINE Louis-Ferdinand, *Voyage au bout de la nuit :
   manuscrit*, Éditions des Saints Pères, 2014, p. 3.

Correspondance Guillaume Apollinaire-Jean Cocteau, éd. Pierre Caizergues, Michel Décaudin et Gilbert Boudar, Éditions Jean-Michel Place, 1991, p. 56.

ÉLUARD Paul, *Lettres à Gala (1924-1948)*, éd. Pierre Dreyfus, Gallimard, 1984, p. 98.

DIDIER Béatrice et NEEFS Jacques (dir.), *Écritures du romantisme II : George Sand*, PUV, « Manuscrits modernes », 1989, p. 118.

SAND George, *Correspondance*, t. I, éd. Georges Lubin, Garnier frères, 1964, p. 925.

SAND George, *Œuvres autobiographiques*, éd. Georges Lubin, Gallimard, « Bibliothèque de la Pléiade », 1983, p. 1384.

DUMAS Olivier, *Jules Verne. Avec la correspondance inédite de Jules Verne à sa famille*, La Manufacture, 1988, p. 311.

LEMIRE Charles, *Jules Verne*, Berger-Levrault, 1908, p. 116.

WEBER-CAFLISCH Antoinette, *Le Soulier de satin de Paul Claudel*, t. I, éd. critique, Les Belles Lettres, 1987, p. 78.

APOLLINAIRE Guillaume, cité dans LEROY Claude, *Rencontres avec Blaise Cendrars : Entretiens et interviews, 1925-1959*, Non Lieu, 2007, p. 169.

BALZAC Honoré DE, *Un début dans la vie*, in *Œuvres complètes*, vol. IV, Furne, sans date [1842 ?], p. 515.

GIRAUDOUX Jean, *Lettres*, éd. Jacques Body, Klincksieck, 1975, p. 53 (lettre du 1er avril 1906).

STENDHAL, *Vie de Henry Brulard*, *op. cit.*, t. II, p. 5.

BAUDELAIRE Charles, *Œuvres complètes*, éd. Yves-Gérard Le Dantec et Claude Pichois, Gallimard, « Bibliothèque de la Pléiade », 1961, p. 1544.

STENDHAL, *Le Rouge et le Noir*, éd. Béatrice Didier, Gallimard, « Folio classique », 1972, p. 248-249.

RIVIÈRE Jacques – ALAIN-FOURNIER, *Correspondance*, t. II, Gallimard, 1926, p. 394.

Règle n° 3

JACOB P.-L., « Simple histoire de mes relations littéraires avec Honoré de Balzac, extrait abrégé de mes *Mémoires inédits* », in *Le Livre*, t. III [1882], p. 187.

BALZAC Honoré DE, *Le Médecin de campagne*, in *Œuvres complètes*, vol. XIII, Furne, sans date [1845 ?], p. 312.

KELLER Luzius, *Les Avant-textes de l'épisode de la madeleine dans les cahiers de brouillon de Marcel Proust*, Éditions Jean-Michel Place, 1978, p. 50.

GIONO Jean, *Le Moulin de Pologne*, Gallimard, 1952, p. 188.

BAUDELAIRE Charles, « La Muse malade », *Les Fleurs du Mal*, in *Œuvres complètes*, *op. cit.*, p. 14 et 1509.

BECKER Colette et LAVIELLE Véronique, *La Fabrique des Rougon-Macquart*, t. V, Honoré Champion, 2011, p. 320.

CHATEAUBRIAND François-René DE, *Mémoires d'outre-tombe*, t. I, éd. Jean-Claude Berchet, Le Livre de Poche, « La Pochothèque », 1989-1998, p. 448.

VERLAINE Paul, « Du fond du grabat », *Sagesse*, in *Œuvres poétiques complètes*, éd. Yves-Gérard

Le Dantec et Jacques Borel, Gallimard, « Bibliothèque de la Pléiade », 1962, p. 276.

BALZAC Honoré DE, *La Femme de trente ans*, Charpentier, 1839, p. 242.

BALZAC Honoré DE, *Lettres à Madame Hanska*, t. I, éd. Roger Pierrot, Robert Laffont, « Bouquins », 1990, p. 547 (lettre du 5 janvier 1842).

Règle n° 4

DU CAMP Maxime, *Souvenirs littéraires* [1892], Aubier, 1994, p. 581-582.

LAMARTINE Alphonse DE, « La Mort de Socrate », in *Œuvres poétiques complètes*, éd. Marius-François Guyard, Gallimard, « Bibliothèque de la Pléiade », 1963, p. 95.

MUSSET Alfred DE, *Lorenzaccio*, in *Théâtre complet*, éd. Simon Jeune, Gallimard, « Bibliothèque de la Pléiade », 1990, p. 1024.

BALZAC Honoré DE, *Eugénie Grandet*, in *Œuvres complètes*, vol. V, Furne, 1843, p. 289.

RIMBAUD Arthur, *Correspondance*, éd. Jean-Jacques Lefrère, Fayard, 2007, p. 537 (lettre du 8 octobre 1887).

RIMBAUD Arthur, *Illuminations*, éd. André Guyaux, À la Baconnière, 1985, p. 37-38.

QUENEAU Raymond, *Zazie dans le métro* [1959], Gallimard, « Folio », 2008, p. 206.

BAUDELAIRE Charles, *Correspondance*, *op. cit.*, t. II, p. 692 (lettre du 11 octobre 1860).

SAND George, *Correspondance*, *op. cit.*, t. I, p. 168 (lettre du 5 septembre 1825).

ARAGON Louis, *Les Beaux Quartiers*, Denoël et Steele, 1936, p. 45.

Règle n° 5

RIMBAUD Arthur, *Les Illuminations*, *op. cit.*, p. 46.

KELLER Luzius, *Les Avant-textes de l'épisode de la madeleine dans les cahiers de brouillon de Marcel Proust*, *op. cit.*, p. 48.

PROUST Marcel, *Lettres*, *op. cit.*, p. 1070 (lettre du 18 janvier 1922).

BALZAC Honoré DE, *La Cousine Bette*, in *Œuvres complètes*, Furne, vol. XVII, 1848, p. 232.

BALZAC Honoré DE, *Lettres à Madame Hanska*, t. I, *op. cit.*, p. 37 (lettre de mars 1833).

HUGO Victor, *Œuvres poétiques*, t. II, éd. Pierre Albouy, Gallimard, « Bibliothèque de la Pléiade », 1986, p. 1578.

LAMARTINE Alphonse DE, *Œuvres poétiques complètes*, *op. cit.*, p. 614.

MAUPASSANT Guy DE, « Un réveillon », *Mademoiselle Fifi*, in *Contes et nouvelles*, t. I, éd. Louis Forestier, Gallimard, « Bibliothèque de la Pléiade », 1974, p. 337.

BALZAC Honoré DE, *La Vieille Fille*, in *La Comédie humaine*, t. IV, éd. Pierre-Georges Castex (dir.), Gallimard, « Bibliothèque de la Pléiade », 1976, p. 829.

Baudelaire Charles, *Correspondance*, *op. cit.*, t. II, p. 728 (lettre du 21 mai 1861).

Follet Lionel, « À propos du manuscrit d'*Aurélien* », *Recherches croisées Aragon-Elsa Triolet*, n° 1, Annales littéraires de l'université de Besançon, Les Belles Lettres, 1988, p. 85-101. Article consulté sur le site suivant : www.louisaragon-elsatriolet.org/spip.php?article175.

Baudelaire Charles, *Correspondance*, *op. cit.*, t. II, p. 937 (lettre du 29 octobre 1865).

Céline Louis-Ferdinand, *Lettres à des amies*, éd. Colin William Nettelbeck, Gallimard, « Les Cahiers de la NRF », 1997, p. 137 (lettre du 29 mars 1936).

Duras Marguerite, *L'Amant*, Minuit, 1984, p. 12.

Règle n° 6

Labiche Eugène, *La Grammaire*, éd. Jasmine Zanotti-Rebellato, Hatier, 2004, p. 29-30.

Baudelaire Charles, *Correspondance*, *op. cit.*, t. II, p. 774 (lettre du 17 mars 1862).

Rimbaud Arthur, *Correspondance*, *op. cit.*, p. 261 (lettre du 25 août 1880).

Balzac Honoré de, *Lettres à Madame Hanska*, *op. cit.*, t. I, p. 85 (lettre du 6 novembre 1833).

Giraudoux Jean, *Siegfried et le Limousin* [Grasset, 1922], Le Livre de poche, 1964, p. 95.

Nerval Gérard de, « Gaieté », in *Œuvres complètes*, t. III, éd. Jean Guillaume et Claude Pichois (dir.), Gallimard, « Bibliothèque de la Pléiade », 1993, p. 413.

Apollinaire Guillaume, *Alcools*, NRF, 1920 (3ᵉ édition), p. 117 et 119.

Balzac Honoré de, *Lettres à Madame Hanska*, *op. cit.*, t. I, p. 700 (lettre du 1ᵉʳ juillet 1843).

Mauriac Dyer Nathalie, « Deux notes à propos du texte de *La Prisonnière* », in *Bulletin Marcel Proust*, nº 53, 2003, p. 23-28. Article consulté sur http://www.item.ens.fr/index.php?id=76074.

Balzac Honoré de, *Le Cabinet des Antiques*, in *La Comédie humaine*, t. IV, éd. Pierre-Georges Castex (dir.), Gallimard, « Bibliothèque de la Pléiade », 1976, p. 1036.

Balzac Honoré de, *Le Contrat de mariage*, in *Œuvres complètes*, vol. III, Furne, 1842, p. 182.

Becker Colette et Lavielle Véronique, *La Fabrique des Rougon-Macquart*, *op. cit.*, p. 260 et 378.

Règle nº 7

Gide André, *Interviews imaginaires*, *op. cit.*, p. 34.

Rimbaud Arthur, *Correspondance*, *op. cit.*, p. 897 (lettre du 17 juin 1891).

Baudelaire Charles, *Correspondance*, *op. cit.*, t. II, p. 852 (lettre du 6 mai 1864).

Balzac Honoré de, *Lettres à sa famille*, éd. Walter Scott Hastings, Albin Michel, 1950, p. 9 (lettre du 6 septembre 1819).

Duras Marguerite, *La Douleur*, POL, 1985, p. 182.

Odouard Nadia, *Les Années folles de Raymond Radiguet*, Seghers, 1973, p. 262.

BAUDELAIRE Charles, *Correspondance*, *op. cit.*, t. II, p. 691 (lettre du 27 septembre 1860).

SAINT-EXUPÉRY Antoine DE, *Lettres à sa mère*, in *Œuvres complètes*, t. I, éd. dirigée par Michel Autrand et Michel Quesnel, Gallimard, « Bibliothèque de la Pléiade », 1994, p. 729 (lettre de 1923).

FLAUBERT Gustave, « Un cœur simple », *Trois Contes*, in *Œuvres*, éd. Albert Thibaudet et René Dumesnil, Gallimard, « Bibliothèque de la Pléiade », 1952, p. 615.

FRANCE Anatole, *La Rôtisserie de la reine Pédauque*, in *Œuvres*, t. II, éd. Marie-Claire Bancquart, Gallimard, « Bibliothèque de la Pléiade », 1987, p. 40.

SARTRE Jean-Paul, *La Nausée*, Gallimard, 1938, p. 21.

CAMUS Albert, *La Peste*, Gallimard, 1947, p. 41.

VERLAINE Paul, *Quinze jours en Hollande*, in *Œuvres en prose complètes*, éd. Jacques Borel, Gallimard, « Bibliothèque de la Pléiade », 1972, p. 388.

PROUST Marcel, *À la recherche du temps perdu. Du côté de chez Swann*, Grasset, 1914, p. 17.

DU CAMP Maxime, *Souvenirs littéraires*, *op. cit.*, p. 582.

PROUST Marcel, *Lettres*, *op. cit.*, p. 650-651 (lettre du 11 décembre 1913).

KOLTÈS Bernard-Marie, *Lettres*, Minuit, 2009 (lettre du 16 février 1986).

Règle n° 8

SAINT-EXUPÉRY Antoine DE, *Terre des hommes*, Gallimard, 1939, p. 184.

PÉLISSIER Georges, *Les Cinq Visages de Saint-Exupéry*, Flammarion, 1951, p. 81-82.

NUITEN Henk, *Les Variantes des* Fleurs du Mal *et des* Épaves *de Charles Baudelaire (1821-1867), étude de stylistique génétique*, APA-Holland Universiteits Pers, 1979, p. 8.

BALZAC Honoré DE, *Le Médecin de campagne*, Gallimard, « Folio classique », 1974, p. 215.

FLAUBERT Gustave, *Correspondance*, *op. cit.*, t. I, p. 223.

HUYSMANS Joris-Karl, *À rebours*, Charpentier, 1884, p. 93.

SAINT-EXUPÉRY Antoine DE, *Courrier Sud*, Gallimard, 1929, p. 47.

DURAS Marguerite, *Les Petits Chevaux de Tarquinia*, in *Œuvres complètes*, éd. Gilles Philippe (dir.), Gallimard, « Bibliothèque de la Pléiade », 2011, p. 860.

LACRETELLE Jacques DE, *Les Maîtres et les amis : études et souvenirs littéraires*, Wesmael-Charlier, 1959, p. 178.

RADIGUET Raymond, *Le Diable au corps, édition critique*, éd. Nadia Odouard, Lettres modernes Minard, 2007, p. 64.

MARIVAUX, *Le Paysan parvenu*, Veuve Duchesne, 1764, p. 46.

DUMAS Alexandre, *La Chasse au chastre et autres nouvelles humoristiques*, éd. Daniel Zimmermann, Actes Sud, « Babel », 1995, p. 302.

GONCOURT Jules et Edmond DE, *Germinie Lacerteux*, Charpentier, 1865, p. 238.

BECKER Colette et LAVIELLE Véronique, *La Fabrique des Rougon-Macquart*, *op. cit.*, t. V, p. 128.

Hugo Victor, *Dieu*, in *La Légende des siècles. La Fin de Satan. Dieu*, éd. Jacques Truchet, Gallimard, « Bibliothèque de la Pléiade », 1950, p. 970.

Hugo Victor, *Les Misérables*, t. I, éd. Yves Gohin, Gallimard, « Folio classique », 1995, p. 856.

Balzac Honoré de, *Une double famille*, suivi du *Contrat de mariage* et de *L'Interdiction*, Gallimard, « Folio classique », 1973, p. 280.

Giraudoux Jean, *Judith*, Émile-Paul frères, 1931, p. 21.

Balzac Honoré de, *La Peau de chagrin*, in *Œuvres complètes*, vol. XIV, Furne, 1846, p. 53.

Dumas Alexandre, *Don Juan de Marana*, in *Théâtre complet*, Michel Lévy frères, troisième série, 1864, p. 325.

Yourcenar Marguerite, *Mémoires d'Hadrien*, Plon, 1951, p. 450.

Règle n° 9

Vigny Alfred de, « La Flûte », *Les Destinées*, in *Œuvres complètes*, t. I, éd. François Germain et André Jarry, Gallimard, « Bibliothèque de la Pléiade », 1986, p. 1098.

Mauriac François, *Les Chemins de la mer* [1939], Grasset, « Les Cahiers rouges », 2000, p. 320.

Hugo Victor, « Ce qui se passait aux Feuillantines vers 1813 », *Les Rayons et les ombres*, in *Œuvres poétiques*, t. I, éd. Pierre Albouy, Gallimard, « Bibliothèque de la Pléiade », 1964, p. 1067.

Balzac Honoré de, *La Duchesse de Langeais*, éd. Michel Lichtlé, Flammarion, « GF », 1988, p. 44.

Stendhal, *Le Rouge et le Noir*, éd. Béatrice Didier, Gallimard, « Folio classique », 1972, p. 59.

Hugo Victor, *Les Misérables*, *op. cit.*, t. II, p. 263.

Flaubert Gustave, *Correspondance*, t. V, éd. Jean Bruneau, Yvan Leclerc, Jean-François Delesalle, Jean-Benoît Guinot et Joëlle Robert, Gallimard, « Bibliothèque de la Pléiade », 2007, p. 430 (lettre du 10 septembre 1878).

Flaubert Gustave, *Novembre*, in *Œuvres de jeunesse*, éd. Claudine Gothot-Mersch et Guy Sagnes, Gallimard, « Bibliothèque de la Pléiade », 2001, p. 797.

Crépet Eugène, *Charles Baudelaire*, Vanier, 1906, p. 427.

Chateaubriand François-René de, *Mémoires d'outre-tombe*, *op. cit.*, t. I, p. 1074.

Marcellus, *Chateaubriand et son temps*, Michel Lévy, 1859, p. 213.

Péguy Charles, *Clio*, Gallimard, 1914, p. 35.

Le Charivari, cité dans Bordas Éric, « Balzac et la question du style », article consulté à l'adresse suivante : http://133.12.17.160/~balzac/colloques/styleBordas.pdf

Balzac Honoré de, *Eugénie Grandet*, éd. Éléonore Roy-Reverzy, Flammarion, « GF », 2000, p. 127.

Balzac Honoré de, *Sur Catherine de Médicis*, La Table ronde, « La Petite Vermillon », 2006, p. 323.

Balzac Honoré de, *L'Auberge rouge*, in *Œuvres complètes*, vol. XV, Furne, 1846, p. 382.

Balzac Honoré de, *Les Comédiens sans le savoir*, in *Œuvres complètes*, vol. XII, Furne, 1846, p. 185.

Febvre Frédéric, *Journal d'un comédien*, t. II, Paul Ollendorf, 1896, p. 71.

Règle n° 10

Goncourt Edmond et Jules de, *Manette Salomon*, éd. Stéphanie Champeau et Adrien Goetz, Gallimard, « Folio classique », 1996, p. 80.

Balzac Honoré de, *Le Cabinet des Antiques*, éd. Nadine Satiat, Gallimard, « Folio », 1999, p. 153.

Stendhal, *Le Rouge et le Noir*, *op. cit.*, p. 124.

Balzac Honoré de, *Le Père Goriot*, éd. Thierry Bodin, Gallimard, « Folio classique », 1971, p. 63.

Hugo Victor, « Le Satyre », *La Légende des siècles*, *op. cit.*, p. 416.

Hugo Victor, *Notre-Dame de Paris*, éd. Jean Maurel, Le Livre de Poche, 1972, p. 260.

Chateaubriand François-René de, *Génie du christianisme*, éd. Maurice Regard, Gallimard, « Bibliothèque de la Pléiade », 1978, p. 496.

Balzac Honoré de, *Maître Cornélius*, in *Le Chef-d'œuvre inconnu et autres nouvelles*, éd. Adrien Goetz, Gallimard, « Folio classique », 1994, p. 172.

Zola Émile, *Son Excellence Eugène Rougon*, in *Les Rougon-Macquart*, t. II, éd. Armand Lanoux et Henri Mitterand, Gallimard, « Bibliothèque de la Pléiade », 1961, p. 274.

Hugo Victor, *Les Misérables*, *op. cit.*, t. II, p. 598.

VERLAINE Paul, « Art poétique », *Jadis et Naguère*, in *Œuvres poétiques complètes*, *op. cit.*, p. 336.

CHATEAUBRIAND François-René DE, *Mémoires d'outre-tombe*, *op. cit.*, t. I, p. 132.

Règle n° 11

LAMARTINE Alphonse DE, *Correspondance*, t. IV, éd. Christian Croisille et Marie-Renée Morin, Honoré Champion, 2005, p. 128 (lettre du 23 décembre 1824).

LAMARTINE Alphonse DE, « Le Poète mourant », *Nouvelles Méditations poétiques*, in *Œuvres poétiques complètes*, *op. cit.*, p. 145.

KOLTÈS Bernard-Marie, *Dans la solitude des champs de coton*, Minuit, 1986, p. 9.

PROUST Marcel, *Sodome et Gomorrhe*, t. IX, Gallimard, 1924, p. 279.

PROUST Marcel, *Jean Santeuil*, Gallimard, 1952, p. 121.

BECKER Colette et LAVIELLE Véronique, *La Fabrique des Rougon-Macquart*, *op. cit.*, t. V, p. 320.

BALZAC Honoré DE, *La Rabouilleuse*, in *La Comédie humaine*, t. IV, éd. Pierre-Georges Castex (dir.), Gallimard, « Bibliothèque de la Pléiade », 1976, p. 434.

GIDE André, *Robert*, Gallimard, 1930, p. 35.

FLAUBERT Gustave, *Madame Bovary*, éd. Thierry Laget, Gallimard, 2001, p. 346.

PAGNOL Marcel, *Le Temps des secrets*, in *Œuvres complètes*, t. XII, Le Club de l'honnête homme, 1977, p. 174.

GIDE André, *Isabelle*, Gallimard, 1929, p. 98.

CAMUS Albert, *La Peste*, Gallimard, 1947, p. 169, cité dans Maurice Grevisse et André Goose, *Le Bon Usage*, De Boeck, 2007 (rééd.), p. 330.

FLAUBERT Gustave, *Correspondance*, t. II, éd. Jean Bruneau, Gallimard, « Bibliothèque de la Pléiade », 1980, p. 707 (lettre du 24 avril 1857).

CLAUDEL Paul, *La Rose et le rosaire*, cité dans le *Bulletin de la Société Paul Claudel*, n° 169, 2003, p. 58-59.

GIDE André, *L'Immoraliste*, Mercure de France, 1902, p. 37.

STENDHAL, *Le Rouge et le Noir*, *op. cit.*, p. 255.

BAUDELAIRE Charles, *Correspondance*, *op. cit.*, t. I, p. 715 (lettre du 27 juin 1838).

FLAUBERT Gustave, *Madame Bovary*, *op. cit.*, p. 50, 82, 223 et 227.

MME DE SÉVIGNÉ, citée dans *Principes généraux de la langue française*, par Noël-François de Wailly, 1803, p. 138.

Règle n° 12

Plusieurs des phrases que nous citons dans ce chapitre ont été relevées par Albert Cim dans *Récréations littéraires*, Hachette, 1920.

STENDHAL, *Vie de Henry Brulard*, *op. cit.*, t. II, p. 647.

BALZAC Honoré DE, *Une ténébreuse affaire*, in *Œuvres complètes*, vol. XII, Furne, 1846, p. 298.

PROUST Marcel, *Le Temps retrouvé*, in *À la recherche du temps perdu*, t. IV, éd. Jean-Yves Tadié,

Gallimard, « Bibliothèque de la Pléiade », 1989, p. 278.

BALZAC Honoré DE, *La Bourse*, in *Œuvres complètes*, Furne, vol. I, 1842, p. 155.

LAMARTINE Alphonse DE, *Jocelyn*, in *Œuvres poétiques complètes*, *op. cit.*, p. 700.

BALZAC Honoré DE, *La Muse du département*, éd. Patrick Berthier, Gallimard, « Folio », 1984, p. 106.

DUMAS Alexandre, *Le Collier de la reine*, éd. Sylvie Thorel-Cailleteau, Gallimard, « Folio », 2002, p. 372.

BALZAC Honoré DE, *La Peau de chagrin*, éd. Nadine Satiat, Flammarion, « GF », 1996, p. 154.

MAURIAC François, *Les Anges noirs*, in *Œuvres romanesques*, Flammarion, 1965, p. 382.

CHATEAUBRIAND François-René DE, *Mémoires d'outre-tombe*, *op. cit.*, t. I, p. 346.

VOLTAIRE, *L'Orphelin de la Chine*, in *Œuvres complètes*, Furne, 1835, p. 688.

ZOLA Émile, *La Débâcle*, in *Les Rougon-Macquart*, *op. cit.*, t. V, p. 692.

MAUPASSANT Guy DE, *Boule de Suif*, in *Contes et nouvelles*, *op. cit.*, t. I, p. 98.

BALZAC Honoré DE, *Physiologie du mariage*, in *Œuvres complètes*, vol. XVI, Furne, 1846, p. 607.

BALZAC Honoré DE, *La Femme de trente ans*, éd. Gérard Gengembre, Flammarion, « GF », 2010, p. 218.

BALZAC Honoré DE, *Le Médecin de campagne*, Gallimard, « Folio classique », 1974, p. 233.

CIZERON-RIVAL, *Récréations littéraires*, Bessiat, 1765, p. 68-69.

Règle n° 13

FLAUBERT Gustave, *Correspondance*, *op. cit.*, t. IV, p. 1010 (lettre de Du Camp, 7 juillet 1869).

FLAUBERT Gustave, *L'Éducation sentimentale*, Conard, 1910, p. 641.

APOLLINAIRE Guillaume, *Correspondance avec son frère et sa mère*, éd. Gilbert Boudar et Michel Décaudin, Corti, 1987, p. 42.

CLAUDEL Louis-Prosper, lettre à son fils (20 janvier 1891), citée dans *Cahiers Paul Claudel*, I, 1959, p. 114.

VIGNY Alfred DE, *Héléna*, in *Œuvres complètes*, *op. cit.*, t. I, p. 1139 et 1140.

PROUST Marcel, *Lettres*, *op. cit.*, p. 966 (lettre du 2 septembre 1920).

DELBLAT Jean-Luc, *Le Métier d'écrire. Entretiens avec 18 écrivains*, Le Cherche Midi, 1994, p. 160.

Règle n° 14

GIDE André, *Journal*, t. II, 15 décembre 1937, éd. Martine Sagaert, Gallimard, « Bibliothèque de la Pléiade », 1997, p. 1276.

BALZAC Honoré DE, *Une fille d'Ève*, in *Œuvres complètes*, vol. II, Furne, 1842, p. 200.

BALZAC Honoré DE, *Ferragus*, in *Œuvres complètes*, vol. IX, Furne, 1843, p. 21.

BALZAC Honoré DE, *Illusions perdues*, in *Œuvres complètes*, vol. VIII, Furne, 1843, p. 253.

APOLLINAIRE Guillaume, « Un fantôme de nuée », *Calligrammes*, Mercure de France, 1918, p. 196.

BALZAC Honoré DE, *La Femme de trente ans*, in *Œuvres complètes*, vol. III, Furne, 1842, p. 57.

BALZAC Honoré DE, *La Cousine Bette*, Michel Lévy, 1871, p. 259.

BALZAC Honoré DE, *Un ménage de garçon*, in *Œuvres complètes*, vol. VI, Furne, 1843, p. 169.

MAUPASSANT Guy DE, *Contes et nouvelles*, *op. cit.*, t. II, p. 73.

FONYI Antonia, « Genèse et censure psychique. L'exemple de Maupassant », in *Genèse, censure, autocensure*, éd. Claire Bustarret et Catherine Viollet, Éditions du CNRS, « Textes et Manuscrits », 2005, p. 97-114. Article consulté à l'adresse www.item.ens.fr/index.php?id=27118

FIRMIN-DIDOT Ambroise, *Essai sur la typographie*, Firmin-Didot, 1855, p. 676.

YRIARTE Charles, *Les Portraits cosmopolites*, Lachaud, 1870, p. 125.

FLAUBERT Gustave, *Bouvard et Pécuchet, œuvre posthume*, Lemerre, 1881, p. 126. Le manuscrit du roman a été consulté sur le site du Centre Flaubert (université de Rouen) : http://flaubert.univ-rouen.fr/.

MALHERBE François DE, *Œuvres poétiques*, éd. Antoine Adam, Gallimard, « Bibliothèque de la Pléiade », 1971, p. 26, 41, 781 et 784.

CERISIER Alban, *Une histoire de la NRF*, Gallimard, 2009, p. 151-153.

LEVILLAIN Henriette, *Saint-John Perse*, Fayard, 2013, p. 129-131.

CHATEAUBRIAND François-René DE, *Mémoires d'outre-tombe*, *op. cit.*, p. 112.

La pierre tombale de Paul Morand est visible à l'adresse suivante : www.findagrave.com/cgi-bin/fg.cgi?page=pv&GRid=16023955&PIpi=4228813.

Règle n° 15

PRÉVERT Jacques, « L'accent grave », *Paroles*, in *Œuvres complètes*, t. I, éd. Danièle Gasiglia-Laster et Arnaud Laster, Gallimard, « Bibliothèque de la Pléiade », 1992, p. 40.

PROUST Marcel, *Du côté de chez Swann*, in *À la recherche du temps perdu*, *op. cit.*, t. I, p. 152.

PROUST Marcel, *Le Temps retrouvé*, in *À la recherche du temps perdu*, *op. cit.*, t. IV, p. 420.

PROUST Marcel *La Prisonnière*, in *À la recherche du temps perdu*, *op. cit.*, t. III, p. 867.

BARBUSSE Henri, *Le Feu*, éd. Denis Pernot, Flammarion, « GF », 2014, p. 241.

MOLIÈRE, *Les Femmes savantes*, in *Œuvres complètes*, t. IV, éd. G. Mongrédien, Flammarion, « GF », 1979, p. 317.

VERLAINE Paul, « À A. Duvigneaux, trop fougueux adversaire de l'orthographe phonétique », *Œuvres poétiques complètes*, *op. cit.*, p. 610.

QUENEAU Raymond, *Bâtons, chiffres et lettres*, Gallimard, « Folio essais », 1965, p. 23.

DREYFUS Robert, *Souvenirs sur Marcel Proust*, Grasset, « Les Cahiers rouges », 1926, p. 26-27.

CLAUDEL Paul, *Œuvres en prose*, éd. Jacques Petit et Charles Galpérine, Gallimard, « Bibliothèque de la Pléiade », 1965, p. 42.

PROUST Marcel, *Lettres*, *op. cit.*, p. 462 (lettre du 6 novembre 1908).

ARAGON Louis, préface aux *Yeux d'Elsa*, in *Œuvres poétiques complètes*, *op. cit.*, t. I, p. 743.

VERLAINE Paul, « Charleroi », *Romances sans paroles*, in *Œuvres poétiques complètes*, *op. cit.*, p. 198.

APOLLINAIRE Guillaume, « Le Pont Mirabeau », *Alcools*, in *Œuvres poétiques*, éd. Marcel Adéma et Michel Décaudin, Gallimard, « Bibliothèque de la Pléiade », 1965, p. 45.

ARAGON Louis, préface aux *Yeux d'Elsa*, in *Œuvres poétiques complètes*, *op. cit.*, t. I, p. 743.

SARTRE Jean-Paul, « Orphée noir », *Situations*, t. III, Gallimard, 1949, p. 247.

CÉSAIRE Aimé, *Cahier d'un retour au pays natal*, Présence africaine, 1983, p. 60-61.

Entretien de Marguerite Duras avec Aliette Armel, cité dans VAUDREY-LUIGI Sandrine, *La Langue romanesque de Marguerite Duras. « Une liberté souvenante »*, Garnier, « Classiques Garnier », 2013, p. 25.

DURAS Marguerite, *L'Amant*, Minuit, 1984, p. 126-127.

STENDHAL, *Le Rouge et le Noir*, *op. cit.*, p. 129.

DIAZ Brigitte, *Stendhal en sa correspondance ou « L'Histoire d'un esprit »*, *op. cit.*, p. 109 (lettre de Stendhal à sa sœur Pauline, octobre 1804).

STENDHAL, *Vie de Henry Brulard*, *op. cit.*, t. III, p. 810.

HUGO Victor, *Lettres à Juliette Drouet*, éd. Jean Gaudon, Fayard, 2001, p. 70 (lettre du 26 février 1838).

RIMBAUD Arthur, *Correspondance*, *op. cit.*, p. 143 (lettre des 4-5 juillet 1873).

BAUDELAIRE Charles, *Correspondance*, *op. cit.*, t. I, p. 101.

MUSSET Alfred DE, et SAND George, *Lettres d'amour*, présentées par Françoise Sagan, Hermann, 1985, p. 150 (lettre d'octobre 1834).

PROUST Marcel, *Lettres*, *op. cit.*, p. 332 (lettre de septembre 1905).

Correspondance Guillaume Apollinaire – Jean Cocteau, *op. cit.*, p. 44 (lettre du 9 juin 1917).

PILLET Maurice, *Le Mal de Maupassant*, Maloine, 1911, p. 185-186.

BALZAC Honoré DE, *Lettres à Madame Hanska*, *op. cit.*, t. I, p. 23 (lettre de fin janvier 1833).

Remerciements

Nous souhaitons exprimer ici toute notre gratitude envers Hélène Fiamma, dont la confiance et l'amitié nous sont infiniment précieuses, ainsi qu'envers Clotilde Meyer et Christophe Guias, pour leur aide et leur soutien.

Nos remerciements chaleureux vont aussi à Muriel Bassou, Pauline Gauthier, Renaud Paquette, Aurélie Serfaty-Bercoff et Christine Vulliard.

TABLE

PROLOGUE 9

Règle n° 1. Commencer par le commen-
cement 15

Règle n° 2. Ne pas se fier à la pronon-
ciation 21

Règle n° 3. Accorder l'adjectif 29

Règle n° 4. Accorder le déterminant 35

Règle n° 5. Accorder le verbe 41

Règle n° 6. Redouter en particulier l'accord
du participe 47

Règle n° 7. Respecter l'emploi des modes
et des temps 53

Règle n° 8. Passer les formes verbales à la
loupe 63

Règle n° 9. Choisir le mot juste 71

Règle n° 10. Éviter pléonasmes et redon-
dances 79

Règle n° 11. Ne pas torturer la syntaxe 85

Règle n° 12. De l'importance de se relire 93

Règle n° 13. Bien choisir ses relecteurs 101

Règle n° 14. Garder un œil sur l'impri-
meur 107

Règle n° 15. Savoir rire de la faute 117

Règle n° 16. Oser la faute 123

Règle n° 17. Écrire avec son cœur 131

AUX LECTEURS 139

SOURCES 141

REMERCIEMENTS 163

Composition et mise en pages : FACOMPO, LISIEUX

Achevé d'imprimer
en novembre 2015
par Corlet Imprimeur
14110 Condé-sur-Noireau

Dépôt légal : septembre 2015
N° d'Imprimeur : 177674
Imprimé en France

PORTRAIT
OF A SCANDAL

Annie Burrows

All rights reserved including the right of reproduction in whole
or in part in any form. This edition is published by arrangement with
Harlequin Books S.A.

This is a work of fiction. Names, characters, places, locations and
incidents are purely fictional and bear no relationship to any real
life individuals, living or dead, or to any actual places, business
establishments, locations, events or incidents. Any resemblance is
entirely coincidental.

This book is sold subject to the condition that it shall not, by way of
trade or otherwise, be lent, resold, hired out or otherwise circulated
without the prior consent of the publisher in any form of binding or
cover other than that in which it is published and without a similar
condition including this condition being imposed on the subsequent
purchaser.

® and TM are trademarks owned and used by the trademark owner
and/or its licensee. Trademarks marked with ® are registered with the
United Kingdom Patent Office and/or the Office for Harmonisation in
the Internal Market and in other countries.

Published in Great Britain 2014
by Mills & Boon, an imprint of Harlequin (UK) Limited,
Eton House, 18-24 Paradise Road, Richmond, Surrey, TW9 1SR

© 2014 Annie Burrows

ISBN: 978 0 263 90937 1

Harlequin (UK) Limited's policy is to use papers that are natural,
renewable and recyclable products and made from wood grown in
sustainable forests. The logging and manufacturing processes conform
to the legal environmental regulations of the country of origin.

Printed and bound in Spain
by Blackprint CPI, Barcelona

Annie Burrows has been making up stories for her own amusement since she first went to school. As soon as she got the hang of using a pencil she began to write them down. Her love of books meant she had to do a degree in English Literature, and her love of writing meant she could never take on a job where she didn't have time to jot down notes when inspiration for a new plot struck her. She still wants the heroines of her stories to wear beautiful floaty dresses and triumph over all that life can throw at them. But when she got married she discovered that finding a hero is an essential ingredient to arriving at 'happy ever after'.

Previous novels by Annie Burrows:

HIS CINDERELLA BRIDE
MY LADY INNOCENT
THE EARL'S UNTOUCHED BRIDE
CAPTAIN FAWLEY'S INNOCENT BRIDE
THE RAKE'S SECRET SON
    (part of *Regency Candlelit Christmas* anthology)
DEVILISH LORD, MYSTERIOUS MISS
THE VISCOUNT AND THE VIRGIN
    (part of *Silk & Scandal* Regency mini-series)
A COUNTESS BY CHRISTMAS
CAPTAIN CORCORAN'S HOYDEN BRIDE
AN ESCAPADE AND AN ENGAGEMENT
GOVERNESS TO CHRISTMAS BRIDE
    (part of *Gift-Wrapped Governesses* anthology)
NEVER TRUST A RAKE
REFORMING THE VISCOUNT

**Also available in eBook format in
Mills & Boon® Historical *Undone!*:**

NOTORIOUS LORD, COMPROMISED MISS
HIS WICKED CHRISTMAS WAGER

Did you know that some of these novels are also available as eBooks? Visit www.millsandboon.co.uk

To the ladies (and gentleman) of flat B1.
You know who you are!

Chapter One

'*Madame, je vous* assure, there is no need to inspect the kitchens.'

'*Mademoiselle,*' retorted Amethyst firmly as she pushed past Monsieur Le Brun—or Monsieur Le Prunc, as she'd come to think of him, so wrinkled did his mouth become whenever she did not tamely fall in with his suggestions.

'Is not the apartment to your satisfaction?'

'The rooms I have so far seen are most satisfactory,' she conceded. But at the sound of crashing crockery from behind the scuffed door that led to the kitchens, she cocked her head.

'That,' said Monsieur Le Brun, drawing himself to his full height and assuming his most quelling manner, 'is a problem the most insignificant. And besides which, it is my duty to deal with the matters domestic.'

'Not in any household I run,' Amethyst muttered to herself as she pushed open the door.

Crouched by the sink was a scullery maid, weeping over a pile of broken crockery. And by a door which led to a dingy courtyard she saw two red-faced men, engaged in a discussion which involved not only a stream of unintelligible words, but also a great deal of arm waving.

'The one with the apron is our chef,' said Monsieur Le Brun's voice into her ear, making her jump. She'd been so intent on trying to work out what was going on in the kitchen, she hadn't heard him sneak up behind her.

'He has the reputation of an artist,' he continued. 'You told me to employ only the best and he is that. The other is a troublemaker, who inhabits the fifth floor, but who should be thrown out, as you English say, on his ear. *If* you will permit…' he began in a voice heavily laced with sarcasm, 'I shall resolve the issue. Since,' he continued suavely, as she turned to raise her eyebrows at him, 'you have employed me to deal with the problems. And to speak the French language on your behalf.'

Amethyst took another look at the two men, whose rapid flow of angry words and flailing arms she would have wanted to avoid in any language.

'Very well, *monsieur*,' she said through gritted teeth. 'I shall go to my room and see to the unpacking.'

'I shall come and report to you there when I have resolved this matter,' he said. Then bowed the particular bow he'd perfected which managed to incorporate something of a sneer.

'Though he might as well have poked out his tongue and said "so there",' fumed Amethyst when she reached the room allocated to her travelling companion, Fenella Mountsorrel. 'I think I would prefer him if he did.'

'I don't suppose he wishes to lose his job,' replied Mrs Mountsorrel. 'Perhaps,' she added tentatively, as she watched Amethyst yank her bonnet ribbons undone, 'you ought not to provoke him quite so deliberately.'

'If I didn't,' she retorted, flinging her bonnet on to a handily placed dressing table, 'he would be even more unbearable. He would order us about, as though we were his servants, not the other way round. He is one of those men who think women incapable of knowing anything and assumes we all want some big strong man to lean on and tell us what to do.'

'Some of us,' said her companion wistfully, 'don't mind having a big strong man around. Oh,

not to tell us what to do. But to lean on, when…
when things are difficult.'

Amethyst bit back the retort that sprang to her
lips. What good had that attitude done her companion? It had resulted in her being left alone in
the world, without a penny to her name, that's
what.

She took a deep breath, tugged off her gloves,
and slapped them down next to her bonnet.

'When things are difficult,' she said, thrusting
her fingers through the thick mass of dark curls
she wished, for the umpteenth time, she'd had
cut short before setting out on this voyage, 'you
find out just what you are made of. And you and
I, Fenella, are made of such stern stuff that we
don't need some overbearing, unreliable, insuf-
ferable male dictating to us how to live our lives.'

'Nevertheless,' pointed out Fenella doggedly,
'we could not have come this far, without—'

'Without *employing* a man to deal with the
more tiresome aspects of travelling so far from
home,' she agreed. 'Men do have their uses, that
I cannot deny.'

Fenella sighed. 'Not all men are bad.'

'You are referring to your dear departed Frederick, I suppose,' she said, tartly, before con-
ceding. 'But given you were so fond of him, I

dare say there must have been something good about him.'

'He had his faults, I cannot deny it. But I do miss him. And I wish he had lived to see Sophie grow up. And perhaps given her a brother or sister...'

'And how is Sophie now?' Amethyst swiftly changed the subject. On the topic of Fenella's late husband, they would never agree. The plain unvarnished truth was that he had left his widow shamefully unprovided for. His pregnant widow at that. And all Fenella would ever concede was that he was not very wise with money. Not very wise! As far as Amethyst could discover, the man had squandered Fenella's inheritance on a series of bad investments, whilst living way beyond his means. Leaving Fenella to pick up the pieces...

She took a deep breath. There was no point in getting angry with a man who wasn't there to defend himself. And whenever she'd voiced her opinion, all it had achieved was to upset Fenella. Which was the last thing she wanted.

'Sophie still looked dreadfully pale when Francine took her for a lie down,' said Fenella, with a troubled frown.

'I am sure she will bounce right back after a nap, and a light meal, the way she usually does.'

They had discovered, after only going ten miles from Stanton Basset, that Sophie was not a good traveller. However well sprung the coach was, whether she sat facing forwards, or backwards, or lay across the seat with her head on her mother's lap, or a pillow, she suffered dreadfully from motion sickness.

It had meant that the journey had taken twice as long as Monsieur Pruneface had planned, since Sophie needed one day's respite after each day's travel.

'If we miss the meetings you have arranged, then we miss them,' she'd retorted when he'd pointed out that the delay might cost her several lucrative contracts. 'If you think I am going to put mercenary considerations before the welfare of this child, then you are very much mistaken.'

'But then there is also the question of accommodation. With so many people wishing to visit Paris this autumn even I,' he'd said, striking his chest, 'may have difficulty arranging an alternative of any sort, let alone something suited to your particular needs.'

'Couldn't you write to whoever needs to know that our rooms, and yours, will be paid for no matter how late we arrive? And make some attempt to rearrange the other meetings?'

'*Madame*, you must know that France has

been flooded with your countrymen, eager to make deals for trade, for several months now. Even had we arrived when stated, and I had seen these men to whom you point me, who knows if they would have done business with you? Competitors may already have done the undercutting…'

'Then they have undercut me,' she'd snapped. 'I will have lost the opportunity to expand on to the continent. But that is my affair, not yours. We will still want your services as a guide, if that is what worries you. And we can just be genuine tourists and enjoy the experience, instead of it being our cover for travelling here.'

He'd muttered something incomprehensible under his breath. But judging from the fact these rooms were ready for them, and that a couple of letters from merchants who might take wares from her factories were already awaiting her attention, he'd done as he'd been told.

At that moment, her train of thought was interrupted by a knock on the door. It was the particularly arrogant knock Monsieur Le Prune always used. How he accomplished it she did not know, but he always managed to convey the sense that he had every right to march straight in, should he wish, and was only pausing, for the merest moment, out of the greatest forbearance for the unaccountably emotional fragility of his female charges.

'The problem in the kitchen,' he began the moment he'd opened the door—before Amethyst had given him permission to enter, she noted with resentment—'it is, I am afraid to say, more serious than we first thought.'

'Oh, yes?' It was rather wicked of her, but she relished discovering that something had cropped up that forced him to admit that he was not in complete control of the entire universe. 'It was not so insignificant after all?'

'The chef,' he replied, ignoring her jibe, 'he tells me that there cannot be the meal he would wish to serve his new guest on her first night in Paris.'

'No meal?'

'Not one of the standard that will satisfy him, no. It is a matter of the produce, you understand, which is no longer fit to serve, not even for Englishmen, he informs me. For which I apologise. These are his words, not my own.'

'Naturally not.' Though he had thoroughly enjoyed being able to repeat them, she could tell.

'On account,' he continued with a twitch to his mouth that looked suspiciously like the beginnings of a smirk, 'of the fact that we arrived so many days after he was expecting us.'

In other words, if there was a problem, it was her fault. He probably thought that putting the welfare of a child before making money was proof that a woman shouldn't be running any kind of business, let alone attempting to expand. 'However, I have a suggestion to make, which will overcome this obstacle.'

'Oh, yes?' It had better be good.

'Indeed,' he said with a smile which was so self-congratulatory she got an irrational urge to fire him on the spot. That would show him who was in charge.

Only then she'd have to find a replacement for him. And his replacement was bound to be just as irritating. And she'd need to start all over again, teaching him all about her wares, the range of prices at which she would agree to do deals, production schedules and so on.

'For tonight,' he said, 'it would be something totally novel, I think, for you and Madame Montsorrel to eat in a restaurant.'

Before she had time to wonder if he was making some jibe about their provincial origins, he went on, 'Most of your countrymen are most keen to visit, on their first night in Paris, the Palais Royale, to dine in one of its many establishments.'

The suggestion was so sensible it took the

wind out of her sails. It would make them look just like the ordinary tourists they were hoping to be taken for.

'And before you raise the objection that Sophie cannot be left alone,' he plunged on swiftly, 'on her first night in a strange country, I have asked the chef if he can provide the kind of simple fare which I have observed has soothed her stomach before. He assures me he can,' he said smugly. 'I have also spoken with Mademoiselle Francine, who has agreed to sit by her bedside, just this once, in the place of her mother, in case she awakes.'

'You seem to have thought of everything,' she had to concede.

'It is what you pay me for,' he replied, with a supercilious lift of one brow.

That was true. But did he have to point it out quite so often?

'What do you think, Fenella? Could you bear to go out tonight and leave Sophie? Or perhaps—' it suddenly occurred to her '—you are too tired?'

'Too tired to actually dine in one of those places we have been reading so much about? Oh, no! Indeed, no.'

The moment Bonaparte had been defeated and exiled to the tiny island of Elba, English tourists had been flocking to visit the country from which they had been effectively barred for the better part of twenty year. And filling newspapers and journals with accounts of their travels.

The more they'd raved about the delights of Paris, the more Amethyst had wanted to go and see it for herself. She'd informed her manager, Jobbings, that she was going to see if she could find new outlets for their wares, now trade embargoes had been lifted. And she would. She really would. She'd already made several appointments to which she would send Monsieur Le Brun, since she assumed French merchants would be as unwilling to do business with a female as English merchants were.

But she intended to take in as many experiences as she could while she was here.

'Then that is settled.' Amethyst was so pleased Fenella was completely in tune with her own desire to get out and explore that for once her state of almost permanent irritation with Monsieur Le Brun faded away to nothing.

And she smiled at him.

'Is there any particular establishment you would recommend?'

'I?' He gaped at her.

It was, she acknowledged, probably the first time he had ever seen her smile. At him, at least.

But then she had never dared let down her guard around him before. She'd taken pains to question every one of his suggestions and to double-check every arrangement he'd made, just to make sure he never attempted to swindle her. Or thought he might be able to get away with any *attempt* to swindle her.

And he had got them to Paris. If not quite to his schedule, then at least in reasonable comfort. Nor had he put a foot out of place.

She was beginning to feel reasonably certain he wouldn't dare. Besides, she had Fenella to double-check any correspondence he wrote on her behalf. *Her* grasp of French was extremely good, to judge from the way Monsieur Le Brun reacted when he'd first heard her speaking it.

'The best, the very best,' he said, making a swift recovery, 'is most probably Very Frères. It is certainly the most expensive.'

She wrinkled her nose. It sounded like the kind of place people went to show off. It would be crammed full of earls and opera dancers, no doubt.

'The Mille Colonnes is popular with your countrymen. Although—' his face fell, '—by the time we arrive, there will undoubtedly be a queue to get in.'

She cocked her eyebrow at him. Rising to the

unspoken challenge, he continued, 'There are many other excellent places to which I would not scruple to take you ladies... Le Caveau, for example, where for two to three francs you may have an excellent dinner of soup, fish, meat, dessert and a bottle of wine.'

Since she'd spent some time before setting out getting to grips with the exchange rate, his last statement made her purse her lips. Surely they wouldn't be able to get anything very appetising for such a paltry sum?

Nevertheless, she did not voice that particular suspicion. Having watched her intently as he'd described what were clearly more expensive establishments, he was probably doing his best to suggest somewhere more economical. He wasn't a fool. His manner might infuriate her, but she couldn't deny he was observant and shrewd. Because she'd made him suffer enough for one day and because Fenella had a tendency to get upset if they quarrelled openly in her presence, she admitted that she rather liked the sound of Le Caveau.

It wasn't long after that she and Fenella had changed, dressed, kissed a drowsy Sophie goodnight and were stepping out into the dimly lit streets of Paris.

Paris! She was really in Paris. Nothing could tell the world more clearly that she was her own woman. That she was ready to try new things and make her own choices in life. That she'd paid for the follies of her youth. And wasn't going to carry on living a cloistered existence, as though she was ashamed of herself. For she wasn't. She'd done nothing to be ashamed of.

Of course, she was not so keen to start becoming her own woman that she was going to abandon all her late Aunt Georgie's precepts. Not the ones that were practical at any rate. For her foray to the bargain of a restaurant that was Le Caveau, she wore the kind of plain, sensible outfit she would have donned for a visit to her bankers in the City. Monsieur Le Brun had just, but only just, repressed a shudder when he'd seen her emerge from her room. It was the same look she would have expected a member of the *ton*, in London, to send her way.

Provincial, they would think, writing her off as a nobody because her bonnet was at least three years behind the current fashion.

But it was far better for people to underestimate and overlook you, than to think you were a pigeon for the plucking. If she'd set out for the Continent in a coach and four, trailing wagonloads of servants and luggage, and made an enormous fuss at whatever inn they'd stopped at, she might as well have hung a placard round her neck, announcing 'Wealthy woman! Come and rob me!'

As it was, they'd had to put up with a certain amount of rudeness and inconvenience on occasion, but nobody had thought them worth the bother of robbing.

And there was another advantage, she soon discovered, to not being dressed in fine silks. 'I can't believe how muddy it is everywhere,' she grumbled, lifting her skirts to try to keep them free from dirt. 'This is like wading down some country lane that leads to a pig farm.'

'I suggested to you that it would be the mode to hire a chair for your conveyance to the Palais Royale,' Monsieur Le Brun snapped back, whiplash smart.

'Oh, we couldn't possibly have done that,' said Fenella, at her most conciliatory. 'We are not grand ladies. We would both have felt most peculiar being carried through the streets like—'

'Parcels,' put in Amethyst. 'Lugged around by some hulking great porters.'

'Besides,' said Fenella hastily,' we can see so much more of your beautiful city, *monsieur*, if we walk through it, than we could by peeping through the curtains of some sort of carriage. And feel so much more a part of it.'

'That is certainly true. The mud certainly looks set to form a lasting part of my skirts,' observed Amethyst.

But then they stepped through an archway, into an immense, brilliantly lit gravelled square, and whatever derogatory comment she might have made next dried on her lips.

And Monsieur Le Brun smirked in satisfaction as both ladies gaped at the spectacle spread before them.

The Palais Royale was like nowhere she had ever seen before. And it was not just the sight of the tiers of so many brightly lit windows that made her blink, but the crowds of people, all intent on enjoying themselves to the full. To judge from the variety of costumes, they had come from every corner of the globe.

'This way,' said Monsieur Le Brun, taking her firmly by the elbow when she slowed down to peer into one of the brightly lit windows of an establishment in a basement. 'That place is not suitable for ladies such as yourselves.'

Indeed, from the brief glimpse she'd got of all the military uniforms, and the rather free behaviour of the females in their company, she'd already gathered that for herself.

However, for once, she did not shake Monsieur Le Brun's hand away. It was all rather more...boisterous than she'd imagined. She'd found travelling to London, to consult with her bankers and men of business after her aunt's death, somewhat daunting, so bustling and noisy was the metropolis in comparison with the sleepy tranquillity of Stanton Basset. But the sheer vivacity of Paris at night was on a different scale altogether.

It was with relief that she passed through the doors of another eatery, which was quickly overtaken by amazement. Even though Monsieur Le Brun had told her this place was economical, it far surpassed her expectations. She had glanced through the grimy windows of chop houses when she'd been in London and had assumed a cheap restaurant in Paris, which admitted members of the public, would resemble one of those. Instead, her eyes were assailed by mirrors and columns, and niches with statues, tables set with glittering cutlery and crystal, diners dressed in fabulous colours and waiters bustling around attentively.

And the food, which she'd half-suspected would be of the same quality she'd endured in the various coaching inns where they'd stayed, was as good as anything she might have tasted

when invited to dine with the best families in
the county.

But what really made her evening, was to see
that the whole enterprise was run by a woman.
She sat in state by the door, assigning customers
to tables suited to the size of their party, taking
their money and tallying it all up in a massive
ledger, spread before her on a great granite-
topped table.

And nobody seemed to think there was anything untoward about this.

They had just taken receipt of their dessert
when a man, entering alone, inspired a grimace
of distaste from Monsieur Le Brun. Her gaze
followed the direction of his to see who could
have roused his displeasure and she froze, her
spoon halfway to her mouth.

Nathan Harcourt.

The disgraced Nathan Harcourt.

Her face went hot while her stomach turned
cold, curdling all the fine food inside it to a
churning mass of bile.

And the question that had haunted her for
years almost forced its way through her clenched
teeth in a despairing scream. *How could you do
that to me, Nathan? How could you?*

She wanted to get up, march across the res-

taurant and soundly slap the cheeks that the pro-
prietress was enthusiastically kissing. Though
it was far too late now. She should have done it
the night he'd cut her dead, after making a point
of dancing with just about every other girl in
the ballroom. The night he'd started to break
her heart.

He hadn't changed a bit when it came to
spreading his favours about, she noted. The pro-
prietress, who'd merely given them a regal nod
when they'd come in, was clasping him to her
bosom with such enthusiasm it was a wonder he
didn't disappear into those ample mounds and
suffocate.

Which would serve him right.

'That man,' said Monsieur Le Brun at his
most prune-faced, watching the direction of her
affronted gaze, 'should not be permitted in here
at all. But it is as you see. He is in favour with
madame, so the customers are subjected to his
impertinence. It is regrettable, but not an insur-
mountable problem. I shall not permit him to
disturb you.'

It was too late for that. His arrival had already
disturbed her—though Monsieur Le Brun's
words had also roused her curiosity.

'What do you mean—subjecting the customers to his impertinence?'

'He does portraits,' said Monsieur Le Brun. 'Quick studies in pencil, for the amusement of the visitors to the city.'

As if to prove his point, Nathan Harcourt produced a little canvas stool from the satchel he had slung over one shoulder, crouched down on it beside one of the tables near the door, took out a stick of charcoal and began to sketch the diners seated there.

'Portraits? Nathan Harcourt?'

Monsieur Le Brun's eyebrows shot up into his hairline. 'You know this man? I would never have thought… I mean,' he regrouped, adopting his normal slightly supercilious demeanour, 'though he is a countryman of yours, I would not have thought you moved in the same circles.'

'Not of late,' she admitted. 'Though, at one time, we…did.'

All of ten years ago, to be precise, when she'd been completely ignorant of the nature of men and from too sheltered a background to know how to guard herself against his type. And from too ordinary a background to have anyone sufficiently powerful to protect her from him.

But things were different now.

Different for her and, by the looks of things, very, very different for him too. Her eyes narrowed as she studied his appearance and noted the changes.

Some of them were just due to the passage of years and were pretty much what she would have expected. His face was leaner and flecks of silver glinted here and there amidst curls that had once been coal black. But it was the state of his clothing that most clearly proclaimed the rumours that his father had finally washed his hands of his youngest son were entirely true. His coat only fit where it touched, his hat was a broad-brimmed affair of straw and his trousers were the baggy kind she'd seen the local tradesmen wearing. In short, he looked downright shabby.

Well, well. She leaned back and observed him working with mounting pleasure. When he'd achieved the almost-impossible feat of becoming too notorious for any political party to put him up for even the most rotten of rotten boroughs, he'd vanished, amidst much speculation. She'd assumed that, like the younger sons of so many eminent families, when he'd blotted the escutcheon, he'd been sent to the Continent to live a life of luxurious indolence.

But it looked as though his father, the Earl of Finchingfield, had been every bit as furious as the scandal sheets had hinted at the time and as unforgiving as her own father. For here was Nathan Harcourt, the proud, cold-hearted Nathan Harcourt, forced to work to earn a crust.

'I shall not be at all displeased if he should come to my table and solicit my custom,' she said, a strange thrill shivering through her whole being. 'In fact, I would thoroughly enjoy having my portrait done.'

By him. Having him solicit her for her time, her money, her custom, when ten years ago, he had been too…proud and mighty, and…*ambitious* to have his name linked with hers.

Oh, what sweet revenge. Here he was, practically begging for a living and not doing too well from the look of his clothing. While here she was, thanks to Aunt Georgie, in possession of so much wealth she would be hard pressed to run through it in ten lifetimes.

Chapter Two

Nathan stood up, handed over the finished sketch to his first customer of the night and held out his hand for payment. He thanked them for their compliments and made several comments witty enough to hit their mark, judging from the way the other occupants of the table flung back their heads and laughed. But he had no idea what he'd actually said. His mind was still reeling from the shock of seeing Amethyst Dalby.

After ten years of leaving him be, she had to go and invade territory that he'd come to think of as peculiarly his own.

Not that it mattered.

And to prove it, he would damn well confront her.

He turned and scanned the restaurant with apparent laziness, hesitated when he came to her table, affected surprise, then sauntered over.

If she had the effrontery to appear in public, with her latest paramour in tow, then it was time to remove the gloves. The days were long gone when he would have spared a lady's blushes because of some ridiculous belief in chivalry towards the weaker sex.

The weaker sex! The cunning sex more like. He'd never met one who wasn't hiding some secret or other, be it only her age, or how much she'd overspent her allowance.

Though none with secrets that had been as destructive as hers.

'Miss Dalby,' he said when he reached her table. 'How surprising to see you here.'

'In Paris, do you mean?'

'Anywhere,' he replied with a hard smile. 'I would have thought...' He trailed off, leaving her to draw her own conclusions as to where he might have gone with that statement. He'd made his opinion of her very plain when he'd discovered how duplicitous she'd been ten years ago. Back then, she'd had the sense to flee polite society and presumably return to the countryside.

He hadn't allowed himself to dwell on what might have become of her. But now she was here, why shouldn't he find out? He glanced at her hand. No ring. And she hadn't corrected him when he'd addressed her as Miss Dalby, either.

So it didn't look as though she'd ever managed to entrap some poor unsuspecting male into marriage with a pretence of innocence. This man, this sallow-skinned, beetle-browed man whose face looked vaguely familiar, was not her husband. What then? A lover?

'Are you not going to introduce me?' He cocked an eyebrow in the direction of her male friend, wondering where he'd seen him before.

'I see no need for that,' she replied with a stiff smile.

No? He supposed it might be a little awkward, introducing a former lover to her current one. Especially if he was the jealous sort. He gave him a searching look and met with one of mutual antipathy. Was it possible the man felt... threatened? He could see why he might look like a potential competitor. Without putting too fine a point on it, he was younger, fitter and more handsome than the man she'd washed up with. Not that he saw himself in the light of competitor for *her* favours. God, no!

'After all,' she continued archly, 'you cannot have come across to renew our acquaintance. I believe it is work you wish to solicit. Is it not?'

Of course it was. She didn't need to remind him that whatever they'd had was finished.

'I explained to *madame*,' put in the man, pro-

claiming his nationality by the thickness of his
accent, 'that this is how you make your living.
By drawing the likenesses of tourists.'

It wasn't quite true. But he let it pass. It was…
convenient, for the moment, to let everyone think
he was earning his living from his pictures. And
simpler.

And that *was* why he'd strolled across to her
table. Exactly why.

There could be no other reason.

'*Madame* wishes you to make her the swift
portrait,' said the Frenchman.

Miss Dalby shot her French lover a look brim-
ming with resentment. He looked steadily back
at her, completely unrepentant.

Interesting. The Frenchman felt the need to
assert his authority over her. To remind her who
was in control. Or perhaps he'd already discovered how fickle she could be, since he clearly
wasn't going to permit her to flirt with a potential new conquest right before his eyes.

Wise man.

Miss Dalby needed firm handling if a man
had a hope of keeping her in her place.

He had a sudden vision of doing exactly that.
She was on her back, beneath him, he was holding her hands above her head… He blinked it
away, busying himself with unfolding his stool

and assembling his materials. No more than one minute in her presence and he was proving as susceptible to her charms as he'd ever been. The Frenchman, on whom he deliberately turned his back as he sat down, had every reason to be jealous. He must always be fighting off would-be rivals. What red-blooded male, coming within the radius of such a siren, could fail to think about bedding her?

Even though she was not dressed particularly well, there was no disguising her beauty. As a girl, she'd been remarkably pretty. But the years—in spite of what her lifestyle must have been like to judge from the company she was now keeping—had been good to her. She had grown into those cheekbones. And the skin that clad them was peachy soft and clear as cream. Those dark-brown eyes were as deep, lustrous and mysterious as they'd ever been.

It was a pity that for quick sketches like this, he only used a charcoal pencil. He would have liked to add colour to this portrait. Later, perhaps, he would record this meeting for his own satisfaction, commemorating it in paint.

Meanwhile, his fingers flew across the page, capturing the angle of her forehead, the arch of her brows. So easily. But then she wasn't a fresh subject. Years ago, he'd spent hours drawing her face, her hands, the curve of her shoulder and the shadows where her skin disappeared into the silk of her evening gown. Not while she was actually present, of course, because she'd been masquerading as an innocent débutante and he'd been too green to consider flouting the conventions. But at night, when he was in his room alone, unable to sleep for yearning for her—yes, then he'd drawn her. Trying to capture her image, her essence.

What a fool he'd been.

He'd even bought some paints and attempted to reproduce the colours of that remarkable hair. He hadn't been able to do it justice, back then. He hadn't the skill. And he hadn't been allowed to pursue his dream by taking lessons.

'It's for young ladies, or tradesmen,' his father had snapped, when they'd discussed what he really wanted to do with his life, if not follow his brothers into one of the traditional professions. 'Not a suitable pastime for sons of noblemen.'

He could do it now, though. He'd learned about light and shade. Pigment and perspective.

His fingers stilled. In spite of what his friend Fielding had said, she wasn't merely a brunette. There were still those rich, warm tints in her hair that put him in mind of a really good port when you held the glass up to a candle. Fielding had laughed when he'd admitted his obsession with it and clapped him on the back. 'Got it bad, ain't you?'

He glanced up, his hand hovering over the half-finished sketch. He might well have *had it bad*, but he hadn't been wrong about her hair. It was just as glorious as it had ever been. After ten years, he might have expected to see the occasional strand of silver between the dark curls. Or perhaps signs that she was preserving an appearance of youth with dyes.

But that hair was not dyed. It could not look so soft, so glossy, so entirely…natural and eminently touchable…

He frowned, lowered his head and went back to work. He did *not* want to run his fingers through it, to see if it felt as soft as it looked. He could appreciate beauty when he saw it. He was an artist, after all. But then he would defy anybody to deny she had glorious hair. A lovely face. And sparkling eyes.

Though none of that altered the fact that she was poison.

He looked up, directly into her eyes, eyes that had once looked at him with what he'd thought was adoration. He smiled grimly. It was easier to read her now that he was older and wiser. She was looking at him assessingly, challengingly, with more than a measure of calculation simmering in the brew. All those things she'd taken such care to hide from him before.

Yes, she was poison right enough. Poison in a tantalising package.

From behind him, he heard her current lover shift impatiently in his chair. He probably regretted allowing her to have her way in this. It must irk him, having her looking at another man with such intent, while he was sitting mere inches away. But he was doing so, as though he was powerless to deny her anything.

God, she must be extraordinarily gifted between the sheets...

His mouth firming, he dropped his gaze to the page on his lap, adding a few deft strokes which put depth to the image he was creating.

'There,' he said, taking the finished sketch and tossing it to her lover.

The man looked at it, raised his brows and handed it across the table to Miss Dalby, who snatched at it.

'This is...' She frowned as she scanned the picture. 'It is amazing, considering you did it so quickly.' The expression in her eyes changed to what looked almost like respect. And he felt that glow which always came when people recognised his talent. His gift.

They might say he was a failure in every other department of his life, but nobody could deny he could draw.

'How much do you charge?'

Miss Dalby was looking at the picture she held in her hands as though she couldn't quite believe it. He stood up, folded up his stool and gave the insouciant shrug he always gave his subjects. And gave her the answer he always gave them, too.

'Whatever you think it is worth.'

Whatever she thought it was worth? Oh, but that was priceless! She would have paid any amount of money to have him sitting at her feet, a supplicant. Ten years ago he'd swaggered everywhere, bestowing a smile here, an appreciative glance at some beauty there, with the air of a young god descended to the realms of lesser mortals. It was worth a king's ransom to see him reduced to working for a living, when at one time he'd thought that she, with her lowly background and her lack of powerful connections, could be tossed aside as though she were nothing. And a delightful notion sprang to her mind.

'Monsieur Le Brun.' She beckoned the courier, who leant closer so that she could whisper into his ear. 'I should like this young man to have the equivalent of twenty-five pounds. In French francs.' It was the annual wage she paid her butler.

'Do you have sufficient funds about you?'

His eyes widened. 'No, *madame*, to carry such a sum on my person would be folly of the most reprehensible.'

'Then you must draw it from the bank and see that he gets it. First thing tomorrow.'

'But, *madame*—'

'I insist.'

After a moment's hesitation, he murmured, 'I see, *madame*', with what looked, for once, bafflingly, like approval. And then, 'As you wish.'

He reached into his pocket and produced a heap of coins, which he dropped into Harcourt's outstretched palm.

'Please to furnish me with your direction,' he said, 'and I will call to settle with you for the rest.'

Nathan's lips twisted into a cynical smile as he scrawled his address on the back of the sketch he'd just drawn. It was obvious this impudent fellow meant to call round and warn him to stay away from the beauty he currently had in his keeping. From the sneer about the fellow's lips, the Frenchman assumed he was penniless. It was the trap so many people fell into where he was concerned, because he wore old clothes when he was sketching, clothes that he didn't mind getting ruined by charcoal dust, or from sitting in the dirt when there was an interesting subject he simply had to capture.

This Frenchman planned to make the point that Nathan need not bother trying to compete. *He* had the wealth to satisfy her. To keep her. And what did he, a shabby, itinerant artist, have to offer?

Apart from relative youth, good looks and a roguish smile?

And all of a sudden, he had an almost overbearing urge to do it. To take her away from this slimy excuse of a man. To pursue her, and win her, and enslave her, and bind her to him...and then throw her away.

Because, dammit, somebody ought to punish her, for every single thing he'd gone through this last ten years. If she hadn't set her sights on him and damn near enslaved him, then he wouldn't have been so devastated when he found out what lay concealed behind the pretty façade. He would not have agreed to the disastrous marriage brokered by his family, or embarked on an equally disastrous political career, from which he'd only managed to extricate himself by committing what amounted to social suicide.

Oh, yes, if there were any justice in the world...

Only of course there wasn't. That was one lesson life had taught him only too well. Honesty was never rewarded. The devious were the ones who inherited the earth, not the meek.

Tucking the pile of coins into his satchel, along with his supplies, he employed the smile he'd perfected during his years in politics, directing it in turn at the Frenchman, at Miss Dalby, and at the mousy woman who was sitting with them at table.

And strode out of the door.

'Goodness,' breathed Mrs Mountsorrel. 'I have heard of him, of course, but I never expected him to be quite so...' She flushed and faded into a series of utterances that could only be described as twittering.

But then that performance was the one he'd used so many times to reduce susceptible females to a state of fluttering, twittering, hen-witted compliance. Having those heavy-lidded, knowing hazel eyes trained so intently on her face would have had the same effect upon her, too, if she hadn't been enjoying seeing him grovelling at her feet quite so much. And then again, there was something about the combination of those aristocratic good looks, and the shabby clothing, that might have tugged at her heart-strings, had she any heart left for him to tug at.

'He has the reputation with the ladies rather unsavoury,' put in Monsieur Le Brun, at his most prune-faced.

'Oh, yes, I know all about *that*,' twittered Fenella. 'Miss Dalby is always reading accounts of his doings that appear in the newspapers. Why, his wife wasn't dead five minutes before the most terrible rumours started up. And then, of course, when he fell from grace so spectacu-larly, there was no doubting the truth of it. He would have sued for libel if the papers had been making it up. Or is it slander?'

'You sound as though you find him fascinat-ing,' he said, with narrowed eyes.

'Oh, no, not I. It is Amethyst who followed his career in public life so closely. I mean, Miss Dalby, of course.'

He turned to her with a frown.

'Well, *madame*, I...I commend you for wish-ing to aid someone you have known in the past. And being so generous, it is one thing, but I im-plore you not to be deceived by his so-charm-ing smile.'

Oh. So that was why, for once, he hadn't argued with her about the way she chose to spend her own money. He thought she was being generous to a friend who'd fallen on hard times.

If only he knew!

'It is rather distressing,' put in Fenella, 'to see a man from his background sunk so low.'

'He brought it all on himself,' said Amethyst tartly.

'And yet you have been so generous to him,' said Monsieur Le Brun.

'Well...' she began, squirming in her seat, and blushing. It hadn't been generosity, but a desire to rub his nose in the reversal of their fortunes that had prompted her to pay him a year's wages for five minutes' work.

'I don't see why you should be so surprised,' said Fenella stoutly. 'I thought you were more perceptive than that, *monsieur*. Surely you have noticed that she doesn't like people to know how generous she is. She hides it behind gruff manners, and...and eccentric ways. But deep down, there is nobody kinder than my Miss Dalby. Why, if you only knew how she came to my rescue—'

Amethyst held up her hand to silence her. 'Fenella. Stop right there. I hired you in a fit of temper with the ladies of Stanton Basset, you know I did. Mrs Podmore came round, not five minutes after Aunt Georgie's funeral, telling me that I would have to employ some female to live with me so long as I remained single or I would no longer be considered *respectable*. So I marched straight round to your house and offered you the post just to spite them.'

'What she hasn't told you,' said Fenella, turning to Monsieur Le Brun who was regarding his employer with raised eyebrows, 'was that she'd never been able to abide the way everyone gossiped about me. But she'd never been able to do much about it apart from offer her friendship until after her aunt died.'

'Well, it was dreadful, the way they treated you. It must have been hard enough, coming to live in a place where you knew nobody, with a small baby to care for, without people starting those malicious rumours about you having invented a husband.'

'For all you knew, I might have done.'

'Well, what difference would it have made? If you had been seduced and abandoned, surely you were due some sympathy and support? What would you have been guilty of, after all? Being young and foolish, and taken in by some glib promises made by a smooth-talking scoundrel.'

Was she still talking about Fenella? Amethyst

wondered as she shakily reached for her glass, and downed the last of its contents. Or had it been seeing Nathan Harcourt that had stirred up such a martial spirit? And bother it, but Monsieur Le Brun was leaning back in his chair, his eyes flicking from one to another with keen interest.

They were both revealing far more about themselves and their past than he had any right to know.

'I think we have said enough upon this subject,' she said, setting her glass down with quiet deliberation.

'She always gets embarrassed when anyone sings her praises,' Fenella informed Monsieur Le Brun. 'But I cannot help myself. For she didn't just give me work to support myself and Sophie, she made sure my little girl finally had all that a gentleman's daughter should have had. All the things,' she said with a quivering lip, 'that my own family denied her, because they never approved of Frederick. A nurse, beautiful clothes, a pony and, best of all, an education…'

'Well, she's such a bright little thing.' And it wasn't as if Amethyst was ever going to have any children of her own. At seven and twenty she was firmly on the shelf. No man would look twice at her if it weren't for the fortune her aunt had left her. As she knew only too well.

'So don't you go thinking,' she said, hauling herself up by the scruff of the neck, 'that I'm…a pigeon for the plucking. Put one foot wrong and I will give you your marching orders,' she finished.

'Miss Dalby!' Fenella turned a puzzled, disappointed face towards her. 'There is no need to keep on treating Monsieur Le Brun as if he is working out ways to rob you. Hasn't he proved over and over again on this trip how very honest, hard working and…ingenious he is?'

And he was sitting right there, listening.

'If you must discuss Monsieur Le Brun's many and various skills, please have the goodness to do so when we return to the privacy of our own rooms.'

'I expect it was the shock of seeing Nathan Harcourt that has made her so out of reason cross,' Fenella explained to Monsieur Le Brun, who was by now starting to look rather amused. 'They used to know one another quite well, you see. He led poor Miss Dalby to believe they might make a match of it—'

'Fenella! Monsieur Le Brun does not need to know *any* of this.'

Fenella smiled at her, before carrying on in

the same confidential tone. 'He was the youngest son of an earl, you know. Well, I suppose he
still is.' She giggled.

And that was when it hit Amethyst.

'Fenella, I think you have had rather too much
to drink.'

Fenella blinked. Her eyes widened. 'Do you
really think so?' She peered down at her glass.
'Surely not. I have only been sipping at my wine,
and, look—the glass is still half-full...'

What she clearly hadn't noticed was the way
the waiters kept topping up the glass. And taking
away the empty bottles and bringing fresh ones.

'Nevertheless, it is time to go home, Monsieur
Le Brun, wouldn't you say?'

It said a great deal for the amount of wine
Fenella had inadvertently consumed that it took
both her and Monsieur Le Brun to get her into
her coat and through the door. Then, when the
fresh air hit her, she swayed on her feet. Monsieur Le Brun proved to have remarkably swift
reflexes, because he caught her arm, tactfully
supporting her before she could embarrass herself. Just to be on the safe side, Amethyst took
her other arm, and between them they steered
her through the crowds milling about the central
courtyard of the Palais Royale.

But she was almost certain she heard him chuckle.

'This is not funny,' she snapped as they ushered her through the archway that led into the street that would take them home.

'She isn't used to dining out like this. Or having waiters going round topping up her glass. And as for that wine...well, it was downright deceitful. It tasted so fruity and pleasant...more like cordial than anything with alcohol in it.'

'It was not the wine. It is Paris,' said Monsieur Le Brun with an insouciant shrug. 'It has the effect most surprising on many people. So we must make sure, as her friends, that we take especially good care of her from now on.'

Her friends? Monsieur Le Brun considered himself Fenella's friend? And what was worse, he was putting himself on a level with her, as though they were...a team, or something.

Well, that would not do. It would not do at all.

And just as soon as she could think of the right words to do so, she was going to put Monsieur Le Brun firmly in his place.

But not until they'd got Fenella safely home.

Chapter Three

'I have let you down,' moaned Fenella.

'Nonsense,' Amethyst murmured soothingly. It had actually been rather cheering to see her friend was not a complete paragon of all the virtues.

'It is just…foreign travel,' she said. 'Or perhaps, as Monsieur Le Brun says, the excitement of being in Paris…'

Fenella rolled on to her side and buried her face in the pillow.

'There is no excuse for what I did…'

'You just had a little too much to drink and became rather more talkative than usual, that is all.'

'But my judgement…' Fenella protested, albeit in a very quiet voice.

'Well, it is not a mistake you will make again,' said Amethyst bracingly, 'if this is how ill you become after partaking too freely. You wince whenever you try to open your eyes. Let me make you more comfortable.'

'I shall never feel comfortable again,' she whimpered as Amethyst crossed the room and drew the curtains, plunging the room into darkness.

'How am I ever going to face Sophie? Oh, my little girl. When she finds out…'

'Why should she find out? I am certainly not going to tell her anything more than that her mama needs to stay in bed this morning, because she is a little unwell. Heavens, she has had to have enough days in bed while we've been travelling to assume that the rigours of the journey have just caught up with you.'

'But to lie to my own child…'

'You won't have to lie. Just not admit to the truth.'

Amethyst strode back to her friend's side and smoothed her hair back from her flushed face. It was an indication of just how ill Fenella really felt that she flinched back from her touch.

'I promised to take her out to see the sights of the city today. She will be so disappointed.'

'No, she won't, for I shall take her myself. You look as though you need to go back to sleep. Don't even think about stirring from this room until after you have had your luncheon, either. Which I shall order the staff to have brought to your room.'

Fenella caught her hand and kissed it. 'You are too good to me. Too kind. I don't deserve your understanding...'

'Fustian! It is about time you stopped being so perfect. I like you the better for it. Makes me feel less of a failure, if you must know.' Usually, she felt like a hardheaded, prickly, confrontational excuse for a woman in comparison to the perfect manners of her elegant and utterly feminine companion.

Amethyst was wealthy, courtesy of her aunt, and she had a good head for business, but she didn't make friends easily and simply could not imagine ever getting married. If a man made up to her, it was because of her wealth, not anything intrinsically attractive about her. She'd learned that lesson the hard way when she'd been too young and vulnerable to withstand the experience. It had scarred her. Wounded her. She'd felt a staggering amount of empathy for those beggars they'd seen so many of, lying by the roadsides of every French town they'd travelled through, for a vital part of her had been ruthlessly amputated in battle and she would never be quite whole again.

Not that it mattered, according to Aunt Geor gie. Lots of people led perfectly good lives in spite of what other people thought of as handicaps. So what if she could never trust a man again? Neither did her aunt.

'Useless pack of self-serving, scrounging scum, if you ask me,' she'd sniffed disparagingly, when she whisked Amethyst from the village on what was supposed to have been a therapeutic trip round the Lakes. 'Don't understand why any sensible woman would wish to shackle herself to one. And I'm beginning to think you are capable of being sensible, if only you will get over this habit of thinking you need a man in your life. All any of them do is interfere and ruin everything.'

After what she'd been through, she'd been inclined to agree.

Fenella moaned again, drawing her attention back to the present, and then she flung the back of one hand over her eyes.

Amethyst pursed her lips. She sympathised with Fenella for having a sore head. She sympathised with her feeling embarrassed at having to be helped home. But...

'Good heavens, Fenella, anyone who is not used to drinking might have made the same error. It is not the end of the world.' And there was absolutely no need for all these theatrics.

'I know what you're doing. You are worrying about what people will say. But nothing is ever solved by worrying about what other people think of you. Especially not the sort of people who would love nothing better than to condemn you. They're mostly cowards, you know. Too scared to take life by the scruff of the neck and live it. Instead, they prefer to sit about gossiping in a vain attempt to liven up the boredom of their useless, unprofitable lives. You should never modify your behaviour in an attempt to win the regard of their sort.'

Good heavens. Had she really just repeated one of Aunt Georgie's favourite homilies? In the very tone of voice her aunt would have employed whenever Amethyst had been a bit blue-devilled?

She had.

She wrapped her arms round her waist and walked rather jerkily over to the window. For years, people had been warning her that if she wasn't careful, she'd end up just like her aunt. But she'd told them she didn't care. She'd been so grateful to her for the way she'd stood up to Amethyst's father. From the moment Aunt Georgie had gone toe to toe with him in his library, telling him he'd been a pompous little boy who'd grown into a pompous prig of a man without a

shred of compassion in him, her life had begun
to take an upward turn. Well, she could hardly
have sunk any lower. So she hadn't listened to a
word of criticism levelled at her aunt, not from
anyone.

But sometimes…

She thought of the single tear she'd seen trick-
ing down Fenella's face, a tear she'd provoked
with that heartless little homily, and wanted to
kick herself. She'd sounded as callous and un-
feeling as Aunt Georgie at her very worst.

'It's different for you,' said Fenella woefully.
'I am a mother. I have to think of Sophie. Whatever I do has an impact on her. And there are
certain things a lady should never do.'

'I know, I know,' said Amethyst, going back
to her bedside and perching on the nearest chair.

'I'm sorry I spoke harshly. It's just—'

'You are so strong that it is hard for you to
sympathise, sometimes, with weakness in others.'

'I wasn't always strong,' she said. 'You know
I would have gone under if Aunt Georgie hadn't
stepped in to rescue me when she did. It was her
example that gave me the determination to do
something for you. I knew what it was like to
be alone, unjustly accused of something I hadn't
done, with nobody to defend me.' It had been

hellish. Her whole family had turned their backs
on her just when she'd needed them the most.
'You needed a friend, to stand with you against
all those wagging tongues. Just as I needed Aunt
Georgie to believe in me. Just as you need me to
be a friend now, not…not tell you to pull yourself together. Forgive me?'

'Yes, of course, but—'

'No. Please don't say another word about it. I
know it must have been distressing to have been
helped home, slightly foxed, last night, but I've
already told you I do not think the worse of you
for it. And who else knows about it? Only Monsieur Le Brun, and if he dares to make you feel
in the slightest bit uncomfortable, he will have
me to deal with,' she finished militantly.

Fenella pressed her hands to her eyes and
whimpered.

'I will leave you now,' she said, far more qui-
etly. It had occurred to her that a loud voice
might bring more distress than comfort, no matter what words she actually said, and that Fenella
just needed to sleep it off.

'I will look after Sophie today,' she said, tiptoeing towards the door. 'And make sure no word
of what you got up to last night ever reaches her
ears.'

She shut the door on yet another moan of anguish, only to jump in shock at the sight of Monsieur Le Brun standing in the corridor, not three feet away.

'I beg your pardon,' he said. 'I did not mean to startle you. I only meant…that is…Madame Montsorrel. How is she?'

'She is feeling very sorry for herself. And very guilty.'

Monsieur Le Brun lowered his head. 'I hope you have not been too harsh with her. Indeed, the fault was not hers. It was mine. I should not have—'

'Oh, don't you start,' she said. 'She made a mistake. That was yesterday. And anyone can see how sorry she is for it. But if you think it was at all your fault, then all you need do in future is to make sure the wine we order is not so strong. And that none of us has more than a couple of glasses. We lived very simply in Stanton Basset and never partook of more than one glass of wine or Madeira, and that only on special occasions.'

'The wine,' he gulped. 'Yes, yes, but—'

'No, I don't wish to discuss this any more.' She was getting a most uncomfortable feeling, seeing him look so concerned about Fenella's health. She'd have assumed he would have been irritated, not remorseful. If she wasn't careful, she might stop disliking him. And then where would she be? Vulnerable!

'We have a busy day ahead of us. Have you dealt with Monsieur Harcourt yet?'

He already had on his coat and was turning his hat round and round as she spoke, as though he had just snatched it off. Or was he just about to put it on?

'Yes, *madame*, I went first thing. I could not sleep, you see. I—'

She held up her hand to silence him. If he wasn't going to volunteer any information about his encounter with Nathan she didn't want to know. 'If your accommodation is unsatisfactory for some reason,' she therefore said tersely, 'you must change it. You can spare me the details.' Only yesterday he'd claimed it was his duty to deal with *the matters domestic*. What was wrong with him today? 'What I do want to hear about is any progress you have made with our contacts. Have you managed to reschedule any of the appointments we missed because of our late arrival?'

He straightened up and gave her a brief, if slightly disappointing, account of his efforts on behalf of George Holdings.

'So the rest of our day is effectively free, then?'

'I regret, *madame*, that yes.' He spread his hands wide in a totally Gallic gesture of apology.

'Well, in that case we can devote it to Sophie. The poor little girl has been through torment to get here. The least we can do is make it up to her by giving her a perfectly splendid day. I want to take her out somewhere today that she will enjoy so much it will prevent her from worrying about her poor mama. Any ideas?'

'Yes, *madame*. Of course *madame*. But—'

'We will be ready to go out in half an hour,' she said, turning on her heel. 'And it's *mademoiselle*,' she threw over her shoulder as she stalked along the corridor to the nursery.

'How are you, my little sweet pea?' she said as she strode into Sophie's room. All her irritation vanished the moment Sophie leapt to her feet, ran across the room and flung her arms round Amethyst's waist.

'Feel better this morning, do you?'

'Yes, Aunt Amy! I have such a lovely view out of my window,' she said, tugging her across the room to show her. 'I have seen so many people walking by. The ladies wear the most enormous bonnets so you can't see their faces and their skirts look like great big bells swinging along the street. And the buildings are all so tall, and grand, but the people who go into them are all muddled up.'

'Muddled up?'

'Yes. You can't tell who the house belongs to by watching who goes in. Not at all. I thought that one over there...' she pointed to the *hôtel* immediately across the street '...must belong to someone very important, because a great big coach drew up last night and people dressed up in fabulous clothes got in, but then this morning, some people came out looking as though they were going to work. A man with a leather satchel and a quite poor-looking woman carrying a bundle...'

'I expect it is the same as this house, then,' she explained. 'Each floor is rented out to someone different. The grand people with the coach would have the ground floor and the woman with the bundle probably lives up in the attics somewhere.'

Sophie's brow wrinkled. 'Are we very grand, then?'

'Because we have rented the ground floor of this house?' Amethyst smiled. 'No. We are not grand at all. Only...quite well off.' Fabulously well off, thanks to her aunt's shrewd business brain. And, lately, to hers. People who knew she'd been her aunt's sole beneficiary expected her fortune to dwindle, now that she was at the helm. Only a trusted few knew that her aunt had trained her in every aspect of managing her vast portfolio, after discovering she, too, had a knack with numbers. An ability to spot an opportunity for investment that others overlooked, which stemmed, in part, from a refusal to accept the general consensus of opinion in the masculine-dominated world of finance.

'I just wanted,' she explained to the inquisitive child, 'you and your mother to have the best that money could buy for our little adventure.'

'Where is Mama?'

'She is not feeling well this morning. I have told her to stay in bed.'

Sophie's face fell.

'She will not be coming out with us today, but Monsieur Le Brun has promised that he will show you a lot of very interesting things.'

'But Mama won't see them. I would rather she was with us...'

'Yes, so would I,' Amethyst replied with feeling. A whole day sightseeing with Monsieur Le Prune, without Fenella's soothing presence to act as a buffer between them, was bound to end in them having words. 'But you can tell her all about them when we come home. And perhaps buy her a little present to cheer her up.'

Sophie's face lit up. 'A monkey. I saw a man with a monkey go past just now, wearing a red jacket and cap.'

'No, sweet pea. I do not think your mama would enjoy having a monkey for a pet.'

Sophie looked thoughtful. 'No, I suppose not. She…likes quiet things, does she not?'

'Yes.' That was very true. Sophie had much more of an adventurous spirit than her mother. She wouldn't be a bit surprised if she didn't take after her rather reckless father in temperament, though she was a miniature image of her mother, with her light-brown hair and soft, smoky blue eyes.

'We could buy her a picture. She would like that, wouldn't she? Are there shops that sell pictures?'

'I am sure there must be.' For there were certainly plenty of artists about. Infiltrating restaurants and invading people's dreams…

She shook herself. He had not invaded her dreams on purpose. It was her own stupid fault for spending the last few moments before she fell asleep savouring the way it had felt to have him come to her and beg for custom. And then imagining all sorts of other ways she could make him rue the day he'd spurned her for that horsey-faced female, simply because *her* father had a seat in Parliament in his pocket, rather than just a modest parish to govern. In her dreams, he'd gone from crouching on that canvas stool, to kneeling at her feet, begging forgiveness and swearing that he'd made a terrible mistake. That he'd been punished, for years, for the callous way he'd broken her heart. And only a kiss from her lips could assuage his torment...

She'd felt most uncomfortable when she awoke. Gracious heavens, she didn't want him to beg her for kisses, or anything else. She was well rid of him. She'd told herself so every time she'd seen his name in print in conjunction with tales of his ineffectiveness, or lack of loyalty to his party and the men who'd sponsored his career. And eventually, when his penchant for sordid sexual scandals got so out of hand that no amount of pressure from his influential family could undo the damage, she had incontrovertible proof.

He was no good.

And she'd had a lucky escape.

'I'm ready!'

She blinked to see Sophie hopping from one foot to the other, her coat buttoned up, her bonnet tied neatly under her chin.

Time to go out.

And push the feckless, faithless Nathan Harcourt from her mind. She had better things to do with her day than think about him. About how much more handsome he was than she had remembered. How much more vital and alive as he crouched with his pencil in his hand in that restaurant than he'd seemed as a young man. He'd strolled through the ballrooms of polite society, in those days, with a jaded air, as though nothing and nobody could possibly interest him. That had been the cynical ploy of a rake, of course. When he'd deigned to pay her a little attention, it had made her feel there must be something special about her to have dissipated the pall of boredom hanging over him. And when he'd smiled at her that first time, in response to some silly quip she'd made, as though it had been something brilliantly witty, she'd felt as though she'd met the one person in the world who completely understood her.

A little grunt of vexation escaped her mouth, which made Monsieur Le Brun, who was waiting for them in the hall, start guiltily.

She didn't correct his assumption that she might be cross with him. It would keep him on his toes.

Besides, before the end of the day, she was bound to be.

Sophie skipped up to him and smiled. 'Aunt

Amy says you are going to show us lots of interesting things. Do you know where the man with the monkey lives?'

His face softened. It was amazing the effect Sophie was beginning to have on him. Even though she'd suspected him of lying about his willingness to take charge of a party that included a child, he had never exhibited the slightest sign of impatience with her. He might have fretted about the delay to his schedule, but he'd never taken out his frustration on her.

'I know Paris well, but alas,' he replied with a shrug, 'I do not know everyone who lives in every house. Especially not now, when my city is so full of visitors. But I can show you the best of it. We shall commence,' he said, gesturing with his hand to the hall door, 'with a stroll along the Boulevard.'

Amethyst grimaced. 'Should I have worn pattens?'

Monsieur Le Brun drew himself up to his full height.

'The Boulevard has gravelled walkways along both sides, shaded by trees. You will not need to worry about soiling your gowns when walking there, I promise you.'

'Hmm,' she said, pursing her lips. Well, she would soon see.

* * *

But as it turned out, the Boulevard was an utter delight. Not only was it flanked by the most impressive buildings she'd ever seen, beyond the trees which provided welcome shade, but also there were stalls selling everything from lemonade to toys. There were street entertainers every few yards, as well: jugglers and acrobats and even a one-man band. Sophie was particularly taken with the man who professed to be a scientist, demonstrating the amazing hydraulic capabilities of water. What he actually did was squirt it at unsuspecting passers-by through a variety of ingenious contraptions, to the delight of his audience.

Eventually, just as her feet were beginning to feel rather too tight for her walking boots, and Sophie's energy was visibly waning, Monsieur Le Brun indicated a café.

'Tortoni's,' he said. 'It is, at night, the most fashionable place to be seen after a trip to the opera. But it also sells the best ice cream in the world. Mademoiselle Sophie will love it.'

Amethyst bit back the urge to enquire how he knew the ice cream was the best in the world, since she was perfectly sure he'd never travelled that far, for Sophie's tired little face had lit up at the mention of ice cream.

And today was all about Sophie. She would do nothing to mar her enjoyment.

She was glad she'd kept her tongue between her teeth when Monsieur Le Brun promptly secured them a table in a very good spot, in spite of the popularity of the café.

'This is lovely,' she therefore said, as they took their places at a table which had a view over the bustling Boulevard.

He almost dropped his menu.

Amethyst couldn't help smiling. He'd got so used to her sniping at him over every little thing that he didn't know how to handle a compliment. She just couldn't resist the urge to shock him even further.

'You have made Sophie very happy this morning. Thank you, *monsieur.*'

His cheeks went pink.

Dear Lord, she'd actually made the poor man blush.

She gave him space to recover by helping Sophie choose what flavour ice to have.

And when she next looked up, it was to see Nathan Harcourt making his way across the crowded café to their table.

What was he doing here?

She took in his unkempt clothing, the satchel over his shoulder, and put two and two together.

Since this was a fashionable place for people to gather, he was bound to pick up custom here.

Yes, that explained his presence in Tortoni's. But why was he coming to her table? What could he possibly want?

And then she noted the determined jut to his chin as he stalked towards them.

Well, she'd wondered how he would react to being given the equivalent of a year's wages for a drawing that had taken him ten minutes, at most. It looked as though she was going to find out.

From the light of battle she could see in his eyes as he drew closer, she'd achieved her aim of humiliating him by highlighting the difference in their stations, just as he'd done to her ten years ago.

Only he wasn't going to crawl away and weep until there were no more tears left, the way she'd done. He looked as though he was going to attempt to get even for the insult.

Well, let him try. Just see how far he could get, that was all. She was no longer some starry-eyed débutante, ready to believe glib flattery and vague half-promises. She was a hardheaded business woman.

And she never, but never, let *any* man get the better of her.

* * *

Indignation carried him all the way across the crowded café to her table. How dare she send her lover to his rooms with all that money?

The Frenchman had been every bit as condescending as he'd expected. The only thing that had surprised him was how early he'd called. Nothing would have dragged Nathan out at that ungodly hour if he'd had Miss Dalby in his bed.

Nor would he have stumbled to the door this morning if he'd had any idea he would have come face to face with the sneering Frenchman, rather than one of his neighbours.

And if he hadn't been so fuddled with sleep he would have refused every last sou. Though it had only been after *Monsieur Le Brun* had sketched that mocking bow and he'd shut the door on him that he'd opened the purse and seen just how great an insult the man had offered him. Without having to say one word.

Sadly for him, he'd given himself away. The moment he'd bowed, Nathan recalled why his face had looked so familiar. So now he had the ammunition to make his stay in Paris extremely uncomfortable, if he chose.

He was here to deliver a warning of his own.

Get out of his city, or by God he would shout the Frenchman's secret from the rooftops.

What a pair they were for secrets. Though it didn't look as though she was trying to keep her secret hidden any more. The proof that she'd lied to him ten years before was sitting openly at table with her. Digging into her bowl of ice cream with a rapt expression, her little feet tucked neatly onto the top rung of her chair. Enjoying the simple pleasure with the total concentration of the truly innocent.

He snatched off his hat and thrust his fingers through his hair. She wasn't just 'an illegitimate baby'. She'd grown up, in the years since he'd learned of her existence, into a very real little person.

And no matter how much resentment he bore the mother, only a blackguard would expose a child to danger by telling the world the truth about its mother's lover.

The child noticed him staring at her and looked straight back at him with unabashed curiosity.

He couldn't see anything of Miss Dalby in her features. Nor her colouring. She must take after her father, he supposed.

Her father. He sucked in a sharp breath.

Of course the child had a father, it was just that he'd been too angry, before, to think of anything beyond the way Miss Dalby had deceived him. The night Fielding had told him about the rumour he'd heard about Miss Dalby's having an illegitimate baby, he'd felt as though he'd been robbed at gunpoint. Those words had stolen his whole life from him. The life he'd planned on having with her. The house in the country, the children he'd imagined running about in the orchard where chickens scratched among the windfalls. Gone in the blink of an eye. He'd been incapable of thinking about anything beyond his own loss.

But she hadn't come by a baby on her own. There had been a man. A man who must have had fair hair and blue eyes.

And no conscience whatsoever.

Damn it all, Miss Dalby had only been seventeen when he'd started to think he was falling in love with her. So she could not have been more than sixteen when...when some rogue had seduced and abandoned her. Nor made any provision for his brat, if she was obliged to hire out her body to men like this one.

He glared at her French lover again, though his anger was veering wildly from one player in the drama to another with confusing rapidity.

Her parents, for instance. They'd brought her up to London for that Season. They must have known. She couldn't have hidden a baby from them. *They* must have told her to pretend to be innocent. At that age, and after what she'd already been through, she wouldn't have dared defy them. Besides, properly brought-up girls did not set up their will in opposition to their parents.

No more than sons of the same age. He'd only been in London himself at the express command of his own father. Forbidden from exploring his talent as an artist, he'd been pretending to think about choosing some other, respectable profession, whilst really trying to work out if there was any honourable way he could break free from family expectations.

For his father wasn't a man to cross, any more than he guessed the Reverend Dalby had been.

It had only been last night that he'd started to wonder what had become of her all these years. Before that, he'd refused to allow his thoughts to stray in her direction. But…it didn't look as though her family had stood by her. Why else would she be sitting here with her daughter in plain sight, a lover at her side and no wedding ring on her finger?

Was her father the kind of man who would wash his hands of his erring child, just because she'd brought disgrace to the family? The way his own father had done? Had her attempt to inveigle him into marriage been her last, desperate attempt to appease them? Had he, Nathan, been her last resort?

No wonder she'd wept when he'd become betrothed to Lucasta instead.

Strange how the years brought a new perspective to the tragedies of youth. There was always more than one side to any story. And before this moment—at least, before he'd watched the child enjoying her ice cream—the only side he'd ever considered had been his own.

'Are you a friend of Monsieur Le Brun?'

He blinked, to find the little girl was smiling up at him, her wide blue eyes full of curiosity.

'No, Sophie,' Miss Dalby hastily put in, while her lover was taking an indignant breath to refute the allegation. 'This is Monsieur Harcourt. He is an artist. He drew a picture of me last night, while we were out at dinner. I expect he is hoping for more custom from us.'

The little girl's face lit up. 'Oh, could he do a picture of me? You said we might buy a picture today. I thought from a shop. But this would be even better!'

'Yes. It would.' Miss Dalby gave him a smug little smile.

And all his sympathy towards her evaporated. She'd found a man who did not care that she'd already borne a child out of wedlock. And she was going to take great pleasure in obliging *him* to sit at her feet and draw the child. The child whose existence had driven them apart. The child whose existence she'd tried to conceal, so that she could entrap him into a marriage that would have been...

At that point, his imagination floundered into a wall of mist. He had no idea what marriage to her would have been like, with an illegitimate child hovering on the fringes of it. Could it possibly have been any worse than the one he'd actually had? With a wife he couldn't even like, never mind desire, once he'd got to know her? A wife who'd broadcast her contempt for him with increasing virulence.

But one thing he knew. He wouldn't have wanted to stop bedding *her*. Even now, ten years later, with a gut full of aversion for her lies and scheming, he wanted her. The reason he'd been so slow on the uptake that morning had been because of the sleepless night he'd spent on her account, either brooding on the past, or suffering dreams of the kind that bordered on nightmares, from which he had woken soaked in sweat and painfully aroused.

Just thinking about the things he'd done to her, and with her, during those feverish dreams had a predictable effect.

Hastily he pulled up a chair to her table, in spite of her French lover's scowl, pulling his satchel on to his lap to cover his embarrassment.

With quick, angry strokes, he began a likeness of the girl he might have been forced into providing for, had Miss Dalby been successful in her attempts to snare him.

Chapter Four

Grimly determined not to reflect on how handsome her father must have been to have produced such a pretty child, he concentrated instead on capturing what he could see of her own nature. With deft sure fingers, he portrayed that eager curiosity and trusting friendliness which had so disarmed him.

'Oh,' the child said when he handed her the finished sketch. 'Do I really look like that?'

'Indeed you do, sweet pea,' said Miss Dalby, shooting him a look of gratitude over the top of the sheet of paper.

She was many things, but she wasn't stupid. She could see he'd restrained his anger with her so as not to hurt the child.

Out of the corner of his eye he saw the Frenchman reaching for his purse. He held up his hand to stall him.

'You do not need to pay me for *this* picture,' he said. Then turning to the little girl, because he was damned if he was going to let either of the adults know that he would rather starve than take another penny of the man's money, he said, 'It is my pleasure to have such a pretty subject to draw.'

The girl blushed and hung her head to study her portrait. Her mother gave him a tight smile, while the Frenchman openly smirked.

And all of a sudden, it was too much for him. He was burning with an unsavoury mix of frustration, anger and lust as he stowed his materials back in his satchel.

A waiter provided a very convenient diversion at that moment by arriving at the table to ask if they required anything else, or if they were ready to pay their bill. While the Frenchman was preoccupied, Nathan leaned towards Miss Dalby and muttered, 'Is he really the best you can do? You are still young and attractive enough to acquire a protector who could at least dress you in something approaching last year's fashions, couldn't you?'

Her eyes snapped with anger as she opened her mouth to make a retort, but then something stopped her. She subsided back into her seat.

'You think I am…attractive?'

'You know you are,' he growled. 'You know very well that ten years ago I thought you so attractive I almost threw caution to the winds and made an honest woman of you. But now…now you've grown even more irresistible.'

From her gasp, he could tell he'd shocked her. But what was more telling was the flush that crept to her cheeks. The way her eyes darkened and her lips parted.

'You should not say such things,' she murmured with an expression that told him she meant the exact opposite.

'Even though you enjoy hearing them?' He smiled at her mockingly. She wanted him. With a little persuasion, a little finesse, he could take her from this mean-looking Frenchman and slake all the frustrations of the last ten years while he was at it.

And then, because if he carried on muttering to her with such urgency, people would start to notice, he said in a clear voice, 'It will be my pleasure to do business with you again, at any time you choose. Any time,' he said huskily, 'at all.'

Amethyst blinked and looked around her. They were standing in some vast open space, though she could not for the life of her recall how she'd got there.

Did Nathan Harcourt really think she was in some kind of irregular *relationship* with Monsieur Le Brun?

And had he really been on the verge of proposing to her? All those years ago? No matter how much she argued that it could not be so, what else could he have meant by those angrily delivered, cryptic sentences?

The Tuileries Gardens. That was where she was. Where the three of them were.

'On court days,' she registered Monsieur Le Brun say, 'crowds of people gather here to watch ministers and members of the nobility going to pay their respects to the King.'

'Can we come and watch?'

While Monsieur Le Brun smiled down at Sophie and said he would see what he could arrange, Amethyst's mind went back to the day she'd stood in her father's study, trying to convince them that she'd believed Harcourt had really loved her.

'If you got some foolish, presumptuous thoughts in your head regarding that young man,' her father had bellowed, 'you have nobody but yourself to blame. If he had been thinking of marriage, he would have come to me first and requested permission to pay his addresses to you.'

She wished she could stand next to the girl who'd cowered before her father's wrath, bang her fist on his desk, and say 'Listen to her! She's right! Harcourt did want to marry her.'

But it was ten years too late. The girl she'd been had trusted her parents would understand. When they'd wanted to know why she'd been so upset on learning of Nathan's betrothal, why she couldn't face going to any more of the balls and routs they were trying to push her to attend, she'd blurted it out. Oh, not all of it, for she'd known it was wrong the very first time she'd let him entice her into a shadowy alcove, where he'd pressed kisses first on the back of her hand, then on her cheek. She couldn't admit that she had hardly been able to wait for the next time they met, hoping he'd want to do the same. She'd been so thrilled and flattered, and eager to join him when he'd taken her out on to a terrace and kissed her full on the lips. They'd put their arms round each other and it had felt like heaven.

All she'd been able to do was stammer, 'But he kissed me...'

And her father had thundered she was going to end in hell for such wanton behaviour. He'd whisked her straight back to Stanton Basset where, in order to save her soul, he'd shut her in her room on a diet of bread and water, after administering a sound spanking.

As if she hadn't already suffered enough. Harcourt had made her fall in love with him, had made her think he loved her, too, had then coldly turned away from her and started going about with Lucasta Delacourt. She'd been convinced he must simply have been making sport of her, seeing how far from the straight and narrow he could tempt the vicar's daughter to stray.

For a while she'd felt as though her whole world had collapsed around her like a house of cards.

Eventually they'd let her out of her room and told her she could eat meals with the rest of the family again, but she had no appetite. She stumbled through her duties about the house and parish in a fog of misery that nothing could lift. Then her mother, rather than offering her comfort, had rebuked her for setting a bad example to her younger sisters.

Her father might have accused her of being a trollop, but her mother had heaped even more crimes upon her head. She'd accused her of being vain and self-indulgent, of getting ideas above her station...

Which was ironic, because the last thing she

had been interested in had been his connections. Others might have simpered and sighed, and tried to capture his attention because his father was an earl, but she'd just liked him for himself. Or the image of himself he'd projected, whenever he'd been with her.

The last straw had been the attitude of her sisters. The sisters she'd cared for as babies, sat up with during illnesses. They'd closed ranks with her parents. Shaken their heads in reproof. Shown not the slightest bit of sympathy.

She understood them doing so when their parents were around. But couldn't one of them have just…patted her hand as she wept alone in her bed? Offered her a handkerchief even?

Surely what she'd done hadn't been that bad? Besides, they could see she was sorry, that she'd learned her lesson. Wasn't anybody, ever, going to forgive her?

She'd begun to sink into real despair. Until the day Aunt Georgie had descended on them. Sat on the edge of her bed and told her, in that brusque way she had, that what she needed was a change of air.

'I shall tell your parents I mean to take you on a tour of the Lake District, to give your mind a new direction.' Though she hadn't, Amethyst recalled with a wry smile, done anything of the sort.

They hadn't been on the road long before Aunt Georgie had been obliged to come clean.

'I've a mind,' she'd said brusquely, 'to buy a couple of factories that some fool of a man ran into bankruptcy.'

Amethyst had been stunned. Women did not go round purchasing failing businesses.

'He's claiming the workers are intractable,' her aunt had continued. 'Has suffered from riots and outbreaks of plague and God knows what else. We'll probably find that he's a drunken incompetent fool. Naturally we cannot let anyone know our true purpose in coming up here.' Aunt Georgie had smiled at her, patted her hand and said, 'Your breakdown has come at a most convenient time for me. Perfect excuse to be wandering about that part of the countryside in an apparently aimless manner. I can sound out people in the know and find out what is really going on.'

'You can't use me as some kind of a…smoke-screen,' Amethyst had protested. 'I'm—'

'Getting angry at last. That's the ticket. Far healthier to get angry than mope yourself into a decline. That young man,' she'd said, 'isn't worth a single one of the tears you've shed over him.

And as for your father...' She'd snorted in contempt. 'What you ought to do, my girl, is think about getting even with them. If not the specific men who've conspired to crush you, then as many of the rest of their sex as you can.'

Get even. She'd never thought a chance would come for her to get even with Harcourt. Though she'd wondered if there wasn't some divine justice at work on her behalf anyway. It didn't seem to have done him much good, marrying that woman. In spite of all the connections she had, in spite of all the money her family spent on getting Harcourt elected, his career never went anywhere. His wife died childless. And then he'd created a scandal so serious that he'd had to disappear from public life altogether.

She'd crowed with triumph over every disaster that had befallen him, since it seemed to have served him right for toying with her affections so callously.

But now he'd admitted that he had been seriously thinking about marrying her. That he'd almost *thrown caution to the winds*.

Thrown caution to the winds? What on earth could he have meant by that?

Oh, only one of half-a-dozen things! There had been the disparity in their stations, for one thing. He was the son of an earl, after all, albeit the very youngest of them, while she was merely the daughter of an insignificant vicar. Nobility very rarely married into the gentry, unless it increased their wealth. And she'd had no dowry to speak of. Not then.

But that Miss Delacourt had. The one he'd become engaged to so swiftly after he'd given her the cut direct.

She shivered as she cast her mind back to the way he'd looked at her that night. As a rule, she tried not to think about it. It hurt too much. Even now, knowing that he hadn't been simply playing some kind of a game with her, she recoiled from the memory of the coldness in eyes that had once seemed to burn with ardour.

She dragged herself out of the past with an effort to hear Monsieur Le Brun was now telling Sophie a gory tale of an uprising that had been quelled upon the very spot where they stood. He pointed at some marks in the wall, telling the fascinated little girl that they'd been made by bullets.

She shuddered. Not at the goriness of the tale, though she would claim it was that if anyone should question her. But, no—what really sickened her was the thought that Harcourt assumed she was having intimate relations with this stringy, sallow-faced Frenchman.

Why was everyone always ready to assume the worst of her? All she'd done was leave Stanton Bassett to take a little trip. She'd followed all the proprieties by hiring a female companion, yet just because she'd stepped outside the bounds of acceptable female behaviour, just the tiniest bit, suddenly Harcourt assumed she must be a…a woman of easy virtue!

Based on what evidence—that she was with a man to whom she was not married, dressed in clothing that indicated she was relatively poor? And from this he'd deduced Monsieur Le Brun must be her protector?

Didn't he remember she was a vicar's daughter? Didn't he remember how he'd teased her about being so prim and proper when they'd first met?

Although he had soon loosened her moral stance, she reflected on a fresh wave of resentment. Quite considerably.

Perhaps he thought she'd carried on loosening after they'd parted.

Next time she came across Harcourt she would jolly well put him right. How dare he accuse her of having such poor taste as to take up with a man like Monsieur Le Brun?

If anyone had bad taste, it was he. He'd married a woman with a face like a horse, just because her family was wealthy and powerful.

Or so her parents had said. 'The Delacourts wouldn't let one of their daughters marry in haste. If they've got as far as announcing a betrothal, negotiations must have been going on for some time. His family might even have arranged the thing from the cradle. It is the way things are done, in such families. They leave nothing to chance.'

The certainty that they were right had made her curl up inside. It had seemed so obvious. He couldn't have walked away from her, then proposed to someone else the next day. Miss Delacourt must always have been hovering in the background.

But now...now she wondered just how deliberate and calculating his behaviour had been after all. He'd talked about finding her so attractive he'd almost *thrown caution to the winds*.

As though...as though he hadn't been able to help himself. As though he'd genuinely been drawn to her.

But in the end, it had made no difference. He'd married the girl of whom his family approved rather than proposing to the girl he'd only known a matter of weeks.

Though none of that explained why he seemed

so angry with her now. Surely, if he had been toying with the idea of proposing to her back then, he should be glad they'd finally met up when both of them were free to do as they pleased?

Only—he didn't think she was free, did he? He thought she was a kept woman.

Oh!

He was *jealous*. Of Monsieur Le Brun.

That was…well, it was…

So preposterous she didn't know whether to laugh or cry. When Monsieur Le Brun shot her a puzzled glance, she realised that, in stifling it, she'd made a very undignified sound, approximating something like a snort.

She made a valiant attempt to form sensible answers whenever Sophie spoke to her, but it was very hard to pretend to be interested in all the things Monsieur Le Brun was telling them about the park through which they were walking and the momentous historical events which had occurred on just about every corner.

When she felt as though her whole life had been flung up in the air and hadn't quite settled into place yet. If she could only get past how angry he'd made her, by assuming she'd sunk low enough to…well, never mind what he thought she and Monsieur Le Brun got up to.

It made her feel queasy. What about the other things he'd said? About finding her attractive?

Never mind *irresistible*. Almost irresistible enough to have lured him away from his sensible arranged match, to live in relative poverty and obscurity.

Had he been serious? Not one man, in the last ten years, had come anywhere near kissing her, yet Nathan claimed to find her so irresistibly attractive he immediately assumed she must be making her living as a woman of easy virtue. He had seethed at her and fumed at her, and only stormed off when he was satisfied he'd rattled her.

She stood stock still, her heart doing funny little skips inside her chest. She'd only ever been sought after seriously by gentlemen *after* they learned she was Aunt Georgie's sole beneficiary.

But Harcourt assumed she was poor and desperate.

And he still claimed to want her.

'Are you getting tired, Aunt Amy?'

Sophie had come running back to her and was taking her hand, and looking up into her face with concern.

'No, sweet pea. I am just…admiring the gardens. Aren't they beautiful?'

She hadn't noticed, not until she'd worked out

that Harcourt was suffering from jealousy, but the Tuileries Gardens were really rather pretty... in a stately, regulated kind of way, in spite of all the gruesome horrors which the citizens had perpetrated within it. The trees dappled the gravelled walks with shade, the sky she could see through the tracery of leaves was a blue that put her in mind of the haze of bluebells carpeting a forest floor in spring, and the air was so clear and pure it was like breathing in liquid crystal.

It was almost as magical a place as Hyde Park had been, when she'd been a débutante. She could remember feeling like this when she'd walked amongst the daffodils with Harcourt. Light-hearted and hopeful, but, above all, pretty. He'd made her feel so pretty, the way he'd looked at her back then, when she'd always assumed she was just ordinary, that there was nothing about her to warrant any sort of compliments.

That was because she'd always had to work so hard to please her exacting parents. She'd done her utmost to make them proud of her, with her unstinting work in the parish and her unquestioning support of her mother in bringing up the younger girls.

And what good had it done her? The minute she slipped, nothing she'd done before counted for anything. All they could say was that she was self-indulgent and ungrateful, and vain.

Though at least now she knew she hadn't been vain. He must have liked more than just the way she looked, if he'd contemplated marrying her. He'd liked *her*. The person she'd become when she'd been with him. The girl who felt as though she was lit up from inside whenever she was near him. A very different girl from the earnest, constantly-striving-to-please girl she was in the orbit of her parents. He'd shown her that it was fun to dance and harmless to flirt. They'd laughed a lot, too, over silly jokes they'd made about some of the more ridiculous people they encountered. Or nothing much at all.

She'd slammed the door shut on that Amy when he'd abandoned her.

She'd tossed aside the former Amy, too, the one who was so intent on pleasing her parents.

It had been much easier to nurture the anger Aunt Georgie had stirred up. She'd become angry Amy. Bitter Amy. Amy who was going to survive no matter what life threw at her.

'It is time I took you to another café,' said Monsieur Le Brun. 'It is a little walk, but worth it, for the pastries there are the best you will ever eat.'

'Really?' She pursed her lips, though she did not voice her doubt in front of Sophie. There wasn't any point. The proof of the pudding, or in this case, pastry, would be in the eating. So she just followed the pair to the café, let the waiter lead them to a table and sank gratefully on to a chair, wondering all the while which, out of all the Amys she'd been in her life thus far, was the real one? And which one would come to the fore if *he* should come into this café, looking at her with all that masculine hunger?

She reached for the sticky pastry the waiter had just brought and took a large bite, wondering if it might be a new Amy altogether. An Amy who was so sick of people assuming the worst of her that she might just as well *be* bad.

She licked her lips, savouring the delicious confection. She sipped her drink with a feeling that before she left Paris, there was a distinct possibility she was going to find out.

Chapter Five

'How are you this morning?' Amethyst asked Fenella, noting that she still looked rather wan and shamefaced.

'Much better,' she said, sliding into her place at the breakfast table and pouring herself a cup of chocolate with an unsteady hand. 'Yes, much better.'

What Fenella needed was something to take her mind off herself, Amethyst decided. She could not possibly still be feeling the after-effects of drinking too much. She was just indulging in a fit of the dismals. Since offering her sympathy had done so little good, perhaps an appeal to her deeply ingrained sense of duty might do the trick. A reminder that she was supposed to be a *paid* companion.

'I hope you do not think I am being strict with you, but I really must insist you get back to work today.'

Fenella sat up a little straighter and lifted her chin. Amethyst repressed a smile.

'I need you to double-check any correspondence that Monsieur Le Brun may have written regarding the trade opportunities we've come over here to secure.'

At Fenella's little gasp of dismay, she held up her hand. 'My grasp of the French language is only very basic, so I need you to keep an eye on everything he does. It is bad enough having to rely on him to represent me at meetings,' she grumbled. 'Anyway, I have to spend some time reading the packet of mail which has caught up with me...' she sighed '...before we can take Sophie out anywhere. It shouldn't take me long, but I must just make sure there is nothing so pressing it cannot wait until my return. Jobbings already thinks I am flighty, because I have come *jauntering off to foreign parts*, as he put it. He fully expects me to fail in this venture,' she said gloomily. 'He doesn't think I have a tithe of my aunt's business acumen.'

'You do not have a high opinion of him, either, do you?'

'He is honest and diligent. Which is more than can be said for most men.'

Fenella cut a pastry into a series of tiny squares, her expression pensive. 'What is your opinion of Monsieur Le Brun, now that you have got to know him better? Sophie said that you did not seem so cross with him yesterday as you usually are.'

'Well, although he looks far too sour to have ever been a child, let alone remember what one would like, he did take us to a whole series of places which were exactly the kind of thing that a lively, inquisitive child like Sophie would really enjoy,' Amethyst admitted.

'Yes, Sophie told me all about it,' said Fenella, lifting her cup and taking a dainty sip of tea.

'I confess,' Amethyst continued, 'I had my doubts when he said that he did not mind having a child form part of our party. I got the distinct impression,' she said with a wry twist to her lips, 'that he would have said anything to get the post, so desperate was he for work. Even the testimonials he provided were so fulsome they made me a bit suspicious.'

'So why, then, did you take him on?'

'*Because* he was desperate for the job, of course. I thought if he would say anything to land the job, then he was likely to work harder to ensure he kept it. And so far, my instincts have not failed me. He has worked hard.'

'Then you do not...' Fenella placed her cup

carefully back on to its saucer '...dislike him as much as you did to start with?'

'I do not need to like the man to appreciate he is good at his job. So far he has proved to be an efficient and capable courier. And though his manners put my back up they have a remarkable effect on waiters on both sides of the Channel. He always manages to secure a good table and prompt service. I attribute that,' she said, digging into her own plate of eggs and toast, 'to that sneer of his.'

'Oh, dear, is that all you can say? Is that really...fair?'

Amethyst raised her brows, but that was not enough to deter Fenella. 'You *did* make a good choice when you employed him,' she said stoutly. 'He is...' She floundered.

'Arrogant, opinionated and overbearing,' said Amethyst. 'But then he is a man, so I suppose he cannot help that. However,' she added more gently, noting from the way Fenella was turning her cup round and round in its saucer that her companion was getting upset, 'I am sure you need have no worries that he may take his dislike of me out on you. What man could possibly object to the way you ask for his advice? For that is what you do, isn't it? You don't challenge his dominance by giving him direct orders, the way

I do, so he has no need to try to put you in your place. You just flutter your eyelashes at him and he does whatever you want, believing the whole time that it was all entirely his own idea.'

To her astonishment, Fenella flushed bright pink.

'I am sorry if that unsettles you. I meant it as a compliment. You handle him with such aplomb...'

Fenella got to her feet so quickly her chair rocked back and almost toppled over. 'Please, I...' She held up her hand, went an even hotter shade of pink and fled the room.

Amethyst was left with a forkful of eggs poised halfway to her mouth, wondering what on earth she had said to put such a guilty look on Fenella's face.

It took Amethyst less than an hour to run her eyes over the latest figures and tally them in her mind with the projected profits. At home, in Stanton Basset, she had always started her day by doing exactly this, and before she'd set out she had seen no reason why she shouldn't keep up with the latest developments as assiduously as ever.

But she'd never felt so relieved to have got through the columns of figures and the dry reports that went with them. She couldn't wait to put on her hat and coat, and get outside and start exploring Paris again.

She'd never enjoyed being in business for its own sake, the way Aunt Georgie had. It had always been more about repaying her aunt's faith in her by making her proud. And as for coming to France to expand the business...

The truth was that the end of the war had come at just the right time for her. Everyone with means was flocking to Paris. It was the perfect time to break away from Stanton Basset and all its petty restrictions. To do something different. Something that was nothing to do with anyone's expectations.

So why had she justified her decision to travel, by telling Jobbings her motive for coming here was to expand the business she'd inherited? Why was she still making excuses for doing what she wanted? Whose approval did she need to win now her aunt had gone? Not Jobbings'. He worked for her.

Was she somehow trying to appease the ghost of her aunt? She'd thought that coming somewhere different would jolt her out of the rigid routine into which she'd fallen and stuck after her aunt had died. But it wasn't proving as easy to cast off the chains of habit as she'd thought it would be. She was still looking over her shoulder to see if her aunt would approve.

She eyed her bonnet in the mirror with dislike as she tied the frayed brown ribbons under her chin. It did nothing for her. She rather thought it wouldn't do anything for anyone.

Well, while she was in Paris, she was going to treat herself to a new one. No woman visiting Paris could fail to come back with just one or two items that were a little brighter and more fashionable than she was used to wearing, would she? It wouldn't exactly be advertising her wealth, would it?

And what was the point of having money, if all you ever did was hoard it?

'I hope,' she therefore said upon reaching the communal hall, where the others were waiting for her, 'that we will be visiting some shops today. Or if not today,' she amended, realising that she had not asked Fenella to make shopping a part of their itinerary, 'tomorrow. I have decided that we should all have new bonnets.'

Fenella flushed and pressed her hand to her throat, but Sophie cheered.

'Monsieur Le Brun has already said he is going to take us to the Palais Royale,' she said, bouncing up to her with a smile. 'He says it is full of shops. Toyshops and bookshops, and cafés like the one where we bought the water ice yesterday. I expect you could buy bonnets, too,' she added generously.

The Palais Royale. Oh, dear. Well, at least she'd already come up with the notion of buying bonnets for all three of them. The prospect of getting something new to wear was bound to help take Fenella's mind off returning to the scene of her downfall.

Though when she took another look at Fenella, it was to find that she still looked rather pink and more than a little uncomfortable.

'A new bonnet,' said Fenella. 'Really, Miss Dalby, that is too kind of you. I don't deserve—'

'Fustian,' she barked as she marched out of the front door. 'You have both been ill. You deserve a reward for putting up so heroically with me dragging you and poor Sophie all the way out here.'

Fenella trotted behind her, twittering and protesting for several yards that the last thing she deserved was a reward.

When they finally reached the Palais Royale and caught sight of the shops by daylight, however, her final protest dwindled away to nothing.

The people thronging the gravelled courtyard

were all so exquisitely dressed. It made their own plain, provincial garb look positively shabby.

And the shops were full of such beautiful things.

It occurred to her that Fenella didn't often have new clothes. She couldn't outshine her own employer, after all. But now Amethyst wondered how much she minded dressing so plainly, when she spent so many hours poring over fashion plates in the ladies' magazines.

'Oh, just look at that silk,' sighed Fenella, over a length of beautiful fabric draped seductively across the display in a shop window. 'I declare, it…it glows.'

'Then you must have a gown made up from it,' declared Amethyst. Before Fenella could come up with a dutiful protest, she interjected, 'It is ridiculous to go about looking like dowds when I have the means for both of us to dress stylishly.'

'Oh, but—'

'Neither of us have had anything new for an age. And nor has Sophie. You have to admit, that shade of blue would suit you both admirably.'

'Well…' Fenella bit her lower lip, which was trembling with the strain of knowing quite the right thing to do in this particular circumstance.

'I have made up my mind, so it is no use arguing. Both you and Sophie are going to return to Stanton Basset in matching silk gowns.'

Sophie's face fell, predictably. She knew that visiting a modiste meant hours of standing about being measured and dodging pins.

'But first, where are those toyshops Monsieur Le Brun promised us?'

Sophie's face lit up again and she skipped ahead of them to a shop she must have already noted, so swiftly did she make for it.

The adults followed more slowly, glancing into all the windows as they went past.

Until they came to a shop that sold all kinds of supplies for artists, at which point Amethyst's feet drifted to a halt. Did Harcourt buy his supplies here? Or perhaps, given the preponderance of tourists milling about, he would frequent somewhere cheaper, known only to locals. Although the money she'd given him for that quick portrait would ensure he could buy the best, for some time to come.

She frowned. She didn't like the way her mind kept returning to Harcourt. It was a problem she'd struggled with for years. Every time his name appeared in one of the scandal sheets, all the old hurts would rise up and give her an uncomfortable few days. It was too bad he'd had to flee to Paris, of all places, when London grew too hot for him.

She heard Sophie laugh and turned to see that the rest of her party were going into the toyshop already. She chastised herself for standing there peering intently into the dim interior of the artist's supplier. She'd actually been trying to see if she could make out the identity of any of the customers. There was no reason he would be there, just because she was.

Sighing, she tore herself away from the window and moved on to the next shop, which was a jeweller's. Once more her feet ruled her head, coming to a halt without her conscious volition. As her eyes roved over the beautiful little trinkets set out on display, she heard her aunt's voice, sneering that women who adorned themselves with such fripperies only did so to attract the attention of men, or to show off to other women how much wealth they had.

'Wouldn't catch me dead wasting my hard-earned money on such vulgar nonsense.'

She bit her lower lip as she silently retorted that it might very well be vulgar to wear too much jewellery, but surely it wouldn't hurt to own just a little?

Her eyes snagged on a rope of pearls, draped over a bed of black silk. She'd worn a string just like it, for the few short weeks her Season had lasted. She'd been so happy when her mother had clasped them round her neck. She'd felt as if she was on the verge of something wonderful. The wearing of her mother's pearls signified the transition from girlhood into adulthood.

Something inside her twisted painfully as she remembered the day she'd taken them off for the last time. They'd gone back in their box when her mother had brought her home from London and she hadn't seen them again for years.

Two years, to be precise. And then they'd been round Ruby's neck.

And her mother had been smiling at Ruby and looking proud of her as she'd walked down the aisle on her father's arm to marry a wealthy tea-merchant she'd met at a local assembly. They hadn't even had to splash out for a London Season for Ruby. No, she'd managed to get a husband with far greater economy and much less fuss. And she therefore deserved the pearls.

Amethyst might not have minded so much if any of her sisters had spoken to her that day. But it was clear they'd been given orders not to do more than give her a nod of acknowledgement. She'd pinned such hopes on Ruby's wedding. She'd thought the fact her parents had sent her an invitation meant that she was forgiven, that they were going to let bygones be bygones.

No such thing. It had all been about rubbing her nose in it. Ruby was the good daughter. She was the black sheep. Ruby deserved the pearls and the smiles, and the bouquet and the lavish wedding breakfast.

Amethyst didn't even warrant an enquiry after her health.

She dug into her reticule, fished out a handkerchief and blew her nose. That was ages ago. She didn't care what her parents thought of her any more. They'd been so wrong, on so many counts. Why should she stand here wasting time even thinking about them, when they probably never spared her a second thought?

And then somehow, before she even knew she'd intended any such thing, her militant feet had carried her into the shop and over to a counter. Her mother had decided she didn't deserve the pearls. And her aunt had held the opinion that wanting such things was vulgar anyway. But neither her aunt nor her mother was in charge of her life, or her fortune, any longer. If she wanted to drape herself with pearls, or even diamonds, she had every right to do so. Why shouldn't she buy something for the sheer fun of splashing out her money on something that just about everyone in her past would have disapproved of?

The shop was a veritable treasure trove of the most beautiful little ornaments she had ever seen. One object in particular caught her eye: a skillfully crafted ebony hair comb, which was set with a crescent of diamonds. Or possibly crystals. Since she had so little experience of such things, there was no way she would ever be able to discern whether those bright little chips of liquid fire were genuine or paste.

But whatever it was, she wanted it. It wasn't as if it was a completely useless ornament, like a rope of pearls would have been. Besides, she sniffed, she didn't want to buy something that would remind her of such a painful episode in her past.

She glanced warily at the man presiding over the shop, who was watching her with a calculating eye. For one fleeting moment she wished she had Monsieur Le Brun at her side. He wouldn't let a shopkeeper chouse him. With that cynical eye and world-weary manner he would put the man in his place in an instant.

She shook the feeling off. She could manage this herself. She might have no experience with jewels, but she had plenty with people. Aunt Georgie had taught her how to spot a liar at twenty paces. She wouldn't let him dupe her into paying more than *she* decided the item was worth.

She took a deep breath and asked how much the comb cost.

'*Madame* does realise that these are diamonds?'

She couldn't help bristling with annoyance. Why did Frenchmen persist in addressing her as *madame*? It made her feel so…old. And dowdy.

And all the more determined to dress a little better.

So she nodded, trying to look insouciant, and braced herself to hear they cost an exorbitant amount, only to suck in a sharp, shocked breath when he quoted her a sum that sounded incredibly reasonable.

Which meant that they couldn't possibly be real diamonds. He *was* trying to trick her.

Like all men, he assumed she must be too stupid to notice. Her eyes narrowed. She stood a little straighter, but was prevented from saying anything when the door burst open and Harcourt strode in.

'I had almost given up hope of catching you alone,' he said, taking hold of her arm. Somehow she found him drawing her away from the counter and into the darker recesses of the shop, away from the window.

She ought not to have let him do any such thing. But then she wasn't in the mood for doing as she ought today.

Besides, there was something in his eyes that intrigued her. It wasn't the anger he'd displayed during their previous two encounters. It was something that looked very much like...desperation. And his words made it sound as though he'd been following her. Seeking an opportunity to speak to her alone. After the Frenchman's attitude, she could help being just a little bit flattered.

'When last we met, I should have said...that is...dammit!' He ran his fingers through his hair, leaving furrows in the thick, unruly mass.

My goodness, but he was worked up. Over her.

'I can't stop thinking about you. I am in torment, knowing you are here, in Paris, so near and yet so...out of reach.'

A warm glow of feminine satisfaction spread through her, almost breaking out in the form of a smile. Almost, but not quite. She just about had the presence of mind to keep her face expressionless.

She hoped.

'Would you consider leaving your Frenchman?'

Well, that put paid to looking cool, calm and poised. She felt her jaw drop, her eyes widen.

She managed to put everything back in place swiftly, but even so, he'd seen her reaction.

And he didn't like it.

'I know I don't look as though I am a good prospect,' he said, indicating the scruffy clothes he was wearing. 'But honestly, I am not as hard up as these clothes suggest. They are practical for when I am working, that is all. I get covered in dust and charcoal, and...but never mind that. The point is, you could do better than him.'

'You...you said that before,' she replied. And she'd been simultaneously flattered and insulted by his assumptions about what sort of woman he thought she was. Well, she might be flattered, but she wasn't going to melt at the feet of a man who kept on delivering his flattery wrapped up in insults.

'You have the unmitigated gall to stand there and criticise both my morals, and my taste, without knowing the first thing about my circumstances. And then have the cheek to say you think you are a better prospect for me?'

That hadn't come out quite right. What she had meant to say was that Monsieur Le Brun was not, and had never been, her protector and that, even if she did need one, she would most certainly be far choosier about the man in question.

'Try me,' he grated. Then, before she had time to draw breath to make her retort, which would have been good and acidic, putting him neatly in his place, he'd grabbed her by the shoulders and kissed her. Hard. Full on the lips.

She froze, shocked into indignant immobility. But only for a moment. Because, amazingly, hard on the heels of her indignation came a wave of such sheer pleasure it made her want to purr.

Oh, but it had been so long since any man had kissed her. Since this man, her first and only love, had kissed her. And that time it had been nothing like this. Back then, his kisses had been almost chaste. Tentative. As though he hadn't wanted to frighten her.

But just as she was starting to wonder if he was trying to punish her with the force of his kiss, his mouth gentled. He slid his hands down her arms and round her waist, tugging her closer to him. And she could no longer see why it was so important not to melt against him, into him. She'd never experienced anything so seductive as the feel of his mouth against hers, his arms tugging her close, the heat of his entire body pressed all along the length of hers. He kissed like a man now, she realised. That was the dif-

ference. He was an experienced man, not an un-
tried boy.

But the most seductive thing about his kiss
was his eagerness. The intensity of his yearning for her flowed off him in waves, making him
shake with it. It was his passion, not his skill,
which was so very irresistible. Because it made
her feel so desirable.

When, too soon, he pulled back, she opened
her eyes, stunned to discover that she'd shut
them.

'You see?'

What? What was she supposed to see? She
hadn't been aware of anything but him, for the
entire duration of that embrace. An entire troop
of Cossacks could have invaded the shop and she
didn't think she would have noticed.

'You still want me.'

Her pleasure dimmed. Was he just trying to
prove something by harking back to their shared
past? And if so, what?

'Why deny yourself, Amethyst? Come to me.'

Why deny yourself? He was talking as though
taking a lover was nothing more significant than
purchasing a bauble to decorate her hair.

When it clearly wasn't. Not even for him. He
was standing there, shaking with the force of
wanting her.

It was flattering. But she wasn't that kind of woman.

She shook her head.

His face hardened. 'What are you afraid of? What hold does that man have over you? Tell me.'

'He doesn't have any hold over me,' she said indignantly.

'Then prove it.'

'I do not have to prove anything to you.'

'So, I repeat, what is holding you back?'

'Can you not think of anything?' Like the fact she might have some morals, for instance?

A look of complete exasperation flitted across his face.

'Explain it to me.'

She glanced over his shoulder towards the door. At any moment Fenella might come in, looking for her, worrying about what was keeping her.

His face softened. 'I forgot. The little girl. Very well. Make an excuse to get away from the others and meet me somewhere where we can talk. And you can tell me exactly why you are reluctant to yield to the passion that is burning between us.'

Talk. She supposed she could agree to that. And, oh, but she did want to see him again. Hear him say such things again. It was almost like the dream she'd had on her first night here, where he'd grovelled at her feet for a chance to kiss her and to beg her forgiveness for the way he'd treated her.

'We are planning to visit the Louvre,' she said. 'I could easily break away from the others...'

'I go there as often as I can,' he said. 'Can you arrange to be there tomorrow?'

'Yes.' Easily. 'Then I will be waiting for you.'

He seized her by the shoulders, kissed her again, then turned and strode out of the shop.

She raised one trembling hand to her lips. What had she done? Agreed to meet him and let him attempt to talk her into having an affair with him, that's what.

She was shaking so much she needed something to lean on for support. Tottering to the counter, she laid both palms on it and took a deep breath. When the contents of the shop eventually swam back into view, she noted the proprietor pushing the comb, now nestled in a little box lined with silk, across the counter towards her.

She glared at him.

He promptly reduced the price by a further two francs.

With the pragmatism of the typical Parisian, he was continuing to haggle as though there was nothing untoward about men storming into his shop, grabbing potential customers, kissing them until their knees turned to jelly and then storming out again.

All of a sudden she felt like laughing.

'I shall take it,' she breathed. It would always remind her of this day, this moment. And the kiss that had tumbled her back to the kind of breathless wonder she'd felt as a girl, whenever he'd stolen a kiss from her in some secluded nook.

She didn't know what tomorrow would bring. But every time she tucked it into her hair, the fire of the gems sparkling from the darkness of their setting would always remind her of the sparks that had flared from this brief moment of twisted, thwarted passion. And she would remember how desirable he'd made her feel.

Amethyst woke the next morning with a smile on her face. Somewhere in this city, Harcourt was stomping around in fury at the erroneous belief she was a kept woman and wishing he was the one to have her in keeping. For the first time in ten years, she felt as though she was an attractive woman—in one man's eyes at least. And since she didn't much care what any other man thought about her, it was enough to make her feel like skipping down the Boulevard, hand in hand with Sophie, laughing with sheer joy.

'Where do you plan to take us today, Monsieur Le Brun?' she asked with bated breath when he came to report to her, after breakfast. 'I hear the Louvre is well worth a visit.'

'I can arrange for a viewing of the works of art for you, *madame*, of course,' he said.

'Oh, but you promised to take me to see the animals in the menagerie,' cried Sophie.

'We can go another day,' put in Fenella hastily, ever the peacemaker.

'No, no,' said Amethyst, making a play of looking out of the windows. 'The weather may not favour a trip out of doors another day. You must take Sophie to see the animals. Especially since she seems to feel you have given your word. Though I rather think I should like you to arrange for my own admission, Monsieur Le Brun. Once I have finished my paperwork for the day, I shall not want to sit about twiddling my thumbs.'

Since Sophie had been so determined to go and look at the animals, Fenella had put up very little resistance to her scheme. And not two hours after they'd departed for the Jardin des Plantes, where the menagerie was to be found, she was walking through the maze of statues on the ground floor, then mounting the stairs which led to the gallery where she'd agreed to meet Nathan.

She gripped her parasol tightly. There were so many other people here, studying the paintings. How was she going to find Nathan amongst them all? And did she really want to? What was she going to say to him?

She hadn't thought this through. Her pulse jumping to her throat, she turned blindly toward the nearest painting, which happened to be Titian's *San Pietro Martire*.

'He looks as though he's taken great pride in the kill, I always think,' said Harcourt, who'd somehow found her in the crowd and managed to approach her without her noticing.

She didn't turn round. She didn't think she could look him in the face without blushing. She'd spent far too many hours, since she'd last seen him, reliving the sensations he'd aroused by kissing her. And then, because he'd made it plain he wanted so much more than kissing, imagining what the rest of it might be like as well. It had left her heated, shaky sometimes, and at other times with a delightful sense in all her limbs as though she was floating a few inches above the muddy streets of Paris, in a kind of hazy-pink romantic cloud.

Which was ridiculous. There was nothing the least bit romantic about what he wanted from her.

Nevertheless, she couldn't help feeling…feminine—that was the only way to describe it—in a way she hadn't since she'd been a hopeful débutante, dreaming of veils and orange blossom.

She was feeling decidedly feminine now, at the rush of his breath against her cheek when he'd leaned close to murmur into her ear. He was standing so close that she could feel the heat of his body along her back and smell the aroma of smoke emanating from his clothing, as though he'd recently been standing near a bonfire.

In an attempt to shake off the spell, she resorted to a challenge.

'Is that any way to greet me?'

'No, I suppose not. It's just that you seemed to be studying it so intently. And as I've already told you, I spend a lot of time here, admiring the works of true masters. I cannot help but admire beauty when I see it. Which is why I am drawn to you, every time I see you about the city with your companions, in spite of knowing better.'

Just as she was drawn to him, too, in spite of knowing better.

'Perhaps I should not have come...'

Only, he'd reached another Amy, one she tried the hardest not to let anyone see. The Amy who'd lain in bed, night after lonely night, wishing someone, anyone, would come and put their arms round her and tell her she wasn't a disappointment. Not to them.

That Amy couldn't resist getting as close to Nathan as she could. To feel the warmth of his body all along her back. The whisper of his breath on the nape of her neck as he murmured into her ear, 'I am glad you did.'

They stood quite still for a few moments, pretending to gaze at the painting, whilst really enjoying the feeling of being so close. At least, that was what she was doing. And if he wasn't, then surely he would move away, instead of standing there, breathing in such a way that her insides were turning liquid with longing?

'You...you spend a lot of time here, you said.'

'I am an artist,' he said abruptly. Was he annoyed she'd deliberately broken the sensual mood that had been shimmering between them? 'Of course I want to study the works of the greats, and see how they managed to produce works like this, when all I...' He paused. 'I have little talent, not compared with men like these. It can be frustrating.'

'Then why continue?'

'Because being an artist is not something you choose. It is something you are. I cannot simply admire a view without wondering how I could capture something of its grandeur on canvas. Any more than I can look at an interesting face and not itch to sketch it. And as for your hair...'

'My hair?' At that she did turn her head to look up at him over her shoulder. He was staring at the few curls that inevitably escaped her bonnet with a kind of fascination.

'I have never seen another woman, anywhere, with hair quite the same shade. It defies analysis. Fielding always used to say it was just brunette,' he scoffed. 'He never glimpsed the rich ruby lights that shone from its depths when you passed under a branch of candles...'

When she gasped, he looked straight into her eyes. They were standing so close that it felt as though they were breathing the same air. He would only have to bend his head, just a fraction, and they would be kissing.

As though the same thought had just occurred to him, his gaze dropped to her lips. For a heartbeat or two they just stood there, looking at each other's mouths and breathing. Heavily.

'If you are really too afraid to risk losing the protection of that Frenchman,' he said harshly, 'then do you think he might give me permission to paint you? Just head and shoulders. I can't sleep for thinking about your hair. And if I could get you up to my studio, then perhaps—'

'Monsieur Le Brun is not my protector,' she said, cutting him off. He might say he only wanted to paint her, but she knew what he really wanted was so much more than that.

And she wanted it too.

Great heavens, she wanted it too. It was wrong. Perhaps even wicked. But it was far too late in her life to dream of romance and wedding bells. And here stood a man who was burning with desire for her. Genuine desire. It must be, for he had no idea how wealthy she was. He even thought she might be in the keeping of some other man. But it hadn't stopped him...lusting after her. To some women it might not seem like very much, but whatever it was that flared between them was real.

'If you want to paint my portrait, you have only to ask me.'

Harcourt's eyes blazed with an intensity that made her heart skip a beat.

'You will have to come to my studio,' he said.

'Yes, of course.'

'You know where it is?'

'Yes.' She flushed. Since the day he'd scribbled the address on the back of that sketch, she'd found out exactly where he lived, by pretending an interest in the layout of the streets through which they walked or drove. She'd even managed to drive past the *hôtel* where he had his lodgings and tried to guess behind which of the many windows his rooms lay.

'Can you come alone?'

Her heart thudded against her chest. She knew it. He wasn't asking her if he could paint her portrait at all, but whether she was willing to become his lover. A thrill of wicked excitement shot through her. Could she really do it? Take a lover?

It would mean an end to any hope of securing the trade agreements she'd ostensibly come to Paris for, if anyone found out.

And as for Fenella—she would be scandalised.

'You will have to paint my portrait, if I do,' she said. So long as he produced some kind of painting by the time they returned to England, she might be able to convince Fenella that nothing untoward had gone on.

And she wanted him so much. Not in the same way she'd wanted him as a girl. It hadn't been marriage she'd been dreaming of as she lay in her lonely, empty bed.

'I *could* come alone...'

He gripped her hand, though they were in full view of dozens of other tourists and might easily be noticed.

Yet she made no attempt to withdraw her hand, for she was held by the gleam of satisfaction that shone from his eyes.

'Tonight?'

'Tonight?' All of a sudden what she was considering became a bit too real. A kiss was one thing, but all the rest? And straight away?

She might be a virgin, but she knew what men and women did in the privacy of their bedrooms.

Her aunt might have sneered at girls who 'lifted their skirts to oblige a man's beastly desires'. But then her aunt had never been in love. If she had, she would know that sometimes you could look at a man and just swoop inside. And melt. And feel as though you would do anything if only he would put his arms round you again.

Not that she was in love.

She just wanted that feeling she'd got when he'd put his arms round her. And have his lips touching hers again. And...when he wanted more, as he surely would, then she—yes, she wanted to find out what that was like too. She'd overheard servants gossiping and giggling about what their menfolk got up to between the sheets.

It had sounded as though they thoroughly enjoyed it.

And if she didn't like it, then she needn't ever do it again. She would have found out the truth for herself. As her aunt had always said—never take anything on trust.

And she'd spent so many years trying to be good. Trying to win approval from people who kept on assuming the worst of her. She'd paid dearly for sins she had never committed.

So what was the point in not committing them?

She lifted her chin and met his look full on.

'Not tonight.' It was too soon. There were preparations she had to make. The one thing she did not want to risk was having a baby, outside of wedlock. And she wasn't going to trip naïvely into his studio assuming he would take care of that aspect of things, let alone trust him to take care of her, should the worst come to the worst.

She didn't need him to take care of her—that was not the point. She was wealthy enough to take care of both herself and any number of children she might have. The point was she did not want to be responsible for burdening some poor innocent child with the terrible stigma of illegitimacy.

'When, then?'

'Tomorrow night', if she could find an apoth-

ecary who spoke English well enough to understand what she needed to purchase and for what
purpose, because the last thing she wanted was
to have to take Monsieur Le Brun along to in-
terpret for her! 'Or perhaps the one after', if it
proved difficult to find such an establishment.

He dropped her hand and took a step back,
his face hardening.

'I might not be there,' he said.

He might not be there? She'd just taken the
momentous decision to fling herself off the precipice of respectability, into the unknown sea
of carnality, and he could just shrug it off, as
though it was nothing?

Well, she could shrug too.

She did so, then said, with as much insouciance as she could muster, 'Then I will have had
a wasted journey.'

She turned to walk away from him. She
wasn't going to beg him to change his mind, or
show a bit more enthusiasm. She wasn't going to
let him see how badly his casual attitude towards
becoming her lover hurt her, either.

'Wait,' he said, coming up and falling into
step beside her. 'Make a definite appointment,
give me a fixed time, and I will be there.'

The way he looked at her calmed her ruf-
fled feathers instantly. He wanted her. He really
wanted her. He was just too proud to beg.

'Saturday, then,' she said. Because in part, he was right. If she didn't set a definite date, she might never work up the courage to go through with it. 'And if, by any chance, I cannot keep our…'

'Assignation,' he supplied, putting paid to any last lingering doubt they might be talking about painting her portrait.

She swallowed. 'I will get word to you, so you will not be disappointed.'

'I will be disappointed if you do not come,' he grated. 'But—' he flung up his chin '—neither will I pursue you. It must be your choice. Come to me freely, or not at all.'

With that, he turned on his heel and stalked away, leaving her frowning after him. That last speech hadn't sounded like the kind of thing a seasoned seducer of women would say at all. In fact, if she hadn't known better, she might have thought his pride might be wounded if she didn't go through with what she'd promised.

Which was absurd. She was only another conquest. Just one more in a long line of women he'd enjoyed and then discarded.

She meant nothing more to him than any of the others. Of course she didn't.

And she'd better not start looking for signs that she might.

Chapter Six

Two nights. She'd made him wait two whole nights.

What kind of game was she playing? What was so important she could put off this raging inferno that blazed between them for two whole nights?

She was letting him know that she was not as desperate to take him as her lover as he was to become hers. He raised his hand and stabbed his brush at the canvas on which he was currently working—the back view of a woman, her head tilted to one side as she tried to make sense of the picture before which she stood.

So be it. Let her play her little games. It was what women did. Lucasta was never happier than when she had some poor victim dangling on a string. But he wouldn't be anyone's puppet, then or now. However long she made him wait, he would do whatever it took to break free of the obsession that had taken hold of him since the night she'd shown up in Paris. And the one sure way to do it would be in bed. Once he'd slaked his lust, there would be nothing left. Wasn't that always the way with women?

Once he'd done with her, perhaps he would be free of the bitterness that had steadily grown throughout his twenties, the rage that made him cruel to his friends, callous towards women and so reckless of his reputation even his father had been forced to agree there was nothing for it but to send him abroad.

Not that he'd minded coming to Paris. Almost as soon as he'd arrived, he'd started to find a measure of...something in his life that had always been lacking before. It wasn't just the fact that he'd broken free of his family's stranglehold, ceased the pretence and the posturing, and was finally doing what he'd always wanted to do. It was more than that. It was the feeling that he could be anyone he wanted here. Nobody thought him odd for tossing aside his entire lifestyle. After all, they'd just overthrown an entire regime. The whole country was making itself over into something new, not just him.

And if a people could depose their own king, a man could conquer his obsession with the woman who'd sent his whole life into disarray. Yes, he could. He put down his brush and picked up the canvas. The romantic aspirations he'd had as a callow youth had long since charred to ashes. And what was left was something he could handle. He carried the painting to the far corner of his studio, where he put it down, facing the wall.

It was lust, that was all he felt for Miss Dalby. All she was good for was bedding. And he knew, from experience, that once he'd bedded her even the lust would pass. He would finally know, in his heart, as well as in his head, that she was... nothing.

'Are you quite sure you know what you are doing?' Fenella was practically wringing her hands as Amethyst tied the ribbons of her new bonnet in a jaunty bow under her chin. She'd been unhappy from the moment Amethyst had admitted she'd met Harcourt in the Louvre and commissioned him to paint her portrait.

'It isn't really...proper...to be alone with a man, you know. And I am supposed to—'

'Do not worry, Fenella,' said Amethyst briskly, giving her reflection one last assessing glance in the mirror. 'I know exactly what I am doing. And since nobody in Stanton Basset will ever know what we choose to do while we are in Paris, unless we tell them, there is no fear of them criticising you for allowing me to behave with impropriety.'

'I cannot help worrying. You are so innocent. If you are alone with a man...even if he says he is only going to paint your portrait...the intimacy of the situation might well lead to—' Fenella broke off, and bit down on her lower lip. 'I am not casting aspersions on your character, please believe me. It is just that you do not understand how very tempting some men can be. And I know that you do find Monsieur Harcourt tempting. Forgive me for speaking so bluntly, but he has hardly been out of your mind for years and years. And now that he is showing an interest in you, I am afraid it might be turning your head.'

Until she'd said those fatal words, Amethyst had been prepared to ignore Fenella's little homily. She was only doing her job after all, which was to protect her reputation. But to hear the very words her own father had used against her, when she'd needed understanding...

'I have no intention of letting any man *turn my head*,' she snapped. 'I am not some silly girl who is still holding out for marriage. Let alone love.' It was passion she wanted to experience.

Just passion. And Harcourt was the perfect man to experience it with. 'There is nothing he can do, or attempt to do, for which I am not completely ready.'

She had no dreams for him to smash, this time. Not that marriage was her dream any longer. She'd come to value her independence. She'd first earned it, then fought for it. And she had no intentions of surrendering it to the likes of Nathan Harcourt, of all men.

Anyway, he'd made it clear, both ten years ago and in the last couple of days, that all he wanted was an affair. Which was exactly what she wanted, too.

'Oh, dear,' said Fenella. 'I can see there is nothing I can say to make you reconsider.'

'Not a thing,' she replied cheerfully. She'd done all her arguing with herself, during the long, sleepless nights she'd spent recalling how wonderful it had felt to be in his arms. Or just having him stand close to her. Her whole body ached to get that close to him again. In vain had she tried to build up a case for abstinence, warning herself of all the potential pitfalls of getting involved with Harcourt again. There was only part of her that was still sensible, cautious Amy. That Amy stood no chance against rebellious Amy and lonely Amy's clamouring for fulfilment.

She was set on her course. And was fully prepared to face the consequences, whatever they might be.

Of course it was easy to say that with a cushion of vast wealth behind her. She couldn't help but compare her own situation with that of the many girls who gave themselves to men who didn't deserve them and paid a terrible price. If the precautions she was taking proved ineffective and she ended up pregnant because of this affair, she would still have a comfortable lifestyle. Even if she was no longer welcomed in the homes of the narrow-minded, morally superior, leading ladies of Stanton Basset, she could simply retire from society and become a recluse. It would not affect her ability to run her businesses. She already did so from behind a screen of companies, with which Jobbings communicated on her behalf. Only...it would be a shame if Fenella felt obliged to withdraw from her employ. Having to work for a woman who had actually committed the crime of which she'd so often been accused might prove too much for her delicate sensibilities.

'I will be discreet, Fenella,' she promised as

she went to the door. 'I wouldn't want to do anything to make you uncomfortable.'

As her carriage drew up outside the *hôtel* where Harcourt lived, she raised her eyes to the top floor where he had his rooms and reminded herself she could still turn round and go home, before things went too far.

Only, why should she? She wanted to have this experience. She'd chosen it. He hadn't seduced her into it, which had annoyed her at one point, but now she was glad of it, or she might have felt as though she'd let him weaken her. Broken down her resolve. Instead, coming here like this, flouting all the rules, taking a risk for once in her life, made her feel brave and adventurous. And more of an equal partner in this venture than she'd ever been in any other relationship in her life.

Fate had given her the opportunity, finally, to lie naked in his arms. To have him the way a wife should have a husband. And she'd never forgive herself if she didn't take it.

With her mouth set in a grim line she entered the house and began to climb the stairs.

But both her trepidation and her excitement at the prospect of finally achieving something of her only girlhood dream had worn off completely by the time she'd climbed all the way to the top floor. All she felt was cross. Oh, yes, and don't forget breathless.

Why on earth hadn't she ordered him to attend her in her own rooms? He could have brought his easel and paints, and…and…

And then she pictured Sophie innocently dancing into the room to see how things were progressing. And finding them locked in a clinch, semi-clothed, on a sofa…

The door flew open just as she imagined Sophie shrieking in shock to see Harcourt doing something unspeakably wicked to her and blushed right down to the soles of her boots.

'I thought you would never get here,' he breathed, fiery-eyed.

'It's your own fault…for living up five… flights of stairs,' she panted. 'Are you going to ask me in, or shall I just expire on your doorstep?'

'My, but you are prickly tonight,' he said with a smile.

Well, that was what came of arguing with herself all the way here—and ever since Harcourt had made his wicked proposition.

He swept her an ironic bow. 'Pray, do come in.'

'You may as well know that I'm nearly always prickly,' she said, moving past him and into his rooms. It was all pretty much as she might have expected a bachelor apartment to look like. The furniture was functional rather than pretty and there was a general air of disorder that was strangely welcoming. There were books piled up on the mantelshelf, interspersed with bottles and glasses. Gloves and a hat tossed carelessly on a side table by the door. Bills bursting from the drawers of a small writing desk and cards of invitation stuck at crazy angles in the frame of the spotted mirror propped up on it. And, permeating through the familiar dusty smell that rented rooms always seemed to have, the distinctive aroma of linseed oil.

'You never used to be,' he said as she drew off her gloves and tossed them on the table next to his. They landed in a kind of tangle, which looked peculiarly intimate, almost as though they represented two invisible people, holding hands.

'When we knew each other in London, I always thought you were...sweet,' he said with a wry twist to his mouth, as though he was mocking himself, or the memory of her.

'You couldn't have been more wrong,' she replied tartly, as she tugged the ribbons of her bonnet undone. 'My sisters always used to call me Thistle.'

'Thistle?'

At least the revelation had wiped that sardonic look off his face. He was openly curious now.

'A variation on Amethyst. I always wanted people to call me Amy, but they invariably ended up following my sisters, and calling me Thistle, or Thistly, because of my prickly nature.'

It was probably why they'd all been so thrilled when she'd come back from London in pieces. She'd been strict with them, coming down hard on their faults because her mother had stressed that, as the oldest, she had to set them all an example and she'd been flattered and pleased, and done her best to make her mother proud. What a waste of effort that had been!

She tossed the bonnet aside in the same way she was mentally tossing aside all the expectations her family had ever had of her. With determination. She'd stopped feeling repentant by the time she'd returned home after her trip 'round the Lakes' with her aunt. Ever since then she'd been angry. The most she'd been guilty of had been *naïveté* where this man was concerned. Had it really been such a terrible sin?

But now she jolly well was going to sin. She'd already been punished for crimes she hadn't committed, so there really was no point in not committing them.

'What would you like me to call you?' His face looked quizzical as she scanned the room, looking for somewhere to sit down.

'I don't really care,' she said. 'I just want to sit down and get my breath back.'

'Then come through here,' he said, indicating a door to his right. 'To my studio. I would like to capture your features as they are right now, all flushed and breathless.'

He hurried through and went straight to a table from which he selected paper and charcoal.

'Sit, sit,' he said, waving his free hand towards a couch under one of the many windows which she could tell would flood the room with light during the day.

She sat, rather disgruntled at his very far from lover-like behaviour. He hadn't offered her any refreshment, he hadn't paid her any compliments and now he was scurrying round, adjusting lamps and candles around the sofa. Then he went back to his stool and started sketching her without saying a word and only looking at her with the dispassionate eye of a workman.

Had she got it wrong? He had said he wanted them to become lovers, hadn't he? Or had she imagined it? Got herself all worked up and gone through that agonisingly embarrassing interview with the apothecary—much of which had to be conducted in signs and gestures—for nothing?

He tossed the sheet on which he'd been working aside and got abruptly to his feet.

'Now for your hair,' he said and stalked towards her. 'I want it loose, tumbling round your shoulders.' Before she could protest, he'd yanked out half-a-dozen pins and was undoing her tightly bound braids. She clenched her fists in her lap. It was beyond infuriating, the way she felt at having him so close. Her heart was pounding, her breath kept catching in her throat and her lips felt full and plump. And he hadn't said or done anything to produce this reaction. He was treating her as though she was just…a subject. An interesting subject he wanted to draw.

But then, as he started to fan her hair out, spreading it like a cloak around her shoulders, something happened to his eyes. They sort of… smouldered. And the lids half-lowered. His fingers slowed in their task and, instead of just arranging her hair to catch the light, he kept on running the strands through his fingers, as though he was getting the kind of pleasure she'd got from stroking the barn cat when she'd been little.

'It's so soft,' he murmured, never taking his eyes from it. 'So beautiful, and lustrous and soft.

It's a crime to bind it up in braids and shove it under an ugly bonnet the way you do. You ought to have it always on display.'

'Don't be ridiculous,' she said, her cheeks heating. To think she'd felt hard done by because he wasn't saying anything lover-like. Now he'd gone to the other extreme, uttering such absurdities. Besides, her bonnet wasn't ugly. Not any longer. It was brand new and quite the prettiest article of attire she'd ever owned.

Nathan quirked one eyebrow at her petulantly clenched mouth. It was as though she felt uncomfortable with his flattery. He looked at her plain jacket, recalled the positively dowdy way she dressed and wondered if she was deliberately hiding her beauty. He supposed being seduced and abandoned when she'd been so young had taught her a harsh lesson.

So why had she decided to come to him like this? He studied her face, the tense set of her shoulders, the way her mouth seemed to settle naturally into a bitter line, and wondered again how she had lived these last ten years.

It couldn't have been easy, with an illegitimate child to care for. Society was harsh upon unwed mothers, while the men who'd seduced them got away scot free, for the most part.

She hadn't been the real villain of the piece at all, he suddenly perceived. She'd been damaged by what had happened in their youth, too. It had made her treat him badly, but then perhaps her experience had soured her against men. Perhaps she hadn't known that he had a heart to break, having been used and tossed aside by some rake.

On a pang of sudden sympathy, he said, 'One day, I'd like you to tell me about that little girl's father.'

'Sophie?' Her eyes widened. Then she frowned. 'Why?'

She clearly didn't want him to pry. Perhaps it was still too painful to speak of, even after all this time. Perhaps she was reminded of the man who'd fathered her, every time she looked at that abundance of fair hair, or into those intelligent and rather mischievous blue eyes.

'Forgive me. You are correct. *That* has nothing to do with *this*, does it?'

'No.'

'Then why not take off your coat?' he suggested with a smile.

'My coat,' she repeated, looking down as though she'd entirely forgotten she was still wearing it.

'Here, let me help you,' he said, when her fingers fumbled at their task. He knelt on the floor beside the sofa, deftly slipping the buttons from their moorings. She tensed at first, but made no move to stop him. And when he went to slide the sleeves down her arms, she leaned forwards, helping him speed the process.

'And now your gown, I think.'

She sucked in a sharp breath as he reached behind her for the tapes that held the bodice fast. She blushed and he could see a pulse beating wildly in her throat. And her eyes darted away, looking anywhere but at him as he slid the loosened gown from her shoulders.

If he hadn't known better, he would have thought she had no experience with this sort of thing at all.

Perhaps she hadn't. Perhaps her seduction and ruin at such a young age had put her off men altogether. He'd already discovered she wasn't being kept by that Frenchman, but was it too much to hope that after that one youthful indiscretion she'd had nobody else?

Her hands went up to her bodice when he went to bare her breasts. And that little show of reluctance made her seem so shy and nervous that he could almost believe he meant something special to her. Whatever had happened to her in her past, whatever had driven her to come to him tonight, she clearly wasn't finding this easy. She didn't seem to be the kind of woman who changed her lovers with as much ease as she changed her gown. She didn't seem to know how to flirt, or tease, or arouse. The fact that she'd got herself here at all made him feel as though she was taking a chance on him, in a way she'd never done with any other man.

And something hot and primitive and possessive surged up within him as he leaned forwards to place a kiss on the pulse that beat so wildly in her neck. For a moment, he felt like a conqueror.

But then he went cold inside.

By God, she was dangerous. All he had to do was get a glimpse of that milky skin and his wits had gone wandering. He was building up a picture in his head of someone he'd once wanted her to be, not looking at the reality of where they both were now.

'Don't move,' he grated, drawing back. He had to get things in perspective. 'Stay exactly as you are, so I can capture that dazed look before it fades,' he said, dashing back to his stool and grabbing hold of a pencil as though it was a lifeline.

Amethyst couldn't believe it. He'd started to undress her, had her practically swooning with desire and then he'd darted away and started drawing her again.

When he finally deigned to speak to her again, it was to make a complaint.

'You are frowning again.'

'You would frown,' she retorted, 'if someone half-undressed you, then shot across the room to do something more interesting instead.'

He smiled in comprehension.

'My apologies. Had I known you were so impatient to share my bed I would have tumbled you first and sketched you in the afterglow.'

He set his sketching pad aside and got to his feet.

'In fact, I think that would probably be for the best.' He stalked slowly towards the sofa. 'I have a feeling you will be a much more co-operative subject once I've released you from all that tension you're carrying around with you.'

Harcourt smiled a wicked smile, then leaned down and scooped her into his arms. She let go of her bodice, briefly, to balance herself in his arms, and the material made an attempt to slide all the way down to her waist, revealing more of herself than anybody had seen since she was about ten years old. Mortified, she grabbed at it again, just as he swung her sideways to manoeuvre through a narrow doorway and into yet another room. His bedroom. Her gaze fixed on the bed, which was in the very centre of the room. The sloping ceilings made that the only sensible place to put it, if he didn't want to brain himself every time he got in or out of it.

She swallowed nervously as he laid her on it, but he didn't give her time to express any last-minute qualms by following her down and showering her cheeks, her neck, her shoulders with brief, tantalising little kisses. They had the effect of stopping the breath in her throat so that she was incapable of speech. Not that she could think of anything to say at such a moment. Except she was making breathy little moans and squirming all over the counterpane, which expressed exactly what she felt far more clearly, to her way of thinking.

She didn't want to protest at all when he went to pull her bodice down again, because he was making little noises expressing his own delight too. And then he proceeded to make her feel as though she was made of some delicious substance, the way he licked, and nibbled at her breasts, before swirling his tongue round her nipples. She had never, in all her life, experienced anything so indescribably wonderful.

When he moved off her, quite suddenly, she wished she'd been bold enough to put her arms round his neck, instead of clutching at the covers, so that she could have held him in place and made him carry on doing what he'd been doing.

But he'd only stood up from the bed to yank his shirt off over his head, slip off his shoes and remove his breeches.

She supposed she ought to avert her gaze, but he didn't seem to mind her looking, so why shouldn't she look? Anyway, she didn't think she could have prevented herself. He was so very much more pleasingly put together than all those cold marble statues she'd glimpsed that day in the Louvre. In fact, the sight of her first naked, adult, flesh-and-blood male just about stole the breath from her lungs.

But before she could catch much more than a glimpse, he was back on the bed beside her, determined to dispense with her clothes.

If he'd paused to stare at her, once he'd got her naked, she didn't think she could have coped with it. But he seemed far more interested in touching and tasting what he was uncovering. And his blatant hunger for everything about her put paid to most of her shyness. Besides, his caresses and kisses were making it just about impossible to think at all. He was reducing her to a molten mass of delightful sensation which drowned out intellect. There was no longer any place on that bed for shyness, or hesitancy, or logic.

She was reacting to his caresses with instincts as old as time, her hips straining towards him, telling both him and her that they were ready for the act she knew almost nothing about.

When he came over her and nudged her legs apart with his own, she found herself flexing up towards him in a way that must have been purely instinctive, because she had certainly never imagined herself doing anything so...unseemly.

And then he began to prod at her.

And then there was a searing pain.

'Ow!'

He pushed into her again.

'Ow, ow, owww!'

All the pleasure had gone. Instead of wanting to flex up towards him, she cringed away from the painful invasion.

'Stop it,' she cried, getting her hands between them and pushing at his chest. 'You're hurting and I don't like it!' How could she ever have thought this was a good idea? It was horrible.

'Stop it, stop it, stop it!'

'What the devil?' He pulled out of her, rearing back so that he was kneeling between her splayed legs. She couldn't have been a virgin. She had a child.

But there was a smear of blood on her inner thigh. He'd been dimly aware of the barrier even before she'd cried out with pain.

She *had* been a virgin.

How the hell was this possible?

A black miasma swirled up before his eyes, which he shut, to blot out the sight of her curling up on her side, thrusting her hands down between her legs, her face crumpled with anguish.

But he could still see exactly how it was possible.

The bastards had lied to him.

Chapter Seven

Ah, God! He placed his fists over his eyes, barely suppressing a cry of anguish as keen as her own had been.

How could his father have done this to him?

And it had to have been his father who'd told Fielding that Amethyst had secretly given birth to a child. He'd known it from the moment his friend had said he'd been told in confidence and hated to have to be the one to break it to him. He'd recognised his father's style of setting up a dupe to do his dirty work.

But he hadn't really questioned the veracity of the tale. He couldn't quite believe even his father would stoop so low as to deliberately blacken a respectable woman's name, just because she stood in the way of his plans, not back then.

He'd naïvely thought his father—with great tact and forbearing—was trying to deliver a warning that he'd strayed into a potential mine-field. Giving him a chance to extricate himself from it, rather than just wading in and throwing his weight around, the way he usually did. He'd felt as though his father was finally giving him a chance to prove that he could do the right thing. That he was offering him an opportunity to go to him, and say he was ready to settle down, to stop resisting his family's efforts to match him up with Lucasta, without either of them having to speak of the disaster he'd almost made of things when left to his own devices.

He'd thought it was that important to his father—their relationship. He'd thought all the subterfuge was about trying to avoid coming to a confrontation between them, which might have resulted in a complete breach.

His insides hollowed out as the truth smacked him in the teeth. It had been the alliance with the Delacourts that had been important to his father. His determination that all his sons should cut figures in society. Even his youngest.

No matter what it cost.

Or who paid the price.

She groaned, then, struggled into a sitting position and shot him a look of loathing.

'I might have known all you'd bring me was pain,' she said, jolting him out of his own agony of mind and reminding him that, right now, she was in actual, physical pain. Pain that he'd caused.

'That you'd lead me halfway...somewhere, then let me down.'

Was that the way she'd seen it? It must have been. She couldn't have had a clue why he'd suddenly turned so cold. For he'd cut her out of his life with brutality. And in public. Her face that night—oh, God, the wounded, bewildered look she'd given him as he'd given her the cut direct. The way she'd crumpled when he'd danced with one girl after another. What had he done to her?

Why hadn't he questioned it? Why hadn't he gone straight round to see his father and demanded proof?

Because he'd finally seen a way to win his father's approval, that's why. Having Fielding carry him that tale had told him the old man was vehemently opposed to the match with Amethyst. He had plans for his youngest son. Plans that did not include him marrying a nobody and settling down in the countryside to live a life of contentment in obscurity.

So he had played along. Hardened himself against her tears. Told himself they were evidence of her guilt. That she was upset at being found out.

But he'd known, deep inside, that he was watching her heart breaking.

He'd known, God dammit!

Just as he'd sensed her innocence tonight. But just like before, he'd thrust the truth aside, preferring to believe the lie. Because it exonerated him from blame. He didn't want to be the man who'd broken her heart. So he kept on telling himself she didn't have a heart to break. That she was manipulative and deceitful.

But he had been to blame for destroying her. He had indeed *led her halfway somewhere, then let her down*, not once, but twice.

He squeezed his eyes shut on the devastating truth—she'd loved him.

And he'd let one lie destroy it.

All those wasted, miserable, hellish years... years during which he'd believed in a lie. A lie so base it had warped his entire outlook on life.

She hadn't had a child in secret. She hadn't come to London to ensnare a man with her practised wiles. She'd been innocent. Innocent!

She moaned again and struggled to sit up.

And he wondered how long he'd been kneeling there, reeling in horror at the terrible mistake he'd made. Too long, however few seconds it had taken for the truth to strike him right between the eyes the way it had. Because she was suffering, shocked at the painfully brutal invasion of her body, and she needed comfort. Not some oaf, kneeling there, so many miles and years away in his head that he might just as well have left the room altogether.

In his mind, it was the hurt he'd dealt her years ago that was the biggest issue, but for her, it was the hurt he'd dealt her tonight.

And that was what he had to deal with. He had to put *this* right, he had to tend to the pain he'd caused her, right now, prove that he wasn't the uncaring, fickle disappointment of a man who'd brought her nothing but grief.

There was no need to bring up what had gone wrong between them ten years ago. Not as far as she was concerned.

He blenched when he thought how close he'd come to quizzing her about the little girl he'd seen her with—the one he'd assumed was hers. And the man he'd thought had fathered it on her. The man he'd thought of as a vile seducer.

But it was him. *He* was the only seducer of innocence she knew. *He* was the man who'd callously, clumsily, ripped her virginity from her. As if shattering her hopes ten years ago hadn't been bad enough. What effect had it had on her? He hadn't stopped to consider that, not before. But she'd fled London at the height of the Season. And she hadn't ever married...

'I will never let you down, or bring you pain again,' he vowed.

'No, you will not,' she said firmly, grabbing the corner of the quilt to cover her breasts as she swung her legs over the edge of the bed. 'Because I won't let you.'

'Hold hard!' He gripped her shoulders and, when she wouldn't look at him, spoke to her rigidly averted profile. 'Do not leave, not as you are. Let me get you…a drink. Yes, a drink. I should have hot water to bathe you and soothe you, really, but it would take too long to fetch it and heat it.'

He winced as the words came tumbling out of his mouth. He was practically gibbering. But then what kind of man would be able to stay calm after discovering that, ten years earlier, he'd spurned the only woman he'd ever loved, because he hadn't had the guts to question a pack of the most dastardly lies about her? And only finally learned the truth of her complete innocence of any kind of wrongdoing because he'd treated her like the veriest lightskirt?

He darted from the bed, out of the room and over to the table where he kept a decanter of good brandy. For a moment or two he could see the attraction of becoming a Papist. It must feel wonderful to be able to go to a priest, confess, and have your guilt absolved through the muttering of a few prayers.

Sloshing a generous measure into a glass, he hurried back to the bedroom, to find, to his relief, that she was still sitting hunched up on the edge of the bed, clutching the quilt round her shoulders and not, as he had feared, hunting round the room for her discarded clothing.

He handed her the glass, which she took from him with a scowl.

'I...I'm sorry it hurt.' *Mea culpa.* 'The first time often does, I believe...'

'I'm amazed anybody ever does it a second,' she said, screwing up her face as she took a gulp of the brandy.

'Perhaps...other men are not as clumsy about it as I just was,' he admitted, running his fingers through his hair. 'If I'd known...' No, he couldn't tell her that, could he? Or he would then have to explain why he'd made such an assumption. 'I misunderstood. That is...I thought you seemed impatient.'

No, that wasn't good enough. He couldn't try shifting one iota of the blame on her. His was the fault. And it was up to him to make amends.

And there was only one sure way of doing that. He took a deep breath.

'We must marry, of course,' he said. It was

the appropriate penalty to pay for all he'd done to her. The ultimate sacrifice to atone for his sin.

But her scowl only grew deeper.

'We will do no such thing!'

'We have to, Amy, don't you see?' He sat down on the bed next to her. 'I have taken your virginity, ruined you…'

'You didn't *take* anything. We were sharing a moment of what I'd hoped would be pleasure. What a stupid mistake to make,' she said bitterly.

He flinched. Had he asked her the same question ten years ago, she would have been overjoyed. She'd loved him, back then, just as he was.

Now he'd become as big a disappointment to her as he'd always been to everyone else.

'It is a mistake, however,' he persisted, 'that can soon be rectified.' He wouldn't be a disappointment to *her* as a husband. He would cherish her. Stay loyal to her. Make up for all the hurts she'd ever suffered on his account and defend her from anyone who ever attempted to do anything similar in future.

'Not by marrying,' she retorted. 'I agreed to your proposition because I believed you were the one man I could trust *not* to want to go all…respectable. You made it quite clear that you had no intention of marrying me, not ten years ago, and not now. You made me,' she said, jabbing

him on his arm with her forefinger, 'believe it
would be *safe* to take up with you. Oh, why do I
never learn? I should have known you would be
nothing but a disappointment. To think I hoped
that because you had the reputation for being
a rake, that you would be able to make this…'
she waved the hand holding the brandy glass
wildly, indicating the rumpled bedding '…enjoy-
able! And not only was that the stupidest mistake I've ever made where you are concerned,
but now you are talking about trapping me into
matrimony.'

She slammed the brandy glass down on his
nightstand and got to her feet.

He had to think of something fast. He couldn't
let it end like this. If she left now, he would never
get her back. Never be free from the guilt. He
went cold inside.

Think, man, think!

Firstly, he got the impression that the tighter
he clung to her, the harder she would struggle
to break free.

And she'd just said she'd wanted to feel safe
with him—which meant free to come and go as
she pleased.

And finally, she'd said she wanted pleasure.

Summoning every last ounce of his ability to
dissemble, he leaned back into the pillows and

folded his hands behind his head as she struggled to get off the bed with her dignity intact, which wasn't easy given all she had to preserve it was a rather moth-eaten quilt that revealed as much as it covered whenever she made an injudicious movement.

'Very well,' he said with feigned insouciance, 'you don't want to marry me. I can understand that. For as long as I can remember, there has been somebody telling me I'm no good.' Except for a few heady weeks ten years ago, when a young girl, fresh from the country, had hung on his every word. Her face had lit up whenever she saw him. Nobody had ever made him feel as though he could be enough for them, just as she was, until he'd met Amethyst.

His calm voice, his apparent nonchalance, had an instant, and highly satisfactory, effect on her. Just as a skilled groom would gentle a skittish, badly broken mare, his retreat roused her curiosity. She stopped scrabbling round on the floor for any item of clothing she could find and looked at him fully for the first time since he'd withdrawn from her body.

Though there was still wariness mingled in with the curiosity.

'What do you mean, no good? You are the son of Lord Finchingfield.'

'He was always my sternest critic. I've never had any ambition, you see, which in his eyes is the greatest sin a member of the Harcourt family can commit.'

It was some consolation that he'd taken a stand and broken free of his father before tonight. Otherwise, he'd have had to go and tell him that he'd never forgive him for what he'd done to Amethyst. For what he'd made *him* do to Amethyst. For making him an accomplice in her heartbreak.

Meanwhile, Amethyst had found a shoe, sat down on the edge of the bed with it and was sliding it on to her foot.

He pulled himself together, sat up, slithered closer and slid his arms round her waist.

'You don't really want to leave, do you?' he murmured the words into her ear. She shivered, but didn't pull away. 'I won't mention marriage again,' he breathed, before nibbling his way down her neck, 'if the prospect of being leg-shackled to a man of my calibre is really so offensive to you.'

'It isn't you,' she huffed, arching, probably involuntarily, to grant him better access. 'I don't want to marry anyone. Ever.'

He wondered why not. It was generally the height of every woman's ambition.

His mouth flattened into a grim line. He had a sneaking suspicion *that* might be his fault too.

'I can understand that,' he said. 'Having gone through the misery of being chained in a bond of mutual antipathy, I would not lightly enter into the state again.'

'But you said…'

'It was the shock, my sweet,' he said, sliding one hand inside the quilt, to cup a breast, 'of finding you a virgin.' Well, it was true, up to a point. 'But if you really don't want to get married, we can forget all about it.'

'There is no *if* about it,' she said vehemently. 'I did not get into your bed in an attempt to extract a marriage proposal from you.'

'Oh?' He nibbled round the outer edge of her ear. 'Perhaps you would like to tell me what you did want to achieve, then. Because you aren't the kind of woman who routinely has affairs, are you?'

'Well, obviously not. You've just discovered that! I…' She faltered into a sigh as he slid the quilt from her shoulders and started kneading at both breasts at once.

'Then tell me,' he urged her. 'Tell me what you want from me.'

'I don't know, exactly,' she protested. 'I just… wanted to know what it would be like.'

'Curiosity? Is that all that drove you here? I don't believe that,' he reproved her by nipping hard at her earlobe.

'Well, no, that wasn't all,' she confessed, her eyes drooping half-shut. 'It is…it has all been building up for some time now.'

'Building up, yes,' he agreed, sliding his hand down her torso until it rested just above the soft downy hair at the juncture of her thighs.

'I'm so sick of people telling me how I ought to behave,' she said, her head lolling back into the crook of his arm. 'Of how to think. And never ever being…happy. I wanted…' She ended on a whimper as he stroked lower.

'You wanted to break free. To be yourself. Even if you're not sure who that is, just yet.'

'Yes,' she moaned. 'Ooh, yes…but how did you…?'

'How did I know? What do you think I'm doing in Paris?'

'I don't know. I don't know what you're doing. But…'

'But it feels good, doesn't it. No pain now. Only pleasure, I promise.'

He pulled her back down on to the bed and shifted so that he was beside her. And kissed her.

She kissed him back for a while, but then stiffened and pulled her mouth away, and said, 'What are you doing?'

'I'm giving you what you want. I'm going to be your lover. For as long as you're in Paris, we are going to keep on coming back to this bed—'

'You must be joking!'

He lifted one leg over hers when it looked as though she was going to struggle out of his arms, pinning her down while he kissed her again. Until she stopped struggling and kissed him back.

'This is too important to joke about,' he said grimly. 'I hurt you. And made you want to run away when I should have given you the greatest pleasure you have ever known.'

'It wasn't all your fault,' she conceded. 'I knew you'd assumed I was being kept by Monsieur Le Brun, and even though I did tell you he wasn't, I did nothing to discourage you from thinking I was the kind of woman who might. And then, when I agreed to your proposition and came straight round here, just as though I was used to doing this sort of thing...'

'Even if you were an experienced woman, I should have been more considerate. But I wasn't thinking straight. I was...' His arms tightened round her convulsively. He'd never, ever, been so insensitive to a bed-partner's needs. He hadn't cared whether she enjoyed the coupling or not, that was the sordid truth. He had been angry with her when he'd carried her to this bed. He had still been blaming her for everything. 'I wasn't thinking about much of anything at all. Only counting the seconds until I could make you mine,' he finished lamely. He couldn't tell her the truth, or anything that might hint at it, because it would only hurt her more. And she didn't deserve more hurt.

She hadn't deserved any of it, ever. Her only crime had been winning his heart and thereby falling foul of his powerful, manipulative, cold-hearted father.

Well, this was where the hurting would stop. From now on, he would only bring her pleasure.

'I may not be good for much,' he said, 'but one thing I am most proficient at is making love.'

She didn't look as though she believed him. He couldn't blame her, considering the way things had gone so far tonight.

'Give me another chance, Amethyst,' he said, sliding his fingers between the legs she'd clamped shut. 'Just see how it goes, hmm?' She was already damp down there. Her body was responding to his kisses and caresses. It was only her mind that was still resisting. 'You can stop me any time you want to. But I don't think, this time, you will want me to stop.'

He nuzzled her neck as he slid one finger inside her. She gasped and tensed. His heart lurched. But as he continued to caress her and nibble at her neck, she slowly relaxed, until he was able to slide another finger inside her.

'Nathan,' she moaned, half-plea, half-protest. 'I really don't think I want to do this...'

'Hush,' he murmured into her ear. 'You don't know what you want. You cannot, because you have never experienced any of this before, have you?'

He groaned into her neck as another wave of anguish assailed him. They'd been on the brink of something, ten years before, which would have resulted in them both becoming very different people. He wouldn't have become the cynic, or the rake he was, if he'd married her. And she... Well, he didn't know what she'd become since they'd last met. But she didn't look any happier than he was. She had that mean, pinched look about her mouth common to impoverished spinsters. She dressed dowdily, as though she had no pride in her appearance.

Well, that was all going to change. While she was in Paris he would show her a new world. A world of sensuality. She'd said she wanted to break free and find out who she really was, who she was meant to be. And he'd be the man to show her. He'd peel back the layers of hurt and caution that shrouded the girl who'd once made his heart dance, as surely as he'd peeled away her clothes tonight. He'd kiss the meanness from her mouth and teach her to love what her body could make her feel.

Starting right now. She might not want to marry him any longer, but she did want him to show her the kind of pleasure most spinsters could only dream of. And…he wanted to give her the wedding night they should have had ten years ago.

For once he was glad he'd had so much experience. In gaining his reputation as a rake, he'd learned a lot about what brought a woman pleasure. Now he could apply it all to Amethyst.

Her neck had proved to be particularly sensitive, so he kept on kissing her there, while toying with the damp folds between her thighs. He dipped and teased, nipped and nuzzled, until her hips began to squirm in a rhythmical response.

And then, when he was sure she'd got to the point where she wasn't going to tell him to stop, he began a leisurely exploration of the rest of her body, paying close attention to anywhere that provoked a gasp, or a shiver, or made her fingers curl a little more tightly round his neck.

She shivered with pleasure when he lapped at the indentation of her waist, moaned when he nipped at the soft flesh on the outside of her hips and squirmed when he trailed his tongue further down, and inward, to the insides of her thighs.

Since she was a total innocent, he hesitated before bestowing the most intimate kiss of all. But had this been their wedding night, he would have made sure she came to orgasm before he made any attempt to enter her. And this was the most reliable way, he'd discovered, of pleasuring a woman.

And he wanted to give her pleasure. Such unimaginable pleasure that she would want to come back to him again and again. He couldn't make amends for every single hurt he'd caused her, but by God, while she was in Paris he could give her pleasure unlike anything she'd known before. Or would ever experience again.

It would be no penance, no penance at all. It wouldn't wash away his guilt. That would stay with him to his dying day.

But at least she wouldn't think of him as the biggest disappointment in her life.

Chapter Eight

Amethyst could not believe the things he was prepared to do with his tongue. Part of her wondered whether she ought to stop him. But it was making her feel so…blissful. And she'd got the idea he wanted to do penance, in some way, so who was she to demur? Besides, when he slipped first one finger, then two inside her, she lost the ability to think anything at all. It was all melting heat, and rivers of delight, and then a kind of starburst that shattered her, yet made her feel completely whole for the first time in her life, all at the same time.

And then he was above her and sliding into her before she'd even recovered her wits enough to tense, or make a protest that she really didn't want him to try again.

And this time it didn't hurt a bit. In fact, it brought another wave of pulsating pleasure shivering through her, making her flex her hips upwards in an instinctively welcoming gesture.

He kissed her on the mouth. Gently, tenderly. A different kiss from any he'd bestowed on her before. He encouraged her to open her mouth, so he could drive his tongue inside. It was almost more shocking than having that other part of him driving into her, though equally as delicious. After a bit, she wondered if he was trying to distract her from the gentle, yet insistent rhythm he'd set up with his body, by teaching her lips to part, her tongue to duel with his.

If so, it was rather...sweet of him.

And then he broke away from her mouth, to pay attention to that sweet spot just beneath her ear, which sent shivers skittering all the way down her spine. And his movements became more insistent, demanding a response from her. And her body gave it, of its own volition. She'd just discovered that touching and kissing a certain spot between her legs resulted in almost unimaginable pleasure. Now, awakened, that place was clamouring for more sensation, more pressure. And the only way to get it was to grind upwards against his pelvis as he thrust down.

She wouldn't have believed that after the pain she would ever permit a man inside her again, let alone want him to go deeper, and harder, but she did. She wouldn't have believed he would be so sensitive to her needs, after the clumsy way he'd started, but he was. It was as though he was completely in tune with her body now, giving it exactly what it needed, a split second before she knew it herself.

So there was no reason for her to thrash about under him, or claw at his back, or wind her legs about his. Not that he seemed to mind. Not to judge by the way he kept on saying, 'Yes, oh God, yes.' Or the way he moaned and shuddered, and showered kisses all over her face and neck.

But then, once again, her mind took leave of her body as delight broke over them both in a great wave.

'Amy,' he cried as she splintered apart. And there was something in his voice that sounded almost as though...

No. It wasn't tenderness. It was just...passion.

And yet the tone of it had plucked at some long-suppressed emotion deep inside her, which made her want to weep.

Which was ridiculous, she panted, as she drifted back to shore. She'd cried enough tears over this man in the past. His purpose in her life now was to teach her about pleasure.

And he had. Once he'd realized just how in-experienced she was, he'd applied his consider-able skill with gentleness.

She should have told him, before they got started, that she hadn't a clue about what went on between a man and woman in the bedroom.

So why hadn't she?

It wasn't just that she'd been flattered he thought her so attractive she could make her living in this way.

No. The truth was much more muddied. He'd accused her of tempting him to marry unwisely in his youth. If he'd known she was a virgin, she'd feared he might have thought this was a renewed attempt on his freedom. And she'd wanted him too badly to allow anything to make him reconsider.

All of a sudden, panic clawed its way to the surface. She wanted him, yes, but not enough to sacrifice her own freedom. Any more than she expected, or wanted, him to sacrifice his.

'I really didn't expect you to propose to me,' she bit out, 'just because I was a virgin. That is not why I chose you to become my first lover.'

'Your first?' He rolled off her and raised himself up on one elbow to glare down at her. 'Do you mean to tell me you now plan to make a habit of taking lovers?'

No, she hadn't meant that at all, but she could see why her words might have made him think so. But he had an infernal cheek to look so disapproving, with the reputation he had!

'I don't know. I might one day, I suppose. After all, I'm not going to stay in Paris for ever. And I most certainly am not going to marry you.'

'You've already made that crystal clear.'

He was positively glaring at her now.

'There's no need to look at me like that, for heaven's sake. You don't want to marry me either! Don't let's spoil this by quarrelling. I was only trying to reassure you that I have no designs on you, just because you happened to be the man to whom I gave my virginity.'

'No, I...no, I see that.' He pursed his lips in a way that, had he been a woman, she would have described as a pout. 'But I cannot help wondering why you did choose me for this singular honour.'

Irritating man! She was trying to reassure him that his precious freedom was not in jeopardy and he was twisting her words to make it sound as though...as though...well, into an insult, anyway.

'There is no need to be sarcastic,' she huffed, reaching down blindly for the quilt. Or a sheet. Or anything to cover herself up with.

He shifted, releasing a swathe of quilt which he tucked up over her breasts.

'Thank you,' she said stiffly.

'You're welcome,' he said drily. 'But for your information, I was not being sarcastic. I do feel that you paid me a great compliment in coming here tonight and permitting me to initiate you into the joys of lovemaking.' He looked troubled when he added, 'I only wish I had done better...'

Her immediate reaction was to try to console him.

'Oh, no, you were very good. Really.' What was the matter with her? Trying to make him feel better? He was a man, for heaven's sake. A fully grown man. Just because he'd pouted like a sulky boy, then looked a bit hurt, that was no reason to pander to his vanity.

'Except to start with,' she therefore reminded him and, feeling a twinge of conscience, hastily added, 'And that was partly my own fault.'

He gave her a lazy smile. 'Thistle,' he said, and kissed her shoulder. The one bit of her that was peeping out from under the quilt. 'You really are prickly, aren't you? Most women would be purring like a contented kitten after that.' But she wasn't most women. And he'd hurt her so badly before, of course she was going to throw up a shield of sarcasm, from behind which she could jab at him with her sharp little tongue. It was all the protection she had.

'Well, if that's going to be your attitude…'

He held her tight when she would have rolled away from him and clucked his tongue.

'I am not criticising you, not at all. It was merely an observation. And a note to myself that I need to do better next time.'

'Next time?' Her eyes were wide, her lips parted, her knuckles white as they clutched the quilt to her chin.

'But you will have to give me a little respite,' he said, rolling on to his back and tucking her into his side.

'Respite? What do you…oh! Well, I didn't think we'd be doing that again. Not now.'

'No, not now,' he said amicably. 'In just a little while.'

'No, really, I…'

'Don't be so demanding, woman,' he said. 'I have told you I need a little rest before the next round.'

'That wasn't what I meant! I…oh…' she glanced up at him when he started to chuckle '…you're teasing me.'

'Has nobody ever teased you before?'

She shook her head. 'Not since…well, you.'

'You must have mixed with some very dull people since we last met then. Want to tell me about them?'

'Not particularly.'

'Well, what would you like to talk about, then?'

Her fingers clutched at the quilt a bit more tightly. Her eyes narrowed warily. If he wasn't careful, she would retreat behind her protective shield and he wouldn't be able to find out anything about her. And he had this burning need to find out what had happened to her after he'd abandoned her. He couldn't bear to imagine her life being as miserable as his had been. If he could just find out that she'd found some contentment in her spinster state, it might assuage his guilt. A tiny bit.

He shrugged one shoulder, as if her next words weren't going to matter to him one way or another.

'If you don't want to tell me anything personal, then...you could recite some poetry, I suppose.'

'Poetry?'

'Yes. To get me back in the mood. I don't suppose you know anything naughty, do you?'

'Of course I don't!'

'Been living a pure and simple life, have you? Tucked away in that rectory with your parents?'

'No. Far from it,' she huffed.

'Oh?' He permitted himself to show curiosity

now. 'Then you've been…travelling the world, posing as a lightskirt, perchance? Using the man who calls himself Monsieur Le Brun as…cover for your work as a spy?'

'Now you really are being ridiculous.'

'It is worth it to see that smile return to your eyes.' He cupped her jaw and turned her face up to his. 'Come on,' he said in a cajoling tone. 'Tell me one thing about yourself. Satisfy my curiosity. Otherwise I am going to imagine all kinds of wild and inaccurate things about you.'

'Such as, for instance, that I have such poor taste that I would sell my body to a man like Monsieur Le Brun?'

'Well, if you cannot give me a better excuse for travelling with him, what else am I to think?'

'That my friend and I hired him, perhaps? To act as courier and guide, since it isn't the done thing for two single ladies to travel without protection?'

Her voice had an acid tinge to it that made him think of tart, ripe berries. Which in turn led to him thinking about puckered, pink nipples. How did she do this to him? Get him roused simply by sniping at him?

'You hired him?'

She tensed again. She really didn't want to let him know anything about her life, which made him all the more determined to find out all there was to know about her. Everything she'd done since she'd vanished so completely from London.

He slid his hand under the quilt and toyed with one of her breasts until the nipple formed into a tightly furled, mouth-watering little berry.

'Who is this friend of yours? How do you know her?'

'What is this? Why are you interrogating me?'

He rolled over, pinning her beneath him.

'Because you won't tell me anything. Tell me just one fact about you. Satisfy my rampant curiosity.'

Her eyes widened at his deliberately suggestive tone. She'd also registered that it wasn't only his curiosity that was rampant.

'One fact,' he growled.

'Very well,' she sighed. 'Fenella and I...' She gave a little wiggle. 'Fenella is a widow, with a small child and no income. I have inherited a house, from a rather eccentric aunt, with whom I lived in the latter years of her life. We have... an arrangement.'

'That's...' his brow furrowed as he tried to concentrate '...seven facts. Very generous of you.' He dropped a kiss on her brow. 'I think that deserves a reward.'

He nudged her legs apart.

'You really are the most arrogant, conceited, infuriating man...'

'Don't forget irresistible,' he said, sliding into her. 'And before you claw my eyes out, remember, I think you are irresistible too.'

Her eyes widened. Her muscles relaxed.

'You do?'

'Utterly irresistible.' He kissed her jaw, then her neck as her head rolled to one side.

'How can you doubt it? I pursued you all over the city, even though I thought you belonged to another man.'

'Oh! Hmmm. You...'

'Yes.' He pulled the quilt down, and started the slow assault on her senses all over again.

It was a long time before either of them spoke again.

Amethyst opened her eyes to find him standing over her with a tray bearing glasses, some cheese, some fruit and a hunk of bread.

Wearing nothing but a lazy grin.

'Refreshments, my lady,' he said, putting the tray down on the bedside table and perching on the edge of the bed. 'Cannot have you fainting away from hunger on your way home.'

And she would have to get up and go home soon, she realised. She wasn't sure how long she'd dozed, but they'd already spent several hours in this bed.

'When can I see you again,' he asked, as he poured wine from a carafe into one of the glasses and handed it to her. 'Soon, I hope?'

The eagerness in his voice soothed some of the sting that his less-than-subtle hint it was time for her to leave had inflicted.

'Tomorrow evening, I should think. I shall tell my...friend, Fenella, that since we won't be staying long in Paris, you need to work on my portrait as often as possible.'

He frowned briefly, turning away to pull some grapes from their stalk.

'I had hoped perhaps we could meet during the daytime, too,' he said, popping one into her mouth. 'I should like to show you something of Paris. The real Paris. Not the one your hired guide will show you. The one that the citizens inhabit. And tomorrow is Sunday.'

He turned back to her, an eager, open expression on his face that reminded her of when they'd both been so much younger and they'd talked about...anything and everything.

'I could take you outside the *barrière*, perhaps to the Jardin de la Gaieté. The locals get paid on Saturday and they tend to go outside the *barrière* to spend their money, where goods don't incur

Paris custom dues. It's like a huge open-air party, with feasting and dancing all day.'

Something seemed to turn over and flip inside her. He had no idea how wealthy she was. He'd looked at her clothes, listened to her story, which had made it sound as though she and Fenella were pooling their resources, and come up with an entertainment that would make what little money he supposed she had go as far as possible. It meant he really wanted to spend time with her.

'I am sorry,' she said, surprised to find that refusing his invitation really had caused her a pang of regret. 'But I have already made plans.'

'You could break them.'

Yes, she could. The trouble was that she wanted to do just that far too much. It felt wonderful to have him look at her like that as he asked her to spend the daylight hours with him, as though he really wanted to be with her. But then he'd made her feel like this when she'd been younger, too. And just look how that had ended!

No, it was more honest to just limit their relationship to what it was truly all about. If they started to behave like a...well, like a courting couple, then she might start to slide into feeling something for him besides the physical fascination she couldn't deny he exerted over her.

'No. I don't break my word,' she said firmly. Besides, it would be much healthier to spend time with her friends, friends who would still be there for her when this *affaire* with Harcourt had burned out. As it surely would. By all accounts he was incapable of sticking to one female for much more than a week.

'What about the evening, then? I have an invitation to a soirée you might find amusing. We could go together.'

She frowned up at him. 'I'm not sure that would be a good idea.' She didn't know what kind of circles Nathan moved amongst these days. It was just possible she might get introduced to one of the merchants with whom she was trying to do business. And then if they spotted her with Monsieur Le Brun, who was acting for her, they might put two and two together. It was only a slight possibility, but still…

He sucked in a sharp breath. 'You want to keep our affair secret. I can understand that.' He shrugged, and smiled, but it was a cynical smile that made her sorry she'd spoken so sharply. 'But you will come to me again?'

Oh, that was better. Much better. He found her so irresistible that he would accept any terms she chose, so long as she returned to his bed.

* * *

She had hugged the sensation to herself all the way home and woken up the next morning with a smile on her face.

She wasn't unnatural and unfeminine, as her father had decreed she must be, for preferring to stay with her aunt and work at her ledgers rather than crawl home to the vicarage and…stultify. She was a desirable woman. Nathan Harcourt, the man who had once spurned her, wanted her. *Her.*

Without knowing a thing about her fortune.

She stretched her arms above her head, wincing as she felt the pull of muscles left tender from all those hours of lovemaking.

No, not *love*making. She wasn't going to mistake his enthusiasm for her body as affection, not this time round. Nor was she going to fall for him, or anything silly like that.

He wasn't anything special. He was just here. At a time in her life when she was ready to explore new possibilities. To find out what she really wanted from life. She'd known it wasn't the cloistered, cramped existence that was all Stanton Basset had to offer. She'd wanted to break free of its petty restrictions, it's narrow-minded parochialism. And she'd thought visiting Paris would do it.

She'd been wrong.

Taking a lover had been what she needed.

They would say she was wanton, if they knew what she'd done last night, the town tabbies. And wicked, to boot, for turning down Harcourt's guilt-induced proposal.

It had surprised her, that proposal. It was the kind of thing an honourable man would do and she'd long since ceased to think of him as anything more than an out-and-out scoundrel.

But he wasn't all bad. He had wanted her, truly wanted her, when he'd been a young man. And if he'd been the villain she'd believed, the rake that the scandal sheets had branded him, he could have taken her virginity then and left her sullied as well as broken-hearted.

But he hadn't bedded her when she'd been a girl. He might have cut her out of his life quite harshly when he'd decided to marry for gain, rather than...well, she hesitated to use the word love, but it really did look as though he had felt *something* for her. But he had left her in such a way that she *could* have married someone else.

If she hadn't been so shattered.

If her parents hadn't added to her misery by heaping all the blame upon her.

If her aunt hadn't swooped down and taken her under her wing. And fostered her poor opinion of the male species until she, too, had grown to dislike them all on principle.

Well, that was all water under the bridge now. It was Sunday and, instead of trudging to church and listening to the moralising of plump and priggish Parson Peabody, she was going out on an excursion of pleasure. Monsieur Le Brun had organised a carriage to drive them out to the Bois de Boulogne. It sounded rather tame, she sighed as she got out of bed, in comparison with the all-day ball that Nathan had invited her to attend. But as she washed and donned her clothes, she reminded herself that it wouldn't do to let him monopolise her time. He was already monopolising her thoughts.

He would have to be content to have the access to her body that no other man had ever known.

Listen to her! Planning to keep her lover at arm's length. She giggled at her newfound confidence in her attractiveness. Oh, if only she'd known how good making love would feel, she would have taken a lover years ago.

Or at least she might have considered it.

Though…actually, she hadn't ever felt the slightest curiosity about what it might have been like to so much as *kiss* a man, until she'd run into Nathan again.

But then, she hastily reminded herself, she hadn't been in Paris, either.

She had just about convinced herself that it was something about the revolutionary atmosphere lingering in Paris that had given her the courage to defy all the rules by the time she went through to the main salon.

And got the shock of her life.

Chapter Nine

'Dare I ask,' said Nathan when he strode into her salon that evening, 'what made you change your mind about accepting my invitation to the Wilsons' soirée?'

'Not here,' she said darkly. 'Wait until we are in the carriage.' So saying, she swept out of the front door and into the street, where the hired carriage he'd come to collect her in was still waiting.

'You look divine, by the way,' he said as he handed her in.

He made her feel divine, too, the way his eyes devoured her as he climbed in beside her.

She was glad she'd succumbed to the urge to dress up for him. She'd briefly wondered whether he would feel more comfortable if she dressed plainly, the way she usually did. But she hadn't been able to resist putting on the prettiest

of her new gowns. And tucking the diamond—
or possibly crystal—aigrette into her hair had
been an act of pure self-indulgence. Just once,
she wanted to look her best and have him look at
her exactly the way he was looking at her right
now. As though she was beautiful. Desirable.

'You look quite…appealing yourself,' she
murmured, looking him up and down with
appreciation. It was a relief to see he still had
some clothes fit to be seen in, in any company.
In fact, they looked as though they'd scarcely
been worn at all. He must have had quite an ex-
tensive wardrobe when he'd been married to his
wealthy, well-connected wife. And he clearly
hadn't pawned it all yet.

'Thank you,' he said, taking her hands and
kissing first one, then the other.

Her toes curled up with pleasure. Oh, but she
had been right to seek the solace that only he
could give her tonight.

'So what is it that has driven you from your
friends this evening? And made you hint at some
mystery? I am all agog.'

'I could not stomach one more minute of
their billing and cooing, if you must know. And
I heartily regretted my decision to turn down
your invitation to spend the day with you not
half an hour after departing for the Bois de Bou-

logne. At least if I'd been dancing with you, you would have noticed I was there!'

'Billing and cooing? The stringy Frenchman and the mousy widow?'

'Yes,' she said in disgust. 'Though they do say that love is blind, I had never before considered how very accurate that statement is until today.' She shot him a sharp look. 'But Fenella is not mousy. She is elegant and poised. Perhaps she is a touch reserved, but—'

'Nondescript,' he said dismissively. 'The kind of woman you barely notice. It amazes me that she managed to produce a daughter so vibrant as that...'

'Sophie,' Amethyst supplied. 'Oh. So that is why you asked about her father.'

He didn't contradict her.

'I've often thought Sophie must take after her father, myself.' She smiled up at him. He couldn't return her smile. Her pleasure in assuming they were of like mind about the girl made him feel so guilty he couldn't even look at her.

'Because Fenella is a quiet person, though neither nondescript, nor mousy. I always think she is a perfect lady, actually.'

'She is not perfect,' he said bluntly. 'She pales into insignificance when next to you. When first I saw you here in Paris, I hardly even noticed she was at the table. But I could not get you out of my head, no matter how hard I tried. I thought of you practically all day. And even in my dreams, there you were, your wonderful hair spread across my pillows, your naked—'

'Did you?'

She loved hearing him say things like that. And even if it was merely the practised patter of a seasoned rake, it was close enough to what she'd felt to be convincing. She hadn't been able to stop her thoughts returning to him either. And he'd infiltrated her dreams too.

'But I am being remiss,' he said. 'To distract you from whatever it was you were going to tell me about your friends. You were so annoyed with them you looked as though you really needed to make a clean breast of it.'

His gaze dropped to the bodice of her gown. And all of a sudden she could imagine him baring her breasts, right there in the carriage, and suckling on them the way he'd done the night before.

'It was all your fault,' she said resentfully. She had decided to get out tonight and risk taking a peek at the glittering whirl that was Parisian society after all. But one heated look and all she wanted was to tell the coachman to take her to his studio, remove every stitch of clothing, slowly, while he watched, and then have him do all the things he'd done to her last night.

Over and over again.

'Mine? I cannot be held responsible for every love affair that springs up in Paris, just because I happen to live here.'

'Oh, that's not what I meant. It was what you said, last night. About, *the man who calls himself Monsieur Le Brun.* I've always thought there was something suspicious about him.' That was not quite true. It was more that she was suspicious of all males as a matter of course.

'But this morning, only he was in the salon where we gather before going out. And although we have been in rooms on our own before, he just looked so...uncomfortable. He could not meet my eyes. Well,' she huffed, her eyes narrowing, 'naturally not, the sneak! It turns out he—' but just then the carriage lurched to a halt. They had arrived at the *hôtel* hired by the minor politician who was throwing tonight's informal rout.

'He what?'

'Are you not going to open the door and help me alight?'

'No. I want to hear what *the sneak* has been getting up to.'

'I will tell you inside.'

'But anyone might overhear.'

'So? I care not. Besides, if we just sit here with the door closed, people will think we are…'

'So?' He grinned at her, echoing her own words. 'I care not.'

'You have to be the most annoying man I've ever met.'

'Worse than Monsieur Le Brun?'

'Far worse,' she said darkly. 'Because I suspect you annoy me on purpose.'

'You should not look so utterly captivating with your eyes flashing fire, then.'

'Captivating? Don't you mean shrewish? That's what most men say.'

'Ah, but I'm not most men. And you warned me about your prickles before you let me get too close. If you were really a shrew, you wouldn't care whether you hurt me or not.'

He leaned forwards, and planted a hard kiss on her lips just as she was parting them to give him a piece of her mind. He kissed her until she'd forgotten what she'd been going to say to him. And then, just as she relented and started to kiss him back, he pulled away and sprang out of the carriage.

Only to lean back in, extending his hand to her with a broad smile, which she somehow found herself returning.

'You are incorrigible,' she said, shaking her head.

'That's me,' he agreed cheerfully. 'But you wouldn't have me any other way, would you? You've needed to find a man who is strong enough not to bleed when you try to sharpen your claws on him.'

'And you think you are that man?'

'I'm man enough for you,' he husked into her ear, just at the moment when a footman stepped forwards to take her coat. Which made her blush. And want to do something to make him squirm, the way he'd just made her squirm. Only she couldn't think of anything that wouldn't make her look a fool as well.

'God, will you just look at this place?' Nathan tucked her hand into the crook of his arm almost absent-mindedly as he stared up at the queue of people snaking half-way down the stairs. 'They must have rented the whole building, not just one floor.'

She took note of the disdainful twist to his mouth. In spite of growing up in exalted circles, in spite of having married into another wealthy family, it looked as though he didn't like people flaunting their wealth either.

'So...' he jerked his eyes away from the marble pillars, the ornate chandeliers, the liveried, bewigged footmen, and turned his attention back to her. 'You were about to tell me what your French hireling said when you told him you knew he wasn't being honest about his name.'

Was she? Oh, yes. She'd been really annoyed about it too.

'That was what started it,' she agreed. 'But then he had the nerve to demand I tell him who had been talking about him, rather than just give me an honest answer.'

'What cheek,' said Nathan with mock horror.

'Yes, it was, actually. He acted as though I had no right to question him, when I am employing him in a position of considerable trust. And I was just pointing out that if he wished to remain in my employ he had better come clean, when Fenella burst into the room and flew to his side. Saying it was all her fault. Well, he tried to silence her, saying that I didn't know the truth, but she just said she couldn't keep it a secret from me any longer and it all came tumbling out. Not about his real identity, not at first, but about how she and *Gaston* were going to marry as soon as we return to England.'

For one terrible moment she'd thought they'd hatched up some plot to swindle her. After all, they had spent so much time together poring over the correspondence from French firms it would have been easy. The thought of Fenella betraying her trust in that way had felt like a knife-blow. Like her sisters all over again. She'd wondered why it was that no matter how much she did for people, nobody had ever stood by her.

It had been a tremendous relief to find out that what they were hiding was merely a romance.

'But why,' he said as the queue shuffled further up the stairs, 'did they need to keep their betrothal a secret from you?'

'It was because he'd seduced her,' she told him grimly. 'The very first night we arrived in Paris. Oh, Fenella said it was all her own doing. She'd had too much to drink and was lonely. And they'd become such good friends during the voyage and had so much in common. And then she said she had missed the kind of closeness a woman can only find with a man. Which, by her blushes, I took to mean in bed.'

And because of the time she'd spent in Nathan's bed, she could actually see why Fenella had succumbed to temptation, when only the day before, she would have been horrified. Sickened.

'Suddenly, a lot of things made sense. Such as the way neither of them could quite look me in the eye any more. And the way he'd gone from being as sarcastic as he dared to being positively ingratiating.' And the way Fenella blushed when she'd made what were, on the face of it, perfectly innocuous remarks.

'And all the while he kept trying to shush her. But when he groaned and covered his face and sort of collapsed on to the sofa, Fenella finally realised we hadn't been arguing about *that* at all. But it was too late. The cat, as they say, was well and truly out of the bag.'

'I wish I had been there,' he said, his lips twitching with mirth.

'It wasn't funny.' Could he take nothing seriously?

'I beg your pardon, but it sounds highly entertaining. When you have a middle-aged couple behaving like some latter-day Romeo and Juliet, with you cast as both sets of disapproving guardians. It's preposterous.'

'To be fair, they were both afraid I would try to part them.'

'Why on earth would you want to do that?'

'Because,' she said, grasping the banister rail with such force it looked as though she was considering wringing someone's neck, 'he'd taken advantage of her. If I'd found out the morning after, when she was so upset about it, you may be sure I *would* have turned him out!'

'But you said Fenella was as keen as he was.'

'I know you don't think there's anything

wrong with jumping into bed with people on the slightest pretext,' she said coldly, 'but Fenella was racked with guilt. So much that she couldn't bring herself to confide in me. And he worked on those fears. And seems to have convinced her that they're experiencing some grand passion that will end in marriage.'

She didn't see him flinch when she assumed he had no morals. That he would, as she put it, jump into bed with any woman, on the slightest pretext. It took an effort, but he managed to carry on with the conversation after only the slightest hesitation.

'And you don't think it will?'

'I...'

He watched the fire go from her. Her shoulders slumped.

'This morning, I would have said not. But having been obliged to watch them...'

'Billing and cooing,' he supplied helpfully.

She shot him a brief, narrow-eyed glare.

'Precisely,' she said bitterly. 'He is certainly very convincing in his role.' Once they'd gone out and Fenella and Gaston no longer felt the need to conceal their relationship, they'd become remarkably demonstrative. Smiling at each other and laughing at silly little jokes that made no sense to her whatsoever. And looking at each other as though, given half a chance, they would dive into the nearest bushes and rip each other's clothes off.

And yet somehow they'd managed to include Sophie in their happy little love bubble. They were bonding into a family unit, right before her eyes.

Leaving her trailing along behind them. Excluded, as usual. She'd felt almost as lonely as when her family had closed ranks against her.

She'd grown increasingly resentful of the fact that she'd stuck to the arrangement she'd made with this pair, thinking it would be bad form to abandon them in order to spend time with her new lover, when they could think of nothing but each other.

As soon as she got home she had sent word that she was ready to accompany Nathan to the party he'd mentioned, to be thrown by some minor politician of whom she'd never heard. If Fenella was going to be wrapped up in Gaston for the duration of their stay in Paris, then she might as well spend every moment she could with her own lover.

'I can see why Fenella believes him to be in earnest,' she admitted. 'But what still worries me is the fact that Fenella really has fallen for him. She was almost weeping when she told me she never thought she'd find love at her time of life, but that Gaston had made her feel like a young bride again.'

And because she'd just spent the earlier part of the day feeling exactly the same, in relation to Nathan, she hadn't been able to utter one single word of rebuke.

'He got to his feet at that point, put his arm round her and claimed that the only reason he did not wish Fenella to tell me of their so-called plans until we returned safely to England was because he was afraid I would turn—' She bit back what she had been about to say, unwilling to let Nathan know that Fenella was also in her employ, rather than just travelling with her as a friend, which was what she'd led him to believe.

'Turn against her, for having loose morals,' she finished lamely.

Monsieur le Prune—and she might as well call him that now, since Le Brun wasn't his real name either—had pointed out that since she'd employed Fenella to give her an air of respect-ability, now that her own morality was in ques-tion, poor Fenella was terrified she would lose her job.

And then had come the only bright spot in her otherwise disastrous day. Fenella had looked up at him with reproach and declared that Amethyst

would never abandon her in a foreign country,
let alone Sophie. Even when he'd muttered that
perhaps she did not know her employer as well
as she thought, Fenella had been unshakeable.
Fenella had stayed true to their friendship.

No matter what happened next, whether the
romance blossomed into marriage, or whether
Monsieur Le Brun turned out to be some kind
of ageing Lothario, Amethyst was not going to
lose her friend.

'I think he had been trying to turn her against
me for some time. He's worked on the guilt she
felt for actually doing what all the ladies of Stanton Bassett accused her of doing—'

'Hold on. Now you have lost me. What, exactly, have the ladies of Stanley Basset accused
her of doing?'

'Stanton. It's Stanton Basset. Well, when
she arrived with a baby, but no husband in evidence, rumours started to fly. You can imagine
the sort of thing that provincial, narrow-minded
women with too much time on their hands can
invent. They're always ready to believe the worst
of people, without a shred of evidence to support it. Particularly if that person has nobody to
vouch for her,' she said indignantly. 'And it was
all the more unfair because Fenella is really a
very moral person. Well, until she started mis-

behaving with Monsieur le Prune, I would have said she had never put a foot wrong in her life. Apart from marrying a plausible rogue the first time round. Honestly,' she huffed, as they moved up yet another place in the receiving line, 'you would have thought she'd have learned her lesson where men are concerned.'

Although had she learned anything from her experience with Nathan? Here she was, seeking him out and confiding everything to him as though he was her closest, most trustworthy friend. Just as she'd done before.

What right had she to question Fenella's judgement when it came to men? At least Fenella had gone for a man she swore was completely different from the feckless charmer she'd eloped with as a girl. Gaston was clever, she declared, and hard working and capable, and he never, ever lost his temper.

After that description of his merits, she saw that he was exactly the kind of man Fenella would fall for. She'd confessed she wanted a man to lean on. Someone dependable and patient. His looks were irrelevant.

She might find the thought of getting amorous with him totally repellent, but he'd managed to put a bloom on Fenella's cheeks. He was making her feel like a desirable, vibrant woman. Just as Nathan—

Nathan, she suddenly realised, had gone awfully quiet. When she darted a glance up at him he was staring fixedly at the back of the stout man in front of them in the receiving line, a forced tightness about his lips.

He was probably getting bored with her stupid prattle. Desperately, she strove to find some other topic of conversation.

'You never did tell me,' she said with determined brightness. 'What is your connection to these people and why they have invited you tonight?'

He turned to her then, his face twisting into a mask of harsh cynicism.

'I know Wilson from my days as a Member of Parliament. We both, at that time, had very ambitious wives. They got on well together.'

He didn't look as though that fact pleased him. And when she frowned her confusion at him, he continued, 'You seem to think that if she is so ambitious for her husband to succeed, they would have done better to stay in England, don't you? Open your eyes, Amy, and look at the people they have attracted to their home.'

As they were almost at the head of the stairs, by peering round the stout man in front of them, and his partner's flounces, she could easily have caught glimpses of the glittering crowd thronging a large salon beyond.

'Not that I am likely to recognise any of them,' she retorted, stung by his patronising attitude.

'Much better you don't,' he said harshly, tucking her arm firmly into his as they reached the landing. 'But I will tell you the kind of people she is gathering about her in Paris. Influential people. She is using this trip to cement friendships she could never have forged in London. When Wilson returns to England, she will continue to use the connections she has made here to push him up the greasy pole.'

'That's not strictly true, though, is it? She invited you, even though...' She trailed off.

'Even though she was my wife's friend, rather than mine, and my career is currently at such a low ebb it would be nothing short of miraculous for me to resurrect it?' He raised one eyebrow, his tone challenging.

'I was going to say,' she replied, 'that you cannot be of use to her any more, since you are no longer involved in politics.'

He looked at her steadily for a few moments, then appeared to relent towards her.

'It isn't easy to understand this world until you've been a part of it. I certainly didn't look beneath the glittering surface to the lethal undercurrents before I plunged in. I was even foolish enough, when I first got elected, to think I needed to go to the House upon occasion and listen to debates.' His mouth twisted into a harsh sneer. 'And that was even though I knew that Lucasta's father had bought the votes of the potwallopers in my borough. But I soon learned that isn't how a man succeeds in politics. He needs to ingratiate himself with the right people. Do deals in secret. Be prepared to perjure his soul in return for promotion.'

'But…'

'You cannot see how I can be of use to these people, is that what you were going to say? Oh, Amy…' he laughed, bitterly '…have you forgotten? My father is, and always will be, the Earl of Finchingfield, and he wields enormous political influence. Who knows but that one day he might forgive me? If I find favour in his sight again, those who have supported me at this…low tide…might find him grateful. And prepared to be generous.'

'That's a horribly cynical way to look at life.'

'I prefer to say realistic. Amy, I spent years amongst these people. I know how they operate. Believe me, the more cynical you are about them, the less likely you are to be hurt by them.'

She frowned. 'I wonder you bothered to come tonight, then. They all sound perfectly horrid.'

'They have their uses,' he said darkly. The most urgent being to send a message to his father. Somebody, from this gathering, was bound to return to England with the news that his reprobate youngest son had taken up with the very woman he'd done his utmost to separate him from. And, for once, *he* would taste defeat. Know that all his machinations had been in vain. Amethyst had found her way back to him.

'Uses? What do you mean?'

Nathan rubbed his nose with his thumb. He couldn't admit that he wanted to flaunt her in his father's face. That he was using her.

She didn't deserve to become a pawn in his ongoing battle with his father. Pawns got hurt. His father certainly hadn't hesitated to blacken her name ten years ago. To him, she was nothing. A mere inconvenience to be swatted aside like a pesky fly.

'I shouldn't have brought you here,' he said, a cold knot forming in his stomach. He could have taken her anywhere. Why had he exposed her to the possibility of getting hurt all over again?

'You are no match for these sort of people. It is like throwing a lamb to the wolves.'

'Nonsense,' she snapped. 'Do you think I am a country bumpkin with straw for brains?'

'No! That is not what I meant at all. You are just too…straightforward to know how to survive in this kind of environment. You have no idea how to smile while uttering a threat, or make someone believe you are their friend whilst plotting how to stab them in the back.'

Simple. He thought she was simple. Not up to cutting it in his world.

Well, why should she be surprised? It was what he'd thought ten years ago, too. Well, she'd show him.

But before she had the chance to work out exactly how she was going to prove that she was not the simpering, weak-willed kind of ninny that needed a man to protect her from all the big bad wolves in the world of politics, the stout couple in front moved away and she and Nathan were finally standing face to face with their host and hostess.

'Oh, Mr Harcourt, what an unexpected pleasure to see you here,' gushed the bejewelled woman, flashing a lot of teeth and bosom in his direction. Though how it could be unexpected, since she must have sent him an invitation, Amethyst couldn't imagine.

'I would have thought our sort of gathering would be much too tame for you,' she said archly, before going off into a peal of shrill laughter.

So why invite him, then? *Because my father is, and always will be, the Earl of Finchingfield and he wields enormous political influence.*

'And who is this delightful young lady you have brought with you? I don't believe I have seen her about anywhere, have I?'

Nathan paused, only very slightly, but the woman promptly leapt to her own conclusion.

'Oh, how very naughty of you,' she said, flattening one hand to her impressive bosom. 'To bring your latest *chère amie* into such a gathering. Oh, but isn't that just like you!' She rapped his arm with her fan. 'Always courting scandal one way or another. But I shall not be cross with you. This is Paris, after all, so what does it really matter? Algernon, dearest,' she rattled on, while Nathan seemed to have turned to stone at her side, 'look who it is. Mr Harcourt and his lovely young...French friend.'

'Harcourt, you dog.' He grinned. 'Still the rake, I see! But do you have a name, you lovely young thing?' Mr Wilson, who looked exactly as she'd imagined a minor politician with delusions of grandeur would look, seized her hand and pressed a wet kiss on the back of it.

She flashed Nathan a swift, challenging glance from under her eyelashes, dropped Mr Wilson a curtsy and, summoning up what little

French she knew, said, in a little, breathy, voice, *'Moi, je suis Mademoiselle D'Aulbie.'*

Nathan let out a choking sound and turned to her with a look of complete shock.

'It is such the honour to meet the very important man of whom I hear so much,' Amy simpered, batting her eyelashes up at her host, the way she imagined a woman of pleasure, who did not know when she was being insulted to her face, would do. 'And Monsieur 'Arcour, he does not want to attend at all, but I did so want zis treat.'

'Did you, my dear?' Mr Wilson puffed up to almost twice his not-inconsiderable size. 'Don't suppose young Harcourt could resist, eh? Don't say I blame him.' He winked at Nathan over the top of her head.

'But what is zis rayk you say of eem?' she said, her execrable accent getting thicker by the second. 'He is the artist, *n'est-ce pas*? Not some kind of gardener.'

At that point, Nathan abruptly came back to life, grabbing her elbow and tugging her into the room, whilst muttering something to their hosts about making room for the next couple in line.

'What the hell,' he said through gritted teeth, 'has come over you? Putting on that ludicrous accent and letting them think…'

'Oh, I don't know,' she said airily, beckoning a waiter who was circulating with a tray of champagne. 'Perhaps I just couldn't resist showing you that I could very easily disguise not only what I am thinking, but also my very nationality, if I put my mind to it.'

He snagged a glass of champagne himself and knocked it all back in one go.

'But why would you want to do any such thing?'

She sipped her champagne whilst considering how to answer him. And then decided to plump for the truth.

'Do you know, I'm not entirely sure. But I've felt on the verge of...revolution ever since I arrived in Paris. I have the strangest feeling that I can be anyone I want to be here. And just for a moment, I rather fancied the idea of letting that stupid woman think I was your *chère amie*. You have to admit it was rather amusing to see the judgemental, pompous, narrow-minded bladders of wind both run to the lengths of their boorishness, wasn't it? Far better than having to explain that actually I am—'

'No. You don't need to say another word.' He'd frozen in horror when Mrs Wilson had expressed curiosity about her. He'd hesitated to give her real name, knowing it could signal the eruption of another battle between him and his father, with Amy at risk of getting caught in the cross-fire.

He'd been relieved, if a little stunned, when Amy had started to poke fun at their hosts. And now that they'd escaped the danger that people who still had connections to his father's world might find out who she was, he had to admit that he would have found her performance amusing if he hadn't been frozen solid with horror at the danger he'd so foolishly exposed her to.

It reminded him of the rather tart sense of humour she'd displayed ten years before. The perceptive and witty comments she'd made about people they met that had chimed so exactly with his own feelings that he'd felt as though he'd found the perfect partner.

And her remark about being anyone she wanted to be here in France was another case in point.

'I know exactly what you mean about the atmosphere of Paris,' he said. 'The moment I got here, something about the attitude of the people made me feel as though I really could make a fresh start. As though I could wipe the slate clean and be whoever I wanted to be. Or perhaps to find out who I was meant to be—yes, that sums it up more neatly. Because none of them assumed I had an inherent value just because of who my father is,' he said, shooting a dark look towards the doorway, where the Wilsons were gushing over the next arrivals.

Amethyst followed the direction of his gaze.

'In fact, they would be as likely to think of that as an impediment, since they have taken such a dislike to anyone connected to the aristocracy.'

'Hasn't it made you feel a little…scared?'

'No. The revolution is over. They've done with executing people just because of their ancestry,' he said.

'I have sometimes felt a little concerned, though,' she said. 'It is as though there is some sort of charge in the air. Like you get just before a storm. And there seem to be soldiers everywhere, loitering in packs, looking mean and hungry.'

'Yes, well I can't blame them, can you? They've had a taste of power. They've overthrown one corrupt regime and spent years forging a military empire. It won't be easy for them to settle back into the kind of lives they had before, if that is all the Bourbons mean to offer them.'

'What do you think will happen?'

He grinned. 'Who knows? Certainly not the Parisians. Everyone has a different opinion about what should happen to their country next, from the lowliest street vendor to the deposed aristocrats who've come flocking back demanding they have their estates restored, and they aren't afraid to voice it. Nobody here accepts the status quo. They feel they have the power to change just about everything. It's…invigorating.'

'I…suppose it is,' she said.

'*I* think it is. Nothing is set in stone here any more. And apart from that, Parisians don't care that I caused such a scandal in London, that no political party would ever back me to stand for them ever again. It makes me feel that the past is gone. Done. I've broken free from my family's expectations, my reputation, everything. It's as though I've been given a blank sheet of paper and what I draw on it is entirely up to me.'

A new start. Yes, she could see why he would want that after the mess he'd made of what should have been a glittering political career. Hadn't she also left Stanton Basset because it was what she was looking for herself? A chance to break free from the expectations of others, the obligations that weighed her down?

'The trouble is,' she said, putting on a frown, 'that since I've come to Paris, people keep on mistaking me for a woman of easy virtue. What do you suppose,' she said, shooting him a coy look from under her lashes, 'that means?'

'I think it means,' he said, setting his empty glass down carefully on the nearest available surface, 'that it is time you fulfilled your potential.'

'Oh, yes?'

'Decidedly yes,' he said, taking her arm and leading her to the nearest exit. 'If you are determined to play the part of my...*chère amie,*' he husked into her ear, 'then it is about time you put in a bit more practice.'

'Does this mean what I hope it means?'

'Yes,' he replied firmly. 'I'm taking you back to my rooms. I've let you see ze most important man, and all zees so important people. Now you need to pay for me giving you zis treat,' he said playfully, imitating her dreadful French accent.

'Ooh,' she breathed. 'You are a hard taskmaster.'

'Hard is the word,' he agreed. 'And these breeches simply don't disguise a thing.'

She blushed. And then began to giggle. And kept on giggling as they pushed their way back through the throng climbing the stairs, as they made their way down.

Chapter Ten

⠀⠀⠀⠀⠀⠀⠀⠀⠀⠀◦⟋⟍⟋⟍⟋◦

They hurried back to his rooms as fast as they could.

'I'm not going to have any breath left for love-making by the time we've climbed up all these stairs,' Amethyst grumbled as they reached the first landing.

'You won't need to do a thing,' he promised her. 'Just lie back on the bed and let me do all the work.'

And he did.

Amy had never had so much attention devoted to her. So much care lavished on her body. Even before he entered her and took her to the heights, it felt really meaningful. What they were doing together was so incredible, so wonderful, so much *more* than anything she'd ever known she could experience that, yes, if she was a naïve, young, uneducated female, she might have mistaken it for love.

Especially since he gave himself to it with such…enthusiasm.

'Amy, Amy, oh God, Amy!'

Nathan's whole body shuddered as he groaned his release. He slumped to one side of her, gathered her in his arms and buried his face in her hair.

No wonder, she sighed, turning and wrapping her arms round his neck, women so very often mistook the attentions of a passionate lover for something deeper. He had made her feel loved

And for the first time in her life, she hadn't had to do anything to earn it, either.

'Why so solemn?'

He'd opened his eyes and was watching her, she discovered. When she didn't know what to answer, he smiled and gently traced the fullness of her lower lip with one finger.

'You are full of contrasts, are you not? Nobody, seeing you so solemn after giving yourself to me, would believe you are the same woman who was so playful earlier tonight, when most people would have been trying to impress.'

'What are you trying to say?'

He shrugged. 'Just that there are so many sides to you I never knew existed when…when I knew you before.'

'I am not the same person I was back then.' In fact, she could scarcely recognise herself any more. She'd certainly never suspected she had it in her to mimic a French accent and play-act at being a lightskirt, for the sheer fun of it. She'd always been sober and serious, even as a girl. Getting her heart broken, having her family roundly rebuke her, then spending years living with her embittered, man-hating aunt had only made her more inclined to look on life as a dull, dreary grind that had to be endured. Her only fun, thus far, had come from pulling the rug out from under self-important people like Mrs Podmore, or giving people private nicknames, as she'd done to Monsieur le Prune. It was as if a new Amy was emerging, day by day, the further she got from Stanton Basset and all its petty restrictions.

What else might she discover about herself as she broke free from the habits she'd acquired without even knowing they were stifling her?

'I know,' he sighed. 'And I'm sorry.'

'Sorry? You don't like me as I am now?' She'd just been likening herself to a butterfly uncurling its wings from a crusty chrysalis and he'd preferred her as she was?

'No. I do. I mean, I am sorry for how things ended between us back then. I was cruel to you.

I hurt you,' he said, kissing her forehead gently. 'I wish I hadn't. I wish it were possible to go back to a time before everything went wrong. I let you down very badly. Can you…could you ever forgive me, do you think?'

A few days ago she would have said no, she would never forgive him. She'd been so full of rage and bitterness. But she must have started to forgive him without any conscious effort, or she wouldn't be in bed with him now, would she? And those same few days ago, she would never have imagined running down the stairs, hand in hand with Nathan Harcourt, giggling like a schoolgirl after the mischievous trick she'd played on their hosts, either.

Had letting go of her anger with him been what had made such a difference? Was that why she felt so much lighter of heart now?

'Forgiveness…is a strange thing to be talking about while we are naked,' she said, reaching for the sheet. It was funny, but she was more aware of her nudity now they were starting to discuss feelings.

'For instance, my parents were adamant that there was nothing to forgive.' And perhaps there hadn't been, not really. He might have toyed with her affections, but he'd drawn the line at seducing her. Given the reputation he'd since gained, it was amazing he'd behaved with such restraint. She'd been so infatuated with him he could very easily have talked her into bed. Well, it hadn't exactly taken much to persuade her into it now, had it? A few smouldering looks, a couple of invitations, one hard kiss and she'd climbed five flights of stairs for the privilege.

'They were quick to point out that you never proposed to me, so I had no right to complain, or even to feel hard done by.' And for the first time, she could see their point. He'd stolen nothing beyond a few kisses. And he could have taken so much more. He could have ruined her before tossing her aside.

He reared up on his elbow.

'What rot! I can't let you shrug off my apology, saying the way we parted didn't matter because I hadn't actually made a formal declaration. I *know* I hurt you. I can still see the look on your face the night I cut you, then danced with every other girl in the place. Admit it. You were in love with me.'

He'd known how badly he'd hurt her that night? She'd shown it on her face? Well, she wasn't an infatuated girl any longer, to wear her heart on her sleeve.

'Why should I admit,' she said haughtily, 'anything of the kind?'

'Because I was in love with you, too, that's why. I did want to marry you.' He rolled on to his back and stared hard-jawed at the ceiling. 'We would have been perfect together,' he said, in a voice that quivered with suppressed emotion. 'My deepest wish, back then, was to live the life of a country gentleman, dabbling with my painting, raising a pack of happy children...'

Her stomach swooped. No matter how many people had told her she'd been mistaken, no matter how often she had told herself that she didn't care, either, to hear him actually admit she'd been right all along gave her a tremendous surge of something that see-sawed between triumph and anguish.

'So,' she said coldly, 'why didn't you?' What possible excuse could he give for ending it the way he had, if he'd really been dreaming the same dreams she had?

A muscle bunched in his jaw.

'Because I was an idiot. A young idiot. I had no confidence in my own judgement. I believed...I was persuaded...that it was better to pursue a career, than to live my life in obscurity.'

Persuaded...

Her anger ebbed. Just a touch.

'I know what it's like to have an implacable, domineering father,' she said, reaching for his hand. 'And since we parted, I learned a great deal more about yours than I'd ever guessed when we were...' She couldn't quite bring herself to use the word *courting*, even though she now knew that was exactly what they'd been doing. 'It is obvious, with hindsight,' she said bitterly, 'that he wanted better for you than a virtually penniless clergyman's daughter from an obscure parish. He forbade the match, is that it?'

He groaned and flung up one hand to cover his eyes. He only wished it had been that simple. 'It wasn't exactly like that,' he admitted 'But if it's any consolation to you, I definitely got my just desserts for not keeping faith with you,' he said with a hollow laugh.

His breathing grew laboured as he considered flinging himself off the precipice of a total confession.

But as he lowered his arm and looked at her pinched expression, he took a mental step back from the edge. He hadn't earned her trust yet, even though she was claiming she'd forgiven him. And if she knew it all...the thought of how she might react made his insides freeze.

'I shouldn't have brought it up, should I,' he said ruefully. His selfish urge to salve his conscience had spoiled what had been a beautiful moment between them. 'It is just,' he said, rolling his whole body to one side to stare down at her, 'that I want to get to know you again. The woman you are now. And we don't have long, do we? You are only spending a short time in Paris.'

'So there is little point in trying, is there?' She swung her legs over the edge of the bed, struggling to keep the quilt covering what modesty she had left, and began to search for her scattered clothing.

As she attempted to fumble one stocking on to her foot without letting go of the quilt, he rolled off the bed and reached for his breeches.

'Would you prefer me to leave you in privacy to dress?'

'Yes. I would, thank you,' she said, flushing, for it seemed foolish to feel shy after he'd had his hands and mouth all over her.

But he didn't mock her sudden attack of shyness. He just smiled at her and walked to the door. Though he hesitated on the threshold, leaning his arm on the jamb.

'I can see you are determined to leave,' he said. 'But I hope I can persuade you to spend tomorrow with me.'

'Oh, and just how do you propose to do that?'

He chuckled. 'Not the way you seem to think.'

'I don't know what you mean,' she said crossly.

He raised one eyebrow. Then straightened his

face. 'Of course you don't. So I will just point out that the mouse and her Frenchman will be so wrapped up in each other that they will drive you to distraction. What's more, they won't even notice whether you are there or not. So you need have absolutely no qualms about spending every moment you have left in Paris with me.'

Which was all true. She had no stomach for trailing around behind Fenella and Gaston. And there was going to be an awful lot more time to endure in Paris, while Monsieur le Prune attempted to strike a deal with the contacts she'd made. Time she might as well spend with Nathan, rather than moping about the changes she'd have to make to her life once Fenella married.

Because she couldn't deny she did enjoy being with him. Tonight, before they'd started talking about the past, and what had gone wrong, she'd enjoyed his company tremendously.

Yes—as a distraction from the prospect of potentially having to spend a bleak lonely future with one hired companion after another, he would be perfect.

'And I still need you to sit for your portrait,' he reminded her. 'That could take hours,' he said, stalking back to the bed and cupping her face before placing his mouth firmly on her own.

Her knees went weak at once. And after only

a little longer, she was wriggling out of the quilt and winding her arms round his neck so that she could pull him back down on to the bed. Only the aggravating man drew back, gave her naked body a scorching look and said, 'Hours and hours.'

The portrait. He was talking about the hours he would spend painting her portrait. Not the hours and hours she could have with him in bed.

Or was he?

That was the trouble with men like Nathan. They could say one thing and mean another. They called it flirting.

Well, no matter. As long as she didn't believe his apparent eagerness to spend time with her was something on which she could base her life, the way she'd done when she'd been younger, she would be fine.

She returned his smile with a brittle one of her own.

'Well, I'd better come for a sitting tomorrow then, hadn't I?'

'It occurred to me after you left last night,' said Nathan as he handed her into the fiacre he'd hired to take her…well, he hadn't told her where he was going to take her, yet. Aggravating man, 'that you never finished telling me about those

two.' He jerked his head towards the window
from which Fenella and Gaston were watching
them drive away. 'And there was something you
wanted to rebuke me for, specifically,' he said,
folding himself into the seat next to her. 'I think
you should get it over with now, don't you? Then
I won't have to live in terror of the moment when
you decide to bring it up.'

'Are you deliberately trying to provoke me?'

'Is it working?' He leaned back in his seat and
spread his arms wide in a gesture of surrender.
'Come on, do your worst. I can take it.'

She breathed in slowly through her nostrils,
then lifted her chin and turned her head to look
out of the window on her side of the carriage.

'Not in the mood for fighting yet? Very well,'
he said, sitting up again and nudging her with
his elbow. 'But you really do need to finish the
tale from which I...distracted you last night.'

'I don't see why. And anyway,' she said
haughtily, 'I cannot recall exactly how much I
told you.' And she didn't want to bore him by
repeating a story that hadn't been able to hold
his attention the first time.

'Just that they saw themselves as Romeo and
Juliet, with you as both sets of parents. And how
you grappled with your very natural desire to
turn him off because he'd not only seduced your

friend while she was foxed, but because he was trying to come between you, persuading her you would judge her for falling from grace.'

Goodness. He had not only been listening to her prattling on, as they'd made their way slowly up the Wilsons' staircase, but had committed the whole thing to memory.

'I was waiting with bated breath for you to get to the part where he confessed his real name, since you accused me of alerting you to the fact he's currently using an alias.'

'You knew, all along, that Monsieur Le Brun is in reality the Comte de...' she frowned. 'Well, he rattled off a very long list of names and honorifics, but I was so stunned that I cannot recall any of them now. It was the last thing I expected to learn about him.'

'What did you expect?'

'Why, that he was wanted by the law for some crime or other...'

'In a way, he is, or was. His parents went to the guillotine, you know. And he only narrowly escaped with his own life.'

'How did you know that?'

'At one time, I played a very minor role in an attempt to make sure that the very many French *émigrés* who cluttered up London were actually who they said they were and not spies.'

'Goodness,' she said, looking at him properly for the first time since he'd made that jest about doing her worst. 'I knew you'd got into Parliament, but I never imagined you ever doing anything useful. I thought you'd been one of those who used their position to cut a dash in town and treated the House of Commons as nothing more than a highly select sort of gentlemen's club.'

'Oh, no, I wanted to use my position to make a difference,' he said bleakly. 'It just…didn't work out that way.'

She decided not to press for reasons why it hadn't worked. It wouldn't be very pleasant for him to talk about his total failure as a politician, even in such a junior role.

'Did you find out much about my Monsieur Le Brun? It is just that he claims to have property in England and the means to look after Fenella, as well as having a string of unpronounceable titles and a claim on some land in France. If he is lying, it would be tremendously useful to know about it now.'

'I cannot recall much about him, to be honest,' he told her. 'It took me some time to work out where I'd seen him before, because I met him at only one or two gatherings thrown for *émigrés* claiming to be friends of England.' And he'd done his best to blot out as much of that portion of his life as possible. If he didn't dwell on it, he'd hoped it would all fade into the mist, rather than remain fixed at the foreground in lurid detail.

'He was only one of many that were under subtle investigation. What has he told you?'

She pouted. 'Well, he *says* that he is using his work as a courier as cover to enter France and see how the land lies. See whether it is possible to have some of what was confiscated from his family restored, now that the Bourbons are back in power. He *claims* he dare not move about openly under his true name, in case there are still enemies lurking in wait for him.'

'It could all be true,' he said. 'There are a lot of people attempting to reclaim land and titles that were once theirs. And he was certainly introduced to me in London as the dispossessed Comte de…somewhere or other. It was what made me refer to him as *the man who calls himself Monsieur Le Brun.*'

'It would certainly account for his excessive arrogance,' she huffed. 'There are times when I can quite understand why French peasants wanted to teach the aristocrats a lesson—though not, of course, quite such a brutal one—whereas Fenella finds his tale wildly romantic. Which was what made the rest of that outing almost unbearable.' Her lips curled in disgust. 'She would keep looking up at him as though he were a hero stepped straight out of the pages of some rubbishing novel. But,' she concluded, 'whether he really is a dispossessed French count, or just a mountebank, makes no difference, I suppose.'

'How so?'

'Well, if he is a mountebank, and has no real intention of marrying Fenella, it will break her heart. And if he is what he says he is and does marry her, it will break up our happy little household.' For no man, particularly not a member of the aristocracy, could stomach the thought of his wife living anywhere but in his own home. 'Neither of which outcome,' she said glumly, 'particularly appeal to me. I suppose that sounds selfish, doesn't it? And it's not that I don't want Fenella to be happy. If anyone deserves to marry a title, even a French one—even a French one that might not actually exist any more—then it is Fenella. For she is a lady, you see. A lady born. She has been obliged to live with me only because her family cast her off when she married against their wishes. They really should have taken care of her,' she added crossly, 'once she was widowed. Yet they refused to have anything to do with her just because she'd married a man she loved, rather than one they approved of.'

He went very quiet for some time, before clearing his throat and saying, 'She sounds like a very courageous woman. I was wrong to say she was mousy just because I couldn't tear my eyes off you.'

She flushed and shifted, avoiding his gaze. She clearly wasn't comfortable accepting compliments. Any more than he was to hear that a woman he'd dismissed as mousy had done what he'd not had the sense to do: defy his family and marry the woman he wanted.

Not that he'd ever got to that point. His father had tricked him into withdrawing before he'd come up to scratch.

The fiacre lurched to a halt.

'Here we are,' he said, leaning over to open the door.

She stepped out of the carriage, to see they were in front of a church that reminded her just a bit of St. Paul's Cathedral.

'The Pantheon,' he said, having paid off their driver. 'After we'd talked about the way the very air of Paris seems full of revolutionary ideals, I thought you might like to come and see the tomb of the man responsible for so much of it.'

'You've brought me to look at a tomb?'

'Not just any tomb. The tomb of Voltaire. Besides, there's much more to see in here than tombstones. Have you ever seen anywhere quite so awe-inspiring?'

She had to admit the building was impressive, with its soaring pillars and multiple domes. They wandered about, admiring the place for some time before coming to a halt before the tomb Nathan had said he'd brought her here to see.

'There was a girl,' she said, 'selling lemonade from a stall on the Boulevard, who had a copy of the *Henriade* in her pocket. I so wanted to ask her what she thought of it, but Monsieur Le Brun wouldn't let me stop.'

'Well, he probably doesn't approve of peasants having any education. Or they wouldn't have risen up and thrown his class out.'

'Your class, too,' she reminded him.

'Ah, but not in Paris. Didn't I tell you, now I'm in Paris I can be whoever I want to be?'

'Do you think…no, never mind.'

'What? You can ask me anything, Amy.'

'You won't like it.'

'How do you know, unless you try me?'

'Because you're a man,' she said with disgust. 'Men don't like women to have their own ideas.'

'Ouch.' He pretended to flinch. 'That is a little unfair, even for you.'

'Very well, then,' she said, flinging up her chin. 'I will tell you what I wanted to ask that lemonade seller, shall I? I wanted to know if women here in France really do have more freedom than the English. Because everywhere I look, there are women presiding over the cash desks of bars and businesses. Clearly the ones in charge. And it isn't just because they've had to, because the men have all gone off fighting. The men are coming back. And instead of taking over their old jobs, they're hanging around in packs, in their uniforms, letting the women carry right on running everything.'

He stroked his chin with one hand. 'I hadn't really noticed it. But you are right.'

She blinked. 'I am?'

'Don't sound so surprised. You are clearly an intelligent woman. And you are looking at this city with a woman's eyes. You are bound to see things I've missed.' When she continued to gape at him, he chuckled. 'Has nobody ever paid you a compliment before?'

'Not about my intelligence,' she said. 'Not men, anyway. Most men want a woman to stay quiet, or agree with everything they say.'

'No chance of that with you, is there?'

'Not any longer, no. Not after the way—' She bit back what she had been going to say.

'The way I let you down?'

She shook her head, frowning. 'It wasn't so

much what you did, Nathan. It was how my family treated me. I was…well, there's no point in trying to deny it, since you claim you knew how badly you hurt me. I was devastated. I needed them to comfort me, but instead they…they turned against me.'

He took her arm and started strolling towards the door. 'I'm so sorry. I wish I hadn't treated you so badly. It was inexcusable. Did I put you off men for life? Is that why you never married?'

'What makes you think I had a choice?' She didn't want to make it sound as if she'd been wearing the willow for him all these years. She had her pride.

'Because you are so beautiful,' he said bluntly. 'Men must have been queuing up to pay their addresses to you.'

She snorted in derision. 'Far from it. The only men who have ever shown an interest in me were…' She'd been about to say tempted by her aunt's money. But she didn't want to go into that. 'Let's say they were put off by the claws I've developed over the years.' She wasn't the dewy-eyed débutante she'd been when she'd gone up to London for her Season. She was as far removed from that open, trusting girl as a domestic cat was from a caged lion. She trusted nobody these days, particularly not if they wore breeches. 'When I see right through their empty compliments, they accuse me of being a harridan.'

'Perhaps not all their compliments are empty, have you ever considered that? Just because I let you down, that doesn't mean all men would.'

There were bound to be men out there, somewhere, who could match her. Who wouldn't be put off by her defensiveness.

He rubbed at his stomach, wondering at the queasy feeling that came from picturing some other man courting her, marrying her and making her happy. Instinctively he made for the open air, where he would be able to breathe more easily.

'It is nothing to do with you, whether I've married or not, you arrogant... Ooh, you make me so angry!'

'Yes, it is,' he said, stopping under the great portico and pulling her into his arms. 'Just a little bit, anyway. Admit it. I ruined you for all other men.'

'You conceited—' But he cut her words off with a kiss. A kiss that started out fiery with her rage and quickly turned heated with passion.

'Nobody else will ever kiss you like that,' he husked, drawing back just far enough that he could speak. But his lips were still so close to hers she could feel their echo. 'No other lover will ever make you feel the way I do.'

When she opened her mouth to make a pithy retort he silenced her with another kiss. A kiss that she felt right down to the core of her being. By the time he finished it, she'd forgotten what they'd been arguing about.

'I think we've done enough sightseeing for one day, don't you? Let's go back to my studio and work on your portrait.'

'In broad daylight?' He wasn't talking about painting her portrait at all.

'The light in my studio will be perfect, about now,' he said, glancing up at the sky, 'to capture...' he cupped her face with his hand, caressing her jaw as his words caressed her other senses '...all those subtle flesh tones.'

For the next few days they didn't bother with the pretence they were going to explore Paris together. Amy went to his studio at first light and let him capture her subtle flesh tones. With his hands, his mouth, and then, later, when she was too sated to bother protesting, she let him arrange her on his couch so he could paint her.

'What are you thinking?' He'd stopped working, and was looking at her steadily from round the edge of the canvas he refused to let her so much as catch a glimpse of.

'Nothing much. Nothing that would interest you, anyway.'

He pursed his lips. 'Amy, how many times do I have to tell you that every single little thing about you fascinates me?'

When she snorted in derision, he shook his head at her. 'It is true. Why would you think I'd bother to lie about it? I can still get you into bed any time I want. I only have to look at you like this...' and he waggled his eyebrows at her suggestively '...and you turn wild.'

Only a few days ago she would have been furious at the suggestion he had any influence on her, but she'd got used to his teasing ways now. Besides, he might joke that he only had to give her a heated look for her to go up in flames, but nine times out of ten she'd done something to provoke the heated look in the first place. Such as lick her lips in a certain manner, or merely twine one of her curls round and round her finger meditatively.

He came across to the couch, knelt beside it and dropped a kiss on her exposed shoulder.

'I will be able to paint a much better portrait if I know your innermost thoughts. I will be able to capture your essence. What makes you uniquely you.'

'Oh, I see, it is for your art.'

'If you like.' He buried his face in her neck to kiss her throat. And breathe her in. And commit her fragrance to memory. The more time he spent with her, the more he regretted letting her go so easily when they'd been young enough to have forged a life together. He couldn't help thinking that if he'd even had the courage of the mousy Fenella, they would have been together for ten years by now. Not that he wanted to get married again. It was just…if he had married Amy, it wouldn't have been hell, that was all. From the things she'd said, he could tell that if he'd gone into politics from choice, rather than drifting into it because he'd stopped fighting his father, and if Amy had been his wife, she would have supported his wish to make a difference. *She* wouldn't have sneered at every opinion he expressed that didn't align exactly with her own. He might even have become a halfway-decent politician. Oh, nothing to compare with a Wilberforce, or a Hunt, but a man who would have been able to look at his own reflection in the mirror without despising what he saw.

But these few days she was in Paris would be all he'd ever have of her, now. He had to make them count. He had such a short time to create a lifetime of memories.

'Well, I was thinking...'

'Yes?' He nuzzled the sheet she'd been using to preserve her modesty to one side.

'About how unfair it is.'

'What is unfair?'

She speared her fingers into his hair as he sucked one nipple into his mouth.

'That the same rules don't apply to men that so restrict women. A single man can take a lover and nobody much cares. But if a woman does so, she runs the risk of becoming a social pariah.'

He looked up at her sharply. 'Are you afraid that there will be repercussions because of our affair, Amy? We've been discreet. I've deliberately kept you out of the public eye as much as possible. Well, after the Wilsons', anyway.'

'Have you?' It hadn't occurred to her that his reluctance to leave the studio for much more than the occasional glass of beer in the nearest café, which was frequented by locals, was anything more than a wish to keep her as near to a convenient bed as possible.

'Of course I have. I have the devil of a reputation. And the last thing I want is for you to be subject to salacious gossip because you've been seen being a bit too...intimate with me.'

'You seem to forget, I am a nobody. I don't move in the kind of circles where a little gossip could ruin my reputation.'

'That's just where you're wrong,' he said fiercely. 'I mean,' he amended, reining himself back with what looked like a struggle, 'just think what it would do if tales about you having a wild affair with the scurrilous Nathan Harcourt got back to Stanton Basset. They would drum you out of the…the sewing circle.'

They could try, she thought. If she'd ever been a member of such an insipid group. But there wasn't all that much they could do. If anyone did try to make her life in Stanton Basset uncomfortable, she would just move away.

In fact, that might not be a bad idea anyway. Nothing would be the same if Fenella really did marry her middle-aged French Romeo. And it was looking increasingly likely. And she did not have any sentimental attachment to the modest house her aunt had bequeathed her, nor the quiet and rather stuffy little town itself. She could buy a much more commodious property elsewhere. Somewhere by the sea, perhaps.

Nathan startled her by getting up and stalking moodily back to his easel. Well, he'd already startled her by sounding so protective of her reputation, when he'd never given a fig for his own.

From the things she'd read about him, particularly in the last weeks before his spectacular expulsion from his party, it was almost as if he'd courted scandal for its own sake.

She would have to be careful she didn't start thinking he cared for her. Just because he hadn't seduced her when she'd been a girl, and had proposed to her when he discovered she'd been a virgin, that did not mean she was anything special to him. It only meant he had a conscience. That he wasn't the hardened rake the newspapers made him out to be.

Not that he might be falling in love with her.

She had to remember that he was a master of this game. He'd had plenty of other lovers. He was probably as charming and apparently tender with all of them. She mustn't lower her guard with him, not even for an instant. Or he would wound her. Oh, he wouldn't mean to. He clearly regretted having hurt her before. It was part of what made him so irresistible.

'You said,' came his disembodied voice from the other side of the easel, 'that your family turned against you after I...married Lucasta. Can you tell me about it?'

'Why do you want to hear about that?'

'Maybe I want absolution. You said that your reasons for not marrying were not my fault and implied other things were far more important than just my abandonment. Besides, I have this insatiable curiosity about you. I want to know every little detail of your life.'

'So you can paint a better portrait of me,' she sighed. 'Yes, you said that before.'

'You don't sound as though you believe me,' he complained. 'If it isn't for that, then what other reason could I possibly have for wanting you to divulge your innermost thoughts?'

She sighed again. 'You are in one of those moods where you won't give up, aren't you?'

He grinned at her from round the edge of the canvas. 'So, surrender. Tell me something. You will only doze off if I don't keep you talking. And I don't want to hand you a portrait of yourself snoring. It won't be flattering.'

Ah. That was a bit more believable. She could easily have dozed off, after the amount of energy they'd expended making love that morning. And at least having a conversation with him would keep her awake.

'You told me you inherited a house from some aunt,' he said. 'Which made me wonder...'

'What?'

'Well, it is a bit unusual for you to throw in your lot with a friend, rather than return to your family after her death, that's all, if marriage wasn't going to be on the cards.'

'Returning to my family was the last thing I'd ever do, after the way they treated me,' she said mutinously. 'They were so awful, when I… broke down after we parted.'

'Saying you had nothing to make a fuss about, I remember you saying so. Are they all idiots? You were obviously broken-hearted.'

She huffed out a surprised laugh. 'I can't believe you are the one person who can understand, and sympathise, when you were the cause of it all.'

'A moment ago you said I was not.'

'Don't be pedantic,' she snapped. 'You started the chain of events and you know it. Only then they were all so…righteous, and mealy-mouthed, and unkind…'

'As I said, idiots.'

'All except my Aunt Georgie. Though, to be honest, I think she may have sided with me simply to spite my father. They'd clearly been at loggerheads for most of their lives. Anyway—' she shrugged '—I went to stay with her for what was supposed to have been a short visit and ended up living there permanently. She…she was a bit of an eccentric. But we got on.'

'So, I'm guessing that staying with her, your

father's arch enemy, didn't endear you to your family?'

'You could say that. Although, to be fair, when Aunt Georgie died, my father did come to the funeral holding out an olive branch. Of sorts.' She sighed. 'He said that in spite of my refusal to show any penitence over our estrangement, he was prepared to take me back into his home and care for me.'

'Oh...oh dear.'

'Are you laughing?' It was infuriating not being able to see his face, but there was a definite trace of amusement in his voice.

'Not exactly. I was just picturing your reaction when he more or less ordered you to surrender, since he thought you had no option.'

'Not only that,' she said indignantly, 'he tried to make sure I *had* no options. As soon as he found out Aunt Georgie had left everything to me, he tried to overturn the will. He told me, in the presence of a lawyer, that since I was merely a woman it would be much safer if he was to handle it all for me.'

Her father had been stunned to discover how much Amethyst was suddenly worth. He'd only been aware that his sister owned a house and a modest amount of capital. He'd assumed that because she lived so modestly, she was just eking out an existence on the interest. Instead she'd invested it in all sorts of ventures that, had he known how risky some of them had been, would have turned his hair white.

'Had he held the position of trustee for his sister, then?'

'No! Which was what made it all so…'

'Humiliating? Infuriating? Unfair?'

'All of those things. But why is it that you seem to be able to understand exactly how I felt?'

'Well, my own father placed no confidence in my judgement, either. Even though I *am* male. Which is possibly even more humiliating, infuriating and unfair.'

'So…you do not blame me for refusing to beg forgiveness and surrender my independence?'

'How could I? Have I not done the very same thing?'

'You mentioned, at the Wilsons', that your father has…'

'Washed his hands of me, yes.'

'But what of your brothers? Do you have any contact with them?'

'Not really. They are all very successful in their own professions and don't want to risk ruining their reputations by being too involved with the black sheep of the family.'

'Same here…' she sighed '…with my sisters. I got invitations to their weddings, but they were too scared of what my father would say to come anywhere near me. It's as if I don't exist for them any more.'

Her only value for them, she'd discovered, was her wealth. Not one of them had contacted her, in all the years she'd lived with Aunt Georgie. It was only after her father had discovered how much wealth she'd inherited that Pearl wrote, telling her that she'd just given birth to a boy, and would be honoured if Amethyst would consent to be his godmother.

She'd very nearly thrown the letter in the fire. It was obvious that having a wealthy godmother far outweighed the risk of drawing down the wrath of an impecunious country parson. If she became Pip's godmother, they would feel entitled to ask her for help with his education and sponsorship in his chosen career. Perhaps even make him her heir, since by then her father would have told them she'd become as confirmed a man-hater as Aunt Georgie and would therefore never marry and have children of her own.

No wonder Aunt Georgie had gone to such lengths to conceal the extent of her wealth from absolutely everyone.

Fortunately, Fenella had pointed out that even if it was from mercenary reasons, at least one of her family had made contact. And that she would regret it, once her anger cooled, if she hadn't taken the opportunity to mend fences.

'So…what will you do if Fenella does marry her French Count?'

She rubbed at her forehead with one forefinger. 'I will have to find someone else to come and live with me, of course, to give me a veneer of respectability. In a way, it won't be all that hard, since I dare say there are any number of single, educated ladies in dire straits. Except… well, none of them would be Fenella. And I will miss Sophie quite desperately.'

'Or,' he said casually, 'you could do something utterly radical. You could marry me. Take me home to live with you.'

'What?' She couldn't believe he'd repeated that idiotic proposal he'd made the first time they'd made love. They were different people now, couldn't he see that? They couldn't go back in time and recapture the youthful feelings they'd had before they'd both had to grow up.

Not that he'd ever mentioned wanting to recapture those feelings. He'd admitted he had been in love with her and wanted to marry her, then. But of how he felt today? He'd said nothing.

So she feigned a laugh. 'Oh, yes, very funny. The answer to all my problems.'

'Well, not all, but possibly some, don't you think? I don't like the thought of you having to live all on your own. Or having to hire a stranger to live with you, for the sake of propriety. It is one thing to invite a widowed friend to live with you, but quite another to have to deliberately hire someone to stay in your home.'

'Well, bringing you home from Paris to live with me, like some…overlarge souvenir is certainly not going to answer. Certainly not the part about propriety, anyway. I can just see the stir it would create, amongst the ladies of Stanton Basset, to have a disgraced politician of your notoriety come live among them. The resulting panic would be akin to shutting a fox up in the henhouse.'

He went very quiet. And still. He wasn't even dabbing paint at the canvas any more, just standing there.

'Nathan?' She sat up and tried to peer at him round the canvas. He was staring at the painting, his jaw hard, his lips compressed into a thin line.

'You were joking, weren't you? A man like you…well, you don't really want to marry anyone, do you? Certainly not to save her from facing loneliness.'

'And you are certainly not that desperate, are you?' he said.

No, she wasn't. But then she looked about the dingy rooms and wondered if perhaps he was. He didn't seem to know exactly how much she was worth, but it was highly suspicious that he'd made that casual proposal just after she'd told him she had a house and admitted to an income of sorts. He would have a roof over his head, guaranteed. And if the sum total of his ambition was to spend the rest of his days messing about with paints...

She shivered.

'You are cold,' he said, flinging his brush aside and coming across the room to drape a blanket over her. 'I'm sorry. I know these rooms are a touch basic, but the light up here is so superb, during the day, that I didn't care about that when I rented them,' he said ruefully.

'Of course,' she said with a tight smile, though if he thought to fool her into believing he was living like this by choice then he'd seriously underestimated her intelligence.

If he was angling for a wife to provide for him, he wasn't going to admit it straight out, was he? And even if he wasn't deliberately trying to deceive her, he was just typical of his class, who refused to admit they were in want. They'd leave bills unpaid, even flee lodgings at dead of night, rather than openly admit their finances weren't in order.

She pulled the quilt up to her chin, but the cold feeling in her stomach wouldn't go away.

'I think it is time I left,' she said in a small voice that didn't sound a bit like her.

'Why? You cannot want to go back to your apartments and have to watch Fenella and Gaston billing and cooing all day, can you?'

'No, but...well, I have to go back some time, don't I? I cannot simply move in with you just because the way they carry on is making me a bit uncomfortable.'

'I wouldn't mind if you did,' he said. 'Though I could wish the place was a bit more comfortable, for your sake.'

That was even worse than proposing marriage. Though it dealt with his earlier assertion that he was being careful of her reputation. A man didn't ask a woman to be his mistress if he really cared about her, did he?

'Hmmph,' she said and stalked to the bedroom to retrieve her clothes. A wave of sadness washed over her as she was pulling her crumpled chemise over her head. If they'd married ten years ago, she was sure they would have been happy. She hadn't any ambitions beyond the kind of life he'd described, after all. She certainly wouldn't have minded him filling up his leisure hours with painting. It was clearly a very large part of who he was. And she would have wanted him to be happy.

But as she swiftly donned the rest of her clothes, she reminded herself that the years had changed them both. She wouldn't be content nowadays to live in some cottage, doing nothing more than raising *a pack of children* and seeing to a man's domestic comforts.

And he'd got used to sampling a different woman whenever the fancy took him. Why, he'd thought nothing of asking her to move in with him, so lax had his morality become.

He didn't really want to marry her.

Any more than she wanted to marry him.

They'd had their chance, ten years ago. And lost it.

By the time she'd tidied her hair in the mirror, and felt ready to leave the room and face him, she'd drawn right back into the crusty cocoon that had kept her heart safe for so many years. Even the grin he sent flashing her way could not pierce it. It just reminded her that Nathan was dangerous.

Because when he smiled at her like that, he could make her say yes to almost anything.

Chapter Eleven

Nathan flung his brush down and plunged his fingers through his hair. Oh, there was nothing wrong with the portrait itself. It was undoubtedly the best work he'd ever done. The trouble was that it was almost finished. Just like his affair with Amy. Only a few more days and she would be leaving Paris, going back to England. And he was going to lose her all over again. And this time it was going to be far worse, because this time round it wasn't all vague dreams of a possible future he would lose. This time he knew exactly what he'd be missing.

Because he'd gone and fallen in love with her, all over again, prickly as she was. He understood why she'd become so defensive. Life had dealt them both some hard knocks, which only made them more compatible, if anything, than they'd been as youngsters. He wouldn't be interested in some shy, naïve young vicar's daughter, straight from the country—not any longer. Tainted by his years in politics, corrupted by the sordid means he'd sunk to in order to obtain his freedom, he'd find such a girl insipid.

But this older, more experienced Amy, the cynical wary woman she'd become, matched him just as he was now. He wouldn't change a thing about her. Not one thing.

Except her opinion of him.

Moodily he stared at her image, staring back at him from the canvas. He'd caught a look in her eyes that...

He flung himself away from the stool and strode to the window. He'd painted her as he wanted her to look at him, that's what he'd done. With love in her eyes, longing expressed in every line of that sleek, lush body.

Which was the height of absurdity. She might enjoy seeing the sights of Paris with him. Might enjoy casting off the restraints imposed on single women, to indulge in this passionate affair. But once it was time to leave, he didn't fool himself that she was going to experience much more than a tiny pang of regret. She would be sorry to have to return to a life of dull respectability, but would she be sorry to bid him farewell?

He didn't think so.

She'd told him at the outset all she wanted

was a fling. And he'd thought he'd be content
with that. He'd certainly never thought he'd contemplate marrying anyone, ever again. And yet
when she'd turned down his guilt-induced, sac-
rificial proposal, he hadn't felt so much relieved
as…a bit insulted. And as the days had passed
he'd begun to find the thought of her being with
anyone else unpalatable. At about the same rate
he'd seen that being married to her wouldn't have
been the ordeal it had been with Lucasta.

And now…well, now he wanted her so desperately, he couldn't stand the thought of her leaving. He leaned his forehead on a pane of glass
and gazed out blindly over the rooftops of the
city he'd started to think he could call home. It
wouldn't feel like home once she'd gone. It would
just be one more cold, inhospitable place where
he would be merely existing.

So what was he to do? Just let her walk away?
Or risk all on one last desperate throw of the
dice?

He was definitely going to lose her if he did
nothing.

But if he stood any chance at having a future
with her, he'd have to tell her everything. He
squeezed his eyes shut as panic clawed at his
stomach. She'd been incensed with the citizens
of Stanton Basset for listening to and believ-

ing unsubstantiated rumours about her friend Fenella being an unmarried mother. How much more angry would she be with him, when he told her he'd believed pretty much the same of her?

And then there was her attitude towards his reputation. She'd made it plain she thought he was the kind of man who would take any woman to bed, under any pretext. He hadn't yet found a suitable opportunity to explain the bitter battle he'd ended up fighting with his father, or how he'd seen that only by taking the most drastic measures would he ever win his freedom. Once or twice he'd very nearly confided in her when she'd told him things about her past that echoed his own battles for independence.

But at the last moment his courage had always failed him. Given all that he'd done, all that he'd become, it was a miracle he'd managed to get even this close to her. He didn't deserve her, not one bit. His father was right about him. Had been right all along. He was no good.

So he'd kept quiet and kept on taking what crumbs she was prepared to throw him. At least for the moment she was sharing his bed. Enjoying his company. But once she knew the depths of him, he'd forfeit even that.

He ran his fingers through his hair again as he reached his decision. It was time he owned up. It might make her hate him, but that would only

be what he deserved. Punishment. For not standing by her. A lifetime of knowing she despised
him would be a just sentence, wouldn't it? For
betraying her. For betraying their fledgling love.

He owed her the truth, so that she could understand what had happened, even if he lost her
because of it. Well, he was going to lose her
anyway, wasn't he? She was leaving. And she'd
made it crystal clear she didn't want him cluttering up her tidy, respectable existence by going
with her.

He drew in a deep, shuddering breath and let
his hands fall back to his sides.

Nothing he'd done so far had helped him to
breach those invisible, but very tangible walls
behind which she hid. So what did he have to
lose?

Perhaps it would take the shock of hearing
what had really gone wrong between them, ten
years ago, to bring them tumbling down. It had,
after all, taken the shock of discovering the truth
to jolt him out of his own emotional prison cell.
And it was beginning to look as though nothing
less would set her free, either.

Amethyst had just picked up her bonnet, a
frivolous article she'd bought from a milliner
who catered to the needs of tourists, rather than

Parisians, when there came a timid knock on her door.

Fenella peeped round it. 'Oh, you are…going out,' she said as Amethyst set the confection of straw, lace and silk flowers at a jaunty angle on her head.

They had not seen all that much of each other since the day of the trip to the Bois de Boulogne. Though Amethyst had made a point of seeing Sophie every day to hear what she'd been doing, she'd deliberately avoided spending time with Fenella alone. And up till now, Fenella had done much the same.

They were both tiptoeing round the fact that though Fenella and Gaston were courting, Amethyst was just having an affair. If they talked in private, one of them might speak rather too frankly.

'With…with *him*, I suppose.' Fenella's face creased into anxious lines.

'Yes, with him,' Amethyst agreed calmly, tying the ribbons under her left ear in a manner that looked positively flirtatious.

'I…I know that you say it is better not to be seen about with Gaston and me, in case someone you want to do a deal with recognises you and starts to ask awkward questions, but…' She tiptoed into the room and shut the door behind her.

Amethyst sighed. Fenella had apparently decided that she wasn't going to avoid speaking frankly any longer.

'I cannot help worrying,' she said, clasping her hands at her waist, 'about the amount of time you spend closeted with Mr Harcourt in his lodgings. And I know that it must sound a bit hypocritical of me, given the way I have behaved with my Gaston, but I fear that...' she took a deep breath and plunged in '...I fear that Mr Harcourt's intentions are not honourable.'

'Well, of course they are not honourable.' Amethyst would have spared Fenella's sensibilities if she'd just carried on pretending she didn't know what was going on. But since Fenella had broached the topic, she wasn't going to be mealy-mouthed about it.

'That was the whole reason for choosing him to become my lover. You know I have no intention of ever getting married.'

'Oh, dear. Oh, dear.' Fenella tottered to the nearest chair and sank down onto it. 'Your...your lover.' She clenched her hands together again so tightly the knuckles went white. 'I blame myself. I have been so caught up with Gaston that I have completely failed to do my duty by you as chaperon.'

'Nonsense.'

'No, it is not nonsense. I have set you a bad

example by allowing my feelings for Gaston to—' She broke off, going pink in the face. 'If ever word of this got out in Stanton Basset, you would be quite ruined. Why, even if people only heard that you have been going all over Paris with a man of *his* reputation, there would be no end of talk. And I...I really don't want you to have to suffer as I did. Even though I was still a completely respectable widow, then, they had no mercy. It will be worse for you, a single lady, if once they get a hint of...of this.'

'Do you know, I don't really care if my reputation does get a bit tarnished,' she replied, pulling on her gloves. 'If I was a young girl looking for a husband, or even a poor person, dependent on the goodwill of others, I might pay more heed to what other people may say of me, or think of me. Besides, you, of all people, must know how good it can make you feel to have an attractive...' She swallowed on the word, as an image of Monsieur Le Brun's sallow face swam into her mind. Well, there were obviously different kinds of attractive. Fenella saw something beneath the unprepossessing exterior Monsieur Le Brun presented to the world which *she* found attractive. 'An attractive man,' she repeated, 'paying me so much attention. I am enjoying having my portrait painted and I am enjoying going out with a man with no sense of decorum whatsoever. He makes me feel…' She paused. She had been about to say he made her feel like a girl again, but on looking back, she rather thought she'd been a bit priggish as a girl. It hadn't been until she'd met Nathan for the first time that she'd discovered she even had a sense of humour. And she'd never just had fun, the way she had fun with Nathan. He'd introduced her to a whole new world of experience and not just in bed.

They'd talked and talked, as she'd never talked to anyone before. He was genuinely interested in her opinions. He didn't always agree with them and sometimes their discussions grew quite heated. But he never seemed to think less of her for disagreeing with him. In fact, if she grew too angry, he would get a wicked gleam in his eyes and tell her she was at her most alluring when she got angry, and then defuse all her irritation by flinging down his brushes, stalking to the couch on which she lay and making her come, over and over again, until she lay limp and sated in his arms. And had totally forgotten whatever it was they'd been arguing about.

'For so long,' she said to Fenella, 'I have felt that I have no appeal as a woman whatsoever. And now the most experienced rake in two countries is hanging on my sleeve.'

Not trying to change her, or form her opinions, or punishing her for disagreeing with him, but allowing her, for the first time in her life, to be herself.

'Do you think worrying about what people might say, if they were to find out, is going to prevent me from making the most of it, while it lasts?'

'No. I suppose not. But…you will be careful, won't you? I don't want you to get hurt.'

She spun round, on the verge of asking Fenella what she thought it was going to do to her when she left her to marry her French Count, and took Sophie away, if not wound her to the core? Sophie had become almost like a daughter to her, while she'd never had a friend as close as Fenella. If Fenella really didn't want her to be hurt, she wouldn't be obliging her to return to Stanton Bassett and bear the brunt of all the talk there would be, and suffer the pitying looks, the moralising and the unsolicited advice—alone.

But she bit her tongue. She mustn't let self-pity or jealousy ruin what they could salvage of their friendship.

Jealousy? She couldn't possibly be jealous of Fenella, having Gaston, could she? No the notion was absurd. She didn't want a husband. She didn't want any man to have the power over her that a husband would have, by law.

'Thank you Fenella, for your concern,' she

said stiffly. 'But I can assure you that I have no intention of getting hurt. This is the man who led me on, then changed his mind once before, don't forget. I know not to trust a single word that comes out of his mouth.'

She'd taken great care not to let Nathan touch her heart. Her body, yes, and her mind. She'd found it liberating to be free with both. But she'd kept her heart safely encased in a block of ice which no amount of passion, no matter how hot, could melt.

'Oh, dear,' Fenella said again. 'That sounds so very...' She shook her head. 'So very sad. To have no hope that things might develop...'

'It is not the least bit sad. It is practical. I am not going to marry some man and let him wrest control of my life from me.'

'Marriage is not like that. I'm sure Gaston will never attempt to *control* me.'

'And has he informed you yet where he plans to set up home, once you are married?'

Fenella flushed and her face fell. 'Actually, he has. He has a little property near Southampton which he says will suit me and Sophie very nicely.'

'Southampton! The opposite end of the country from Stanton Basset. About as far away from me as he can take you.'

'It isn't deliberate. It isn't as if he bought the place on purpose to keep us apart. He knew nothing about either of us when he bought it.'

Amethyst drew a deep breath. 'I will make quite certain he does not keep us apart,' she said grimly. 'I had already toyed with the idea of moving away from Stanton Basset. After this trip, going back there would feel like going back to a cage. So I had thought about taking a place by the seaside. Southampton will be as good a location as anywhere.'

It eased all the hurt of hearing Fenella was going to live on the south coast when her face lit up.

'Oh, that will be wonderful. I was a little worried,' she admitted, 'about how I would cope in a new town, all on my own. Because Gaston is going to be away quite a lot.'

'Is he?'

'Well, yes. He's…he's hoping to continue working as a courier for English tourists. So he can return to France again and again, until the matter of his estates is settled. You will give him a good reference, won't you?'

'Is that why he sent you to speak to me this morning?' A cold sliver of uncertainty snaked through her middle.

'Oh, no! He is convinced that you hate him. He is even a bit worried you might try to take some form of revenge on him for stealing me away from you.'

'But you don't?'

Fenella laughed. 'Of course not! I know you better than that. You haven't a vengeful bone in your body. You are all that is good,' she said, pressing Amethyst's hand affectionately. 'Otherwise you couldn't have let that man…Mr Harcourt…back into your life, could you?'

All of a sudden Amethyst felt like crying. Fenella's faith in her was so touching. She was the one person who always chose to see some good in her, even when everyone else chose to think the worst.

She delved into her reticule for a handkerchief and blew her nose.

'I suppose I shouldn't mention him, should I?' said Fenella. 'It must be so difficult for you, having to bid him farewell and never be able to hope you will see him again.'

It was going to be a wrench, she couldn't deny it. Nathan had made her feel…so alive.

'I will always have the portrait to remind me of this time, though,' she said, putting her hanky away.

'You mean there really is a portrait?'

'Yes. I'm going to view it today. And I'm going to buy it,' she said decisively, 'even if it is a bit of a daub.'

'That is so like you,' said Fenella, almost worshipfully.

'Fustian! I won't be doing it for him.' Though she'd already decided she would find something complimentary to say about it, because he cared so greatly about his art. More than he cared about anything else in his life, if she'd read him aright. He'd told her, rather wistfully, when they'd first known each other, that he wished being a painter was an acceptable profession for a gentleman. But it wasn't until these last few weeks that she'd realised that it was all he'd ever really wanted to do with his life. And now that his brief career as a politician had ensured nobody could possibly think of him as a gentleman any more, he was finally free to live the life he'd always dreamed of.

No, after all he'd done for her these past weeks, the way he'd made her feel, she wasn't going to be the one to tell him he didn't have the talent, if that was the case.

'It is just that the painting is a bit, shall we say, *risqué*. I have to ensure that it cannot fall into the wrong hands.'

'Oh, my word. Did he paint you...?'

'Without benefit of clothing, yes,' she said, checking her appearance in the mirror one last time. 'I shall most probably have to shroud it in holland covers and hide it away in the attics.'

She walked briskly to the door. 'I hope you and Sophie enjoy your day. I shall see you... later.' And with that, she left.

She was glad she'd gone prepared to speak with tact, rather than total honesty, when she saw how on edge Nathan appeared the moment he opened the door to her.

As she followed him through to the studio, she wondered at her decision to keep the painting, rather than simply burn it the moment she had the freedom to do so. She wasn't normally prone to making decisions based on sentiment.

Although...it would be pleasant to have a tangible reminder of this heady month, spent in a foreign country, in a handsome man's arms. When she was old and grey, she could creep up to the attic, pull off the covers and warm herself at the memory of having, for one month of her life at least, had a man who found everything about her utterly feminine, and deliciously desirable, to boot. Or even before then. Whenever her father made one of his sporadic attempts to assert his will, she could remind herself that she'd been right and he'd been wrong about Nathan's intentions. And by extension, everything else about her.

That wasn't being sentimental. It was…providing herself with armour against the life she was going to have to live once Fenella left and she stood alone against a harsh, judgemental world.

Nathan paused in the doorway to the studio for a moment or two, before stepping aside and letting her enter. Before he let her see the finished portrait, which he'd turned on its easel to face the door.

'Oh,' she said, coming to an abrupt halt as the full impact of it hit her squarely in the chest.

Not that it was dreadful. She didn't know why she'd ever thought it might be, given the skill he'd demonstrated when producing those swift pencil sketches. There was no problem with perspective, or the way the light shone on the drapery which made it look as though it flowed over her body, or anything like that. There was no mistaking that the woman in the picture was her, either.

Nevertheless, this painting was most definitely going to be consigned to the attics. She couldn't possibly risk letting anyone see her portrayed like this. And it wasn't just because he'd depicted her reclining on a couch, strategic folds of linen preserving her modesty, whilst advertising the fact that she was naked beneath it. It was the expression on her face that she daren't let anyone ever see. He'd made her look like... like a woman in love. She was gazing out of the canvas as though she adored the man who was painting her. He'd made her look... She swallowed back something that felt very like tears. Younger. Less cynical. Vulnerable, even.

Yes, that was what she objected to. She didn't mind a reminder that she was capable of being feminine, but he'd gone too far. There was not a trace of the hardheaded businesswoman she'd become. Let alone the rebellious daughter, who was the despair of her father, or the shrew from whom Monsieur Le Brun had thought he needed to protect his gentle, ladylike Fenella.

'You don't like it.' His voice was flat.

She shook her head. 'Nathan, you have real talent. I can see that. You have made me look... beautiful. Which is very flattering. But it is not me, that woman there. It makes me feel as though you don't really know me. Or as though you have been looking at me through a...through a prism.'

'That is the most perceptive thing I have ever heard you say.' He turned her round when she couldn't tear her eyes from the vision of womanly submission on the canvas, obliging her to look directly into his face. 'In a way, I have been looking at you through a kind of prism. I have been looking at you through the eyes of a man in love. Desperately in love.'

Something coiled in her stomach and slithered its way up her spine. The hairs on the back of her neck stood on end.

There was only one thing that could account for him saying such a thing. Somehow he must have found out how wealthy she was.

'Love?' She shook her head. 'Do you take me for some kind of fool? You don't love me. You don't even know me,' she cried, waving her hand at the portrait of a woman who was a far cry from the person she knew herself to be.

'But I do know you, Amy. I know better than anyone else how badly you were hurt as a girl and that it made you close yourself off from the possibility of ever getting hurt again. I understand why you have become a cynic. I also know you don't want to hear what I'm going to say next, but I'm going to say it anyway. I don't know what I'm going to do with myself when you leave here and return to England. I can't bear to lose you again. Marry me, Amy.' He went down on his knees. 'Please. I asked you before if I could come back to England with you because

I couldn't bear the thought of you being lonely. But now I can't bear the thought of you finding someone to save you from that loneliness, if that someone isn't me.'

She drew back.

'I am not going to be taken in by you,' she hissed. 'I won't let you deceive me. You chose your last wife for what you could gain and I—'

'No! That is not true.' He got up. 'I'm not going to let you believe that lie for one second longer.' He clenched his fists. 'I did not marry my first wife for gain.' His face leached of colour. 'I married her to wound you.'

'You…what? But why? Why would you want to wound me?'

'I was deeply in love with you, Amy. Well,' he hedged, 'as deeply as a boy of that age could be. I've already told you that I wanted to marry you. I confided as much to one or two people, one night, at one of my clubs. They'd been teasing me about what a stranger I was becoming there and how I seemed to be spending all my time mixing with, forgive me for repeating their words, but they described your set as the shabby-genteel.'

She flushed. It was true that he'd seemed out of place at most of the gatherings she'd attended. That she'd always known he was way above her own more humble station. But that was no excuse for doing what he'd done.

'You stopped courting me because your friends teased you about marrying below your station?'

'No! How could you even think I'd do something so…shallow?' He turned away, took a few paces away from her, then turned back, his face implacable. 'I'm just trying to help you see how it must have all come about. I paid no attention to the teasing, knowing it was nothing compared with the opposition I'd have to face from my father. And probably yours. I was plucking up the courage to approach him and ask for your hand in form, knowing that I had little to recommend me. If I could get him to look favourably on my suit, I would have been more than capable of braving my own father's displeasure. I had reached a crossroads in my life. I'd always been something of a disappointment to him, whereas my brothers had all made him proud. So I stopped asking his permission to travel to Italy to study art. I'd agreed to spend that Season in London considering professions he deemed suitable for a man of my background. And then I met you. And—'

He broke off, paced away, paced back again.

'Well, before I got round to approaching either

of them, one of my friends told me he'd heard something that made it impossible for him to stand back and let me throw myself away on you.'

He was shaking, she noted with surprise. Actually trembling. He licked his lips, with what looked like nervousness, before saying, 'He told me that he'd heard, from a reliable source, that you were no innocent. That you'd actually borne a child out of wedlock and had come up to town for the sole purpose of luring some poor unsuspecting male into the trap of providing for you and your child. Preferably a man with a title, a man powerful enough to protect you from the scandal.'

She gasped. 'But that's absurd! You know it is. Why, I was a virgin when we...'

The edges of the room seemed to blur and darken. There was a roaring sound in her ears as her mind flew back to his shock, the night he'd first taken her to bed. How his attitude towards her had gone from scornful and aggressive to remorseful and caring.

'You believed it,' she whispered. 'You believed I would be that wicked.' Now her own legs were shaking. For a moment, she wondered if she was going to faint. But then fury surged through her veins, giving her strength to stand

and speak her mind, instead of crumpling under the weight of hurt and shock.

'You didn't even demand proof from this so-called friend of yours. You couldn't have done. You didn't confront me with the tale either. You just...you just spurned me!' Why had everyone, at that period in her life, been so ready to assume the worst of her?

'I was devastated, Amy. I was so angry and hurt to think you could deliberately set out to deceive me that I lost my head.'

'Because you believed it. How could you?'

'Because Fielding, the friend who plucked up the courage to come to me with the tale, had been well chosen,' he said bitterly. 'He was the one friend I had who I knew would never tell a deliberate lie. He was not only too honest, but also not bright enough to spin any kind of yarn. He'd never have been able to keep all the threads straight. And he was torn, Amy. He hated having to speak ill of a lady. He only did so because he was convinced someone had to do something to save me from the clutches of an ambitious schemer.' He huffed out a strange, bitter laugh. 'That was what made him so convincing. The fact that he believed it so completely. The poor sap was such a slow-top that he couldn't imagine anyone inventing a deliberate lie about a lady.

He was so gullible he genuinely believed that if my father had breached the gentleman's code by repeating such a foul tale about a lady, it could only have been from the best of intentions.'

'You have a nerve to describe him as a slow-top,' she breathed. 'You fell for exactly the same lie he did.'

'Did I? I'm not so certain any more. Deep down I think I always knew my father was behind it. I knew what my father was like. I should have known he would thrust a spoke in my wheel, if he were to discover I'd decided to marry you, rather than tamely submit to the plans he'd started making for me. He must have been livid when his spies brought back tales of me planning to marry a nobody, and settle down in obscurity, just as he thought he'd finally got me to knuckle under. And even if it wasn't true, about you...but I told myself it must be. It made sense, you see.'

'What do you mean? How could it make sense? What had I ever done to make you think I was...that kind of woman?'

'You'd appeared to fall for me practically at first sight,' he said bleakly. 'When everyone else knew there was nothing special about me. I was only the youngest son of four. The runt of the litter. The one with no ambition. The one whose only talent was for drawing, a subject more suited to women than to real men.'

'That's utter nonsense.'

'It was what I felt, at the time. That you couldn't possibly have seen anything in me to admire, apart from my susceptibility to your charms. I could believe you might have seen me as a pigeon ripe for plucking. And then there was the matter of your behaviour.' The corners of his mouth pulled into something very like a sneer. 'You were the daughter of a vicar. At first you seemed so prim and proper, but in no time at all you were letting me lure you into secluded places. Nay, you encouraged me to lure you into secluded places so that I could kiss you, Amy. So you could set my blood on fire. And I was always the one to call a halt. I got the feeling you would have let me do whatever I wanted...'

Yes, she would have done. Because she'd loved him. Loved him! And all the time...

Something inside her snapped. She flew at him, pounding at his chest with her fists. He grabbed her wrists to hold her at a distance, which so infuriated her she kicked out at his legs, twisting and hissing like a cat.

But Nathan was far stronger than her. He just held her at arm's length until, exhausted, she would have collapsed into a sobbing heap at his feet if he hadn't scooped her up into his arms and carried her to the sofa where he cradled her on his lap, rocking her as she carried on weeping.

'I hate you,' she said, when she could at last find the breath, and the control, to form words.

'It's no more than I deserve.'

'You…you…destroyed me…'

'My father destroyed us both. The last ten years have been sheer hell, Amy—'

'No. *You* destroyed us. You had no faith in me. Not even when we met again. You deliberately seduced me, for…for revenge, I suppose.'

'Yes.' There was no point in denying it. That was exactly what he'd done. 'At first, I did want revenge. Until I discovered the truth. And then all I felt was remorse. I wanted to make reparation for all the misery I caused you. I wanted to wipe out the misery by making you happy instead. By giving you one perfect month. A month where you had all you'd ever wanted. But somewhere along the way I fell in love with you all over again.'

'You don't love me. You never loved me. You couldn't, to have believed such foul lies.'

'I did love you, Amy. Not enough, it is true. But I love you more now. For knowing that you were innocent. For growing into the woman you are now. Strong, and independent, and wary, and fiery…'

'You don't know me any better now than you knew me then,' she cried, wriggling off his lap. 'Not if you think I'm going to have anything to do with you ever again, after learning what you did to me.'

'Amy, please…'

He reached for her, but she darted away from him, towards the door.

'Don't leave like this,' he begged her. 'Not while you are so upset. You shouldn't be alone…'

'I have been alone,' she breathed, 'for the last ten years.' She dashed a tear from her cheek with an angry swipe of her hand. 'And alone is exactly how I like it. If you don't let anyone near you, then nobody can hurt you.'

'That's true. But it's going to be a lonely life, if you cling to that belief and never let anyone near.'

'No. It won't be. Lonely is when you are surrounded by people who betray you. And despise you. And only pay you attention when they want something. *That* is loneliness.'

She flew to the door and ran out.

Oh, God, she was so angry she couldn't see straight. He should know. He'd been in just such a fury on the night Fielding destroyed his hope in the possibility of marrying for love. So he plunged straight after her. He couldn't bear it if some harm befell her on the crowded streets.

He didn't try to stop her, for he knew she was in no fit state to listen to reason. He just kept her in his sights, ready to intervene should she run into danger, until he'd seen her reach her lodgings safely. And then he went to find her friend, and her French lover, to tell them that she needed them. She wouldn't tolerate him anywhere near, for a while, but she must not be alone.

Eventually, the first flood of her anger would recede, and then, by hook or by crook, he would make her listen to him again.

That was the one advantage he had now, which she had lacked the last time this same lie had driven them apart. She'd had no weapons with which to defend herself. No idea she'd even needed to prove her innocence. She'd been completely in the dark.

But this time, they both knew exactly where they stood. And he wasn't going to give her up without a fight. He was no longer an insecure youth, torn between staying loyal to his family and taking a chance on love. He was a man now. A man who'd learned that love was worth fighting for.

Whatever it took. No matter how long it took.

Chapter Twelve

She had to get the portrait from him.

She couldn't believe, now, that she'd been stupid enough to pose for it. Naked. She pressed her hands to her cheeks, which were burning with mortification.

If he was desperate enough for security to ask her to marry him, he'd have no compunction about selling it if she left it behind in Paris. Or deliberately displaying it somewhere if he decided to take a more humiliating revenge for her refusal. He had a reputation for not being particularly kind to former lovers. And she had turned him down in the most insulting terms. She'd called him a slow-top, she'd accused him of being shallow and marrying his first wife for her money, of being faithless and worthless and she didn't know what else.

Oh, yes. She'd told him she hated him, and

then, when ten years of repressed rage had swelled up, the dam had burst and she'd physically attacked him.

Not that he didn't deserve every name she'd called him, but it hadn't been a wise move to make an enemy of him all over again. Only look what lengths he'd gone to the last time, when he'd only *thought* she'd betrayed him. He'd coldly, deliberately done the very worst thing he could have done to her. He'd flaunted another woman—a rich, titled woman—in her face. Even gone so far as to marry her to make doubly sure he inflicted the maximum hurt he possibly could.

Not only that, but he'd held on to his anger for ten years. He'd admitted he started up their affair because he wanted revenge.

No. Nathan Harcourt wasn't a man to cross with impunity. He'd get his own back on her somehow.

Well then. Her mouth compressed into a hard line. She'd just have to force herself to go and see him, one last time, before she left Paris. Offer him whatever he wanted to release the portrait to her.

Any sum of money, that was, no matter how steep. She would pay it.

And if his demands were not of the financial kind?

Well, he would be wasting his time trying to blackmail her into anything other than monetary payment. Marry him she would not. Nor let him touch her again.

Anything but that!

She'd just risen from her chair to get ready to go and tell him so when Fenella knocked timidly on her door.

'I know you said you wanted to be alone this morning, but I thought I'd better let you know... that is...he's here. Mr Harcourt.'

Amethyst dropped back down into her chair.

'I tried to turn him away,' Fenella continued apologetically, 'but he's most insistent...'

She'd just bet he was. He'd already worked out that he had a valuable bargaining chip in that portrait and was clearly determined to start negotiations for it before she left.

Her fingers clawed round the arms of her chair

'Show him in.'

'Are you sure?'

'Quite sure. His visit has saved me the bother of going out and seeing him, actually, which I had planned to do later on. He and I have a few matters we need to settle before I leave France. Private matters,' she added, giving Fenella a stern look that sent her scuttling away just like the mouse Nathan had so disparagingly likened her to.

She took a deep breath as soon as the door shut behind her companion, suddenly wishing she'd taken a bit of care over her appearance when Fenella had persuaded her to roll out of bed this morning. She hadn't bothered looking in a mirror, but since she'd scarcely slept last night, and spent most of the day before weeping, she must look a fright. Had she even brushed her hair? She raised a shaky hand to her head and confirmed her suspicion that she had not, when they met with a riot of tangled curls.

She let her hand drop to her lap where she clenched it into an impotent fist. She should have told Fenella to make him wait while she tidied herself up. She didn't want to give him the satisfaction of seeing how low he'd managed to bring her.

For the second time in her life.

But it was too late to do so much as reach for a comb. There was a scuffling sound from just outside the door, then it swung open and Nathan slid in sideways, his movements hampered by a huge, square package done up in brown paper.

A package that was the exact size of the portrait.

She shot to her feet. 'Is that what I think it is?'

He propped up the package against the wall to the right of the door before looking her way. He seemed tense, but defiant, turning his hat round and round in his hands.

'Thank you for agreeing to see me,' he began.

'Never mind all that.' She made a dismissive gesture with her hand as she strode across to what might be her portrait.

'I was hoping you would want to keep it,' he said. 'So I took the chance that it might be my ticket in to see you.'

She shot him just one suspiciously wary glance before tearing at the wrapping with her fingers to find out exactly what it was he'd brought with him. Who knew what kind of trick he might be trying to play on her? She cursed under her breath when she broke a fingernail. Where were the scissors when she needed them?

'Here,' he said, handing her a pocketknife.

She took it from him with an indefinable noise, halfway between the words thank you and a snarl, and severed the string.

It was the picture. Of her. Half-naked and looking at the artist as though she wanted to devour him.

With a shiver, she twitched the slashed wrappings back in place, then dragged the whole

thing across the room and tucked it safely behind a sofa.

'You may be able to hide that away,' he observed, 'but you can't hide from what has passed
between us this past month.'

'Can you blame me for wanting to?'

'Not if this was just some tawdry affair, no.
But it is so much more. I've asked you to marry
me, Amy—'

'And I have said no.'

'You said it when you were angry with me
for discovering what an idiot I'd been before.'
The corners of his mouth tilted into a rueful, yet
hopeful smile. 'I was hoping your temper might
have cooled somewhat since then.'

'Oh, I'm perfectly cool today,' she assured
him haughtily. 'You might say, to the point of
chilliness. Why, towards you, I feel…positively
frigid.'

'Do you, though?'

He tossed the hat aside, strode across the
room, hauled her into his arms and kissed her.

And even though she was still furious with
him, especially since he had the nerve to try
smiling at her, her body melted into him the moment he took her in his arms. Her own arms
went round his neck. Her foolish lips parted for

his and kissed him back. Only her pride stood apart, shaking its head in reproof.

'You want me, Amy,' he breathed, breaking their kiss. 'Even though I'm no good, you want me. Don't pretend you don't. Don't be a liar. That kind of behaviour is beneath you.'

'Who are you to tell me how to behave?' Injured pride had her pulling out of his arms. She managed to take two steps away from him, spied her chair and took another two steps, so that she'd put it between her and him.

'The man who loves you,' he said.

'Oh, don't start that again. You never loved me. You couldn't have.'

'Are you saying that because of the way I behaved, or because you believe there is something in you that makes you unworthy of love?'

'What?' She flinched. 'I don't know what you mean.'

His eyes narrowed. 'Oh, I think you do. I think you know exactly what I mean. I recognise that aspect of you, Amy, because I have it, deeply ingrained in me, too. Like me, I think you've always had to try to prove yourself to parents who expect more from you than you are capable of being. Who want you to be someone you will never be. And I wouldn't be a bit surprised to learn that, since we parted, you've carried on living the kind of life where people around you always measure you by a different set of standards from those that matter to you.'

She gasped and pressed one hand to her chest. It was as if he'd looked right into her soul and divined every last one of her secrets.

So she had no choice but to fight back. She reached for the cruellest weapon she had at her disposal.

'You said it yourself, Nathan,' she sneered. 'You are no good. I can't depend on a single word you say. You made me fall in love with you, then decided I wasn't good enough. And now you talk about marriage, when all the world has seen what a dreadful husband you can be...'

'I've already told you it wasn't because you weren't good enough! I confessed my darkest shame to you. You know why I spurned you, Amy, so don't give me that excuse...' He stalked up to the chair, stopping only when his knees touched the upholstered cushions. She gripped the back, but he was so close it scarcely formed a barrier between them at all now.

'And as for being a dreadful husband—I'll tell you about my first marriage, shall I? How I fell into it because I'd ceased caring what happened to me? There was great gaping hole in my future, a void where my dreams of being *your* husband had once been. My father was telling me that I had exhibited poor judgement and that it was better to let him organise my life. And I believed him. I thought I'd made a terrible error of judgement by falling for you. I had only two things left: a chance to redeem myself with my father, of making him proud of me by going along with his plans, and a burning desire to wound you the way you wounded me. Marrying Lucasta achieved both those ends. She was the perfect weapon. To prove to you that I didn't care. To show you that I would rather marry a girl with a pedigree, and a fortune, than one with a pretty face.'

Amethyst flinched. She'd known it. She'd known he'd done his utmost to wound her. That he wasn't the kind to turn the other cheek.

Any more than she was. Hadn't she just said the very worst thing she could think of, with intent to wound him?

'Father had chosen Lucasta for me because she was intelligent and ambitious, and of course well connected. He'd picked the same kind of wife for each of my brothers. Women who would be a help to them rising through the ranks, in whatever career they'd chosen. He matched Freddy to the daughter of an archbishop, the moment he chose to take holy orders. And Berty got the granddaughter of both an earl and a general when he joined the army. The only difference was that others had decided I ought to go into politics, rather than me showing any inclination for it. But nobody thought it would matter. Unlike any other profession, a man doesn't need any aptitude to have a successful career in politics. He only needs the right connections.

'The terrible irony of it all was that initially I fell in with my father's scheme, because I thought he was showing faith in me. But it was the very opposite. He was putting his faith in Lucasta. He thought she would make me a success, no matter how inept I was. She was the one with all the ambition. She wanted me to reach the top by fair means or foul, whereas I...'

Something he said came back to her. 'You wanted to make a difference.'

He snorted in derision. 'She just wanted me to vote the way I was told. She was furious when she discovered I wasn't the shambling, indolent wastrel my father had persuaded her she could push into doing whatever she wanted. I started to wake up, you see, not long after the nuptials were over. And stopped dumbly agreeing with everything that everyone told me. Voiced a few opinions of my own. Once or twice I even had the unmitigated cheek to vote according to my conscience. A young pup like me, who had no experience, no brains, no *judgement*... They kept telling me I shouldn't think for myself. That I should let older and wiser heads guide me. Which had the opposite effect. I made a couple of dramatic, rebellious gestures that made me look more of a fool than ever.'

In spite of her determination not to believe one word he said, this rang so true she couldn't help it. Hadn't she made the dramatic, rebellious gesture of going to live with her spinster aunt rather than back down when her family had told her she hadn't known her own mind, that she'd misunderstood his intentions?

'And as soon as Lucasta saw she'd been sold a pig in a poke, as she put it, she started to try to punish me.'

He gave a bitter laugh that tugged at a place deep inside her that had long lain dormant. She swallowed it back down, nervously.

'Her opening gambit was to start spreading tales about her disappointment with my prowess between the sheets. I suppose in a way she had cause to complain. I'd never had that much enthusiasm for her, and what little I managed to muster waned remarkably swiftly once I realised what she was like. But still, I had this stupid, unfashionable notion that what went on between a husband and wife was private. She didn't. She wanted a life lived in the public eye. And when I refused to employ the kind of tactics she wanted me to take in order to start climbing the greasy pole, she took her revenge in public.'

His cheeks flushed dull red as she recalled some of the things she'd read about him in those days. The hints that he wasn't much of a man. The cartoons depicting him as a sort of wilting flower, blowing about with every breeze as he voted not according to the party line, but with the prevailing wind of public opinion.

'Even the fact that I wouldn't break my marriage vows made her despise me more. I made it a point of honour, you see, to show the world that I wouldn't sacrifice my integrity for my own comfort, let alone her ambition. But she even managed to twist that into something…foul.' His mouth twisted with bitterness.

'When, eventually, I suggested we might both be happier if I retired to the country, out of her way, she reminded me that her family had paid a great deal of money for me and I owed it to them to at least go through the motions. Even if I couldn't be a husband she could be proud of, I had no right to make her forfeit the life she loved. Hosting political gatherings, being in the thick of all the intrigue…

'She was right, of course. I stayed in London and...endured. My God, but I was relieved when she died. That makes me sound heartless, doesn't it? But you have no idea what it's like to live with that level of contempt, day in, day out.'

Actually, she rather thought she did. She'd had a taste of it from her family, before her aunt had swooped in and rescued her. Only she hadn't had to endure it for years. Only a few months.

'I wasted no time in embarking on a very public affair with a notoriously rapacious widow,' he said with a touch of defiance. 'A notoriously gossipy, rapacious widow, who was not averse to telling anyone who showed any interest that I was most definitely not a disappointment between the sheets. And after her, I went a little mad, I suppose. Taking whatever was on offer, proving Lucasta a liar, over and over again. Nobody has any doubt about my masculinity, not any longer.'

'Oh,' said Amethyst faintly. That made perfect sense. She could see exactly why he'd gone out and proved his manhood, over and over again, in as flagrant a way as possible. He hadn't let her leave his bed that first time, until he'd demonstrated his ability to take her to the heights of pleasure. He took pride in his prowess as a lover.

'That's right. Your sexual career made all the papers.'

His face darkened.

'Yes. All of it. I made sure it all got published, even though my father tried his damnedest to suppress it. It was my way out.'

'Your way out?' She injected as much cynicism into her voice as she could muster. She couldn't believe that in a few short minutes he'd practically demolished beliefs she'd held firmly for ten years. But she wouldn't let him convince her he had any excuse for being involved in that Season's most lurid scandal. Lifting her head, she looked down her nose at him. 'The way I heard it, they threw you out.'

'Precisely! If I hadn't done something that drastic, my father would have picked another girl, from another political dynasty, and it would have started all over again.'

Dammit! She knew he'd come up with something to make even the end of his political career seem justified.

'So, those last affairs you had, with…'

'Two of the most influential women I could seduce,' he agreed with a cold, hard smile. 'At the same time, too, so that even if their husbands could overlook the affairs, the offended wives could not. If there is one thing a certain

type of woman will not tolerate, it is infidelity
in her lover.'

'Indeed?' She'd thought he would at least tell
her that the stories about that last scandal had
been exaggerated. Instead he was confirming
them. She shuddered.

The thought of him coldly seducing two
women, married women at that, concurrently,
made her feel sick.

His face shuttered.

'You didn't question a single word of it, did
you? You read it in print, so you thought it must
all be true.'

She glanced up at him as he huffed out a bitter laugh.

'But you've just told me that it was...'

'And you were ready to condemn my behaviour without knowing what lay behind it. Or considered there might have been people whose sole
aim in writing the stories was to blacken my
name.'

She drifted blindly away from the chair behind which she'd been cowering and sank down
on to the nearest available sofa she could reach
without having to walk past him.

'I can excuse you for not seeing my true motives for the way I've behaved,' he said. 'Because you knew nothing of my misery, my sense

of utter failure. So now, will you have the honesty to think about my earlier failure to believe in you? Remember, all I knew of you was that although you professed to be from a very strict background, you never protested when I crossed the line. You did not put up even a token protest that first time I kissed you. You wanted me to kiss you. You didn't seem to care if we got caught, either.'

'But that was because...'

'You loved me. I know that now. And I should have believed in it at the time, too. But what Fielding told me put a very different complexion on your behaviour. It was all just credible enough to make me wonder. So before you condemn me for not being able to somehow discern that you were totally innocent of all the charges laid at your door, let me ask you this: When the situation was reversed, did you believe in me?'

No. She hadn't. She'd been so angry with him for the way he'd cast her aside that she'd wanted to believe the worst of him. Stoking up her hatred had given her the strength to go on living. She'd pored over those newspaper stories, believing the very worst of him without a shred of evidence to back any of it up.

So how could she condemn him for believing what a true, honest, good friend had told him, from the best of motives? Especially when, now she looked back on it openly and honestly, her own behaviour might have made the accusations against her seem plausible?

She'd been so bowled over when the handsome, charming young son of such a notable family had paid her attention that she'd forgotten every principle she'd ever had. She had encouraged him, as much as she'd dared. When he'd snatched that first kiss, a hasty peck on the cheek, she hadn't protested. She'd blushed and giggled, and let him engineer situations where he could do it again. They'd rapidly progressed to kisses on the lips. Then heated kisses on the lips.

She caught her lip between her teeth.

'What a pair we are,' he said. 'Neither of us can quite believe in love. I couldn't believe you loved me ten years ago and you cannot believe I love you now. Or perhaps you are just looking for excuses to escape me. I'm not much of a catch, am I? You've made it clear that I'm good enough for a fling, but not a lifetime.'

He walked over to the window and stood with his back to her for some time, in complete silence. When she darted a glance in his direction, it was to see his shoulders hunched in an attitude of defeat.

She wanted to cry out that she'd been too

hasty. That, perhaps, if he gave her time to think it over, she might be able to…

To what? Believe in him? Trust her entire future to his hands? When by his own admission he'd proved himself capable of the vilest kind of behaviour?

'I may as well go,' he said, whirling round and making for the door. 'Forgive me for haranguing you. I hope your voyage back to England will be uneventful and that your memories of your stay in Paris are…sweet.'

And with that, he walked out.

Leaving his hat lying on the floor where he'd dropped it.

Amethyst stared wide-eyed at the closed door through which he'd gone. He'd given up. He'd seen that she couldn't ever trust him fully again and he'd given up. And gone.

Just like that.

She got to her feet and ran to the window. One last look. She would take one last look at him as he walked away until the crowd in the street swallowed him from sight. She laid her hand flat on the window pane, as though she could reach through it and touch him. Knowing she couldn't.

She'd blamed him for destroying what they'd had, before. But this time, he was right, *she* was the one who'd destroyed it. She hadn't been prepared to trust him. To forgive him. Worse than that, she hadn't even tried.

She could justify ignoring that first proposal. The night he'd discovered she was still a virgin and guilt had reared up and slapped him round the head for what he'd done. But the subsequent ones? If he didn't know about her wealth, if he was really trying to get her to marry him because he loved her...

She shook her head, tearing herself away from the window and returning to her chair.

Where her eye fell on the portrait that he'd brought to her. For no other reason, according to him, than that he thought it might be a way to get to speak to her again. Was that true? He certainly hadn't attempted to use it against her, the way she'd expected.

A shaft of cold dread speared down to her stomach. What if he'd meant it? What if he really did think he was in love with her?

No. She took a deep breath, pushing the possibility to the back of the sofa where she'd stashed the portrait. It couldn't possibly be love. He probably thought marrying her would mean returning to a time before his life had gone so catastrophically wrong. To a time when he'd thought he could just marry a simple country girl and live in a sort of bucolic idyll.

But she wasn't that girl any more. She ran businesses. She could never retreat to the country and live the way he'd said was his own fantasy.

It just wasn't possible.

He wasn't the rather dreamy boy he'd been either, who talked about the beauty of nature, and how wonderful it would be to visit Italy and see the works of art on display in so many cities. He'd become a rake. A man who was capable of carrying on affairs with two women at the same time, to deliberately wreak as much destruction and pain as he could.

That wasn't a man she could love, was it? If she was capable of loving anyone at all.

And anyway, why was she sitting here arguing with herself about it? He'd gone. Defeat in every line of his body. He'd realised it was over between them. That it had been destroyed ten years ago and there was no putting it back together.

So that was that.

Chapter Thirteen

Men were good at saying all the right things, but actions spoke louder than words.

Nathan had said he wanted to marry her, that he loved her, that he couldn't bear to think of her leaving Paris. But after one rebuff, he'd disappeared. If he'd really meant what he said, he would have called, every day, begging her to reconsider.

But he didn't call.

Though what would be the point, she didn't know. It had been one thing having an affair with him here, but to make a new life with him in England? Impossible. Even if he still wanted her, which, apparently, he didn't.

Or he would have called.

And since he hadn't, it meant that he'd lost interest.

He was probably painting another woman

right now. Telling her she had glorious hair as he sifted it through his long, supple fingers.

Telling her whatever was most likely to get her into bed.

She straightened up from the trunk she was packing, welcoming the flare of anger that had just flowed through her. Anger was what had kept her going for so many years. Without it, she didn't know what might.

She certainly didn't want to return to Stanton Basset looking as if she'd had all the stuffing knocked out of her, which is what she'd felt like after that final scene with Nathan.

Only she couldn't seem to get a solid grip on it. It was as if she didn't have the energy to sustain a decently solid bad temper.

She slumped on to a chair, looking at the belongings strewn across the room. They'd acquired so much stuff since arriving in Paris. It would be no use trying to travel home the way they'd come. It was a symptom of her state of mind that she hadn't raised even a token protest when Monsieur Le Brun decided to hire a wagon to carry all the trunks that contained both hers and Fenella's new wardrobes. And a second carriage to contain the maid he'd insisted on employing for Fenella. A French woman, naturally. He didn't consider English domestics worthy of a place serving his wife.

Amethyst picked up a scarf and absentmind-edly rolled it into a ball. Far from being annoyed with Monsieur Le Brun for taking over all the arrangements that had at one time seemed so im-portant, she'd been grateful. Left to herself, she wasn't sure she'd have managed to leave Paris at all. Because once she did, then it really was over.

A peremptory knock on the door heralded Monsieur Le Brun's entrance. He never waited for permission to enter a room these days. Since confessing that he was a French aristocrat, he'd dropped any pretence at servility.

'We must speak,' he said sternly. 'About my Fenella. And Miss Sophie.'

She sighed and waved to the chair opposite. As a gentleman, he had at least waited until she indicated he might sit, she would give him that much credit.

'What do you wish to say?'

'I know that you do not like me. That to start with you would have done all in your power to prevent me marrying her if you had not seen it would cause the rift of permanence between you. But I tell you this—' he leaned forwards, glar-ing at her '—if you had tried to keep us apart, or given me to lose my employ with you, I would have followed you both back to England and sto-len her away in marriage.'

Oh, but that hurt. Here was this man, prepared to follow his lady love across the ocean—well, the English Channel at least—because Fenella was the kind of woman who deserved to find love. She was a good, kind-hearted creature. Not a cold unfeminine shrew without an ounce of trust in her nature. Fenella had trusted Gaston. Given him her heart along with her body. And this was her reward. This determined, dogged devotion.

If she'd been able to trust Nathan, he wouldn't have walked away from her. They might all be going back to England together and arranging a double wedding.

And so what if he was only after her for her money? Or trying to recapture a fleeting moment of their youth when they'd had hope and trust, and belief in goodness? Did that really matter? It wasn't just her money he liked. It wasn't the memory of a girl he'd talked to and danced with, and argued with and made love to, either. It was her, as she was now. He'd enjoyed every minute they'd spent together. She knew he had.

But she'd pushed him away. Once too often.

'I know,' continued Monsieur Le Brun belligerently, 'so you have no need to say it, that she deserves a better man than me. That I cannot provide for her in the way I would wish. But I have hope that one day the estate of my family will be restored and that then she will come to live with me here, in France, as my countess.'

A lump formed in her chest as she contrasted his determination to win Fenella against all obstacles, with Nathan's swift defection.

'And why, exactly,' she said, tossing the balled-up scarf into an open trunk, 'do you feel the need to tell me all this?'

He gripped the arms of the chair, his jaw working.

'She tells me that you plan to move to Southampton to be near her.'

'What of it?'

'Only this. I am a proud man, *mademoiselle*, as you are well aware. Fenella is to be my wife. Sophie will be my daughter. Mine is now the task of providing for them and ensuring their happiness. I give leave to inform you I shall not tolerate your interference in the way I run my household or permit you to do anything that will make either of them question where their loyalty must now lie.'

'I have no intention of *interfering*,' she replied coldly. 'But have you given any thought to how lonely Fenella is going to be while you are away, pursuing your dream of getting your château back? She will have nobody to support her. No family, no friends in that area. I didn't think you disliked me so much that you would seriously wish to deprive Fenella of the one friend she does have.'

His scowl deepened. 'This is what she has told me, too.' He thrust his bony fingers through his hair, then slapped his hand down on the chair arm. 'That only you stood by her in her darkest hour. For that, *mademoiselle...*' he swallowed, as if something painful lodged in his throat '...I have to thank you,' he bit out through gritted teeth. 'And I do not wish for her to be left lonely. But...'

Amethyst held up her hand. 'I don't like you any more than you like me. The only thing upon which we will ever agree is that Fenella deserves better of both of us. I propose, for her sake, that we come to some kind of...truce.'

'A truce?'

'Yes. I will agree to keep my distance when you are at home. But I will be purchasing a property near enough so that I can support Fenella while you are away.'

'That sounds reasonable. Though she will not like it, I think, if you never visit while I am home. She will want us to become friends...'

'Oh, I have thought of the perfect way to calm her fears on that score. And that is to offer you employment.'

'I beg your pardon?'

'Well, unless you have a burning desire to

carry on working as a courier to English tourists, I had thought you might prefer a permanent position within George Holdings. As my French agent. There are bound to be outlets for my wares wherever in France you need to travel in pursuit of your quest, so you can fit in my business around your own agenda. It will surely be better for you if you don't have to dance attendance on demanding tourists all day long?'

'It would, but...'

'I know I haven't been an easy person to work for, but I've been most impressed by your tireless energy and efficiency, not to mention your patience. Besides, Fenella loves you...'

'I do not want you to give me work as a favour to my wife! We both know that I have had very little success in procuring for you the new outlets for your goods.'

'On the contrary, you managed to secure two contracts, under almost impossible conditions.' Whilst acting as tour guide, and sweeping Fenella off her feet. 'I propose paying you a small basic wage and meeting your expenses while you are travelling in France. Plus a percentage of any profits my companies make through your efforts.'

'You would really put me in a position of such trust?'

'Without hesitation. You have plenty of sterling qualities. Not least of which is your devotion to Fenella.'

'I...I suppose I could say the same of you,' he said grudgingly. Then his mouth twisted into a wry grimace. 'I think since I have seen what that pig of a man has done to you—both now and when you were just a girl—that you think you have cause to distrust men. And that is perhaps why you have treated me as though I am a worm. And also...you wish not to see your friend hurt, the way you have been hurt.'

'Who says I have been hurt?'

He shook his head reprovingly. '*Mademoiselle*, ever since he came here to give you the *congé*, you have been a shadow of yourself. You do not eat. You do not speak. And most telling of all, you do not assert your will over mine.'

It was all true. There didn't seem to be any point in anything. It was as if a grey pall hung over her now, which she couldn't ever see lifting.

'Do not,' said Monsieur Le Brun in alarm, 'be so upset. I did not mean to make you weep. *Merde!*' He pulled out a handkerchief and thrust it at her. Only then did she realise that tears were streaming down her cheeks.

'It is not your fault,' she said through his handkerchief as she blew her nose.

'Fenella will never forgive me if she learns I have made you cry. Please cease.'

'I just told you, you have not made me cry. No man will make me cry. I won't let any of you,' she said defiantly, though tears still streamed down her cheeks.

'Now go away,' she said, burying her face in his handkerchief. 'And leave me…alone.'

Alone. As she would be now for the rest of her life.

She had travelled back to England in the second carriage with Sophie, her nurse, Francine, and the new French maid. She'd realised she would much rather hold the child's head over the bowl as she vomited than watch her former companion and courier makings sheep's eyes at each other all the way to Calais.

Both she and Monsieur Le Brun were on their best behaviour whenever Fenella was watching, though she couldn't resist taking one last swipe at his masculine pride by insisting on paying all the wedding expenses and then making it as lavish as she possibly could. She met the groom's objections by pointing out that Fenella had been robbed of a society wedding the first time round and she deserved the best.

There was more than a hint of retaliation in the way he promptly invited a veritable crowd of remarkably well-connected people to both the church and the wedding breakfast, since most of them looked down their aristocratic noses at her. But she shrugged it off. She'd been mean to him, so…

Or perhaps it wasn't anything to do with her at all. Perhaps he really was responding to what she'd said about Fenella deserving a society wedding and was just doing his utmost to provide it?

Fenella had thoroughly enjoyed her day, which was the main thing. Though she was very tearful when it came time to part on the morning after.

'I hate to think of you going back to Stanton Basset all on your own,' she said.

'I do not plan to stay for very long. I will just see that my aunt's house is cleared for sale, or rent, and then come to join you. Not in your marital home, I hasten to add,' she put in when Monsieur Le Brun looked distinctly alarmed. 'But in some nearby hotel, while I view the properties on offer.'

'Still, I don't like the thought of you travelling all over the country by yourself,' persisted Fenella.

'I do not like it myself,' put in Monsieur Le Brun, to her surprise. 'You hired me to act as your courier from Stanton Basset to Paris and home. London is not your home.'

'If you think I can stomach the sight of you two fawning all over each other in a closed carriage for the next three days you are very much mistaken,' she retorted. 'And I am quite certain that the last thing you want is a former employer joining you on your bride trip.'

The newly married couple blushed.

'Besides, it is not as if I shall be travelling alone. I have employed a woman to act as escort and chaperon.'

Fenella and Monsieur Le Brun both glanced across the inn yard at the nondescript wisp of a woman Amethyst had hired from an agency not two days earlier.

'She doesn't look as if she will provide you with much company, though,' said Fenella with an anxious frown.

'Believe me, I shall not pine for conversation after that last trip with the two French maids jabbering away incessantly like a pair of magpies. Peace and quiet will suit me very well.'

'*Ma chère*, Mademoiselle Dalby has clearly made up her mind. Have you ever been able to sway her, once she has done so?'

With one arm round Fenella's waist, and Sophie's little hand clasped in his own, Monsieur Le Brun firmly ushered his new little family into the coach that stood waiting for them.

A swell of resentment surged through Amethyst as she boarded her own carriage. If it wasn't for him, they would all be going home together. She would still be smarting from losing Nathan, but at least she would have...

She shook her head, angry at herself. When had it ever done her any good relying on others? She was stronger than this.

She consoled herself, for the first few miles of her own journey, with visions of Monsieur Le Brun's discomfort, shut up with a child whose reaction to the bouncing and swaying of their coach was going to be inevitable. Served him right for breaking up her happy home!

Except...Fenella loved him. And if he felt anything like she did about those two, he wouldn't be finding it a trial. Caring for each other was part of being a family.

Or it should be. It was what she'd always wanted, deep down. She knew herself so much better since being with Nathan. He'd let her express her opinions, rather than trying to form them, and the more she'd done so, the more she understood what she really thought and felt about everything.

And she'd seen that, all her life, she had just wanted to have somebody love her. It was what had made her strive so hard to please both her parents, and then her aunt.

And what had made her fall into Nathan's bed.

It hadn't been just adventure she craved. It wasn't just about rebelling and proving that a woman could do anything a man could do. She'd wanted him to love her. Yet when he'd claimed he did, she hadn't been able to believe it. Why should he love her? Nobody else ever had. They'd made her believe there was something intrinsically unlovable about her. And so she'd pretended she didn't care. Hardened herself against hurt. Pushed people away before they had a chance to make so much as the slightest dent in her defences.

But it did hurt, knowing that Nathan didn't love her, any more than anyone else ever had.

She slumped into the squabs, that grey pall making the mere act of breathing feel like an effort.

England was such a damp and dreary place. People scuttled about, heads bowed into the drizzle, as though they were the nation that had just been defeated, rather than the French.

Or was it just the air of defeat hanging over Amethyst that made the rest of the world look so bleak?

The woman she'd hired from an agency to lend her respectability on the journey very soon gave up attempting to converse with her taciturn employer. And no doubt gave thanks, reflected

Amethyst on one of the stops to change horses, that her employment was only temporary.

Amethyst gave her a generous tip when at last they reached their destination.

'I hope your return trip is more pleasant,' she said to the startled woman. 'It couldn't have been very comfortable for you, having to travel so far with an employer who had only roused from her depression to make acid remarks about the deficiencies of any stray male unfortunate enough to cross her path,' she said self-deprecatingly.

'I...I don't like men any more than you, madam,' said the woman, with just the hint of a sympathetic smile, before dropping a curtsy and scuttling off towards the town square and the coaching inn where she would rest overnight before taking the stage back to London the next morning. Amethyst half-wished she was going with her. She had to brace herself before walking up the path to Aunt Georgie's front door. After the glorious freedom she'd known on her travels, setting foot inside the house would be rather like putting on a stiffly starched collar. The minute she crossed the threshold, she got the urge to fling open all the windows. Only, since it was raining, all it would achieve would be to make her cold, as well as depressed.

'There is a fire in the morning room, Miss

Dalby,' said her butler, a long-suffering individual she'd inherited from her aunt along with the house.

'Thank you, Adams,' she said, suddenly wondering why he'd borne the brunt of her aunt's displeasure for so many years. He wasn't paid much more than the average for his position. 'But I would rather take tea in the study.'

'Of course. I had the fire lit in there, too, thinking you might like to cast your eye over the correspondence awaiting you.'

'That was very thoughtful of you,' she said with real gratitude. 'Thank you.'

He dipped his head in a kind of truncated bow, swiftly, but not before Amethyst had caught a startled look on his face. Good grief, had she really been so lacking in manners towards the man that a mere 'thank you' could surprise him?

She went to the study while Adams made his stately way in the other direction to see to the tea things. There was quite a pile of correspondence piled up on her desk. Hours' worth of work.

She sighed and went to the window, which looked out over her garden. She hadn't come in here because she was keen to put her nose back to the grindstone. It was just that she'd made this room her own, since Aunt Georgie's death. She'd moved the desk so she could see out over the gardens by merely lifting her head. She'd had the walls painted a light, creamy colour, pretty new curtains hung and even put up some watercolours she'd purchased herself, whereas she hadn't got round to doing anything about the gloom that pervaded the morning room. And she'd got the strangest feeling that the room would disapprove of her jaunt to the Continent. That it would gloat at her, too. What good had it done her to go abroad? The solid, heavy furniture would imply. Or buying new clothes, and going dancing and taking a lover? She'd still ended up having to come back alone. More alone than before, since even Fenella had abandoned her. Fenella, the nearest thing to a friend she'd ever had.

And yet…all those ledgers lining the shelves and the correspondence stacked neatly on the desk reminded her that her life still had some purpose. Within those reports lay the livelihood of hundreds of workers. The decisions she made regarding them would affect the prosperity of swathes of Lancashire and the Midlands.

It was probably coincidence that at that moment the sun managed to break through the heavy pall of cloud hanging over the scenery, making the damp shrubbery glisten as though covered with hundreds of tiny jewels. At that exact same moment Amethyst saw a ray of light of her own.

Towards the end of her aunt's life she'd begun

to liken her to a dragon, zealously guarding her hoard. She'd accumulated great piles of money simply for the sake of having it. But it had never made her happy. On the contrary, she'd grown increasingly fearful that someone would find out about it, then try to steal it from her, one way or another.

She turned round and stared at the piles of paperwork lying on her desk. She didn't need to follow blindly in Aunt Georgie's footsteps. She didn't need to carry on amassing more and more wealth, for its own sake. She might remain a spinster, secretly running a vast financial empire, but she could do it in her own way. She'd already made a start, she realised, by expanding into France, which would mean increasing output in the manufactories she had, rather than extracting as much profit from one, in order to raise capital to buy the next one, the way her aunt had. Which meant she could start looking after the workers a bit better. She could found schools for the workers' children and organise some kind of welfare fund for the sick, and—

Adams interrupted her train of thought by knocking on the door and informing her that she had a visitor.

'Already?'

'Mrs Podmore,' he said as though that explained it.

'Oh, dear lord,' she groaned, laying her forehead against the window.

'Shall I tell her you are too tired to receive anyone just yet,' ventured Adams, 'having so recently returned from such a long journey?'

'It is tempting, but, no.' She sighed. 'The wretched woman will only call back, again and again, until she's said whatever it is she wants to say. Or ambush me in the high street, or on the way back from church. So I may as well get it over with by taking the tea you were going to bring me, with her.'

If Adams was surprised to be on the receiving end of such a frank speech, he betrayed no sign of it. Merely nodded his head and offered to take the tray she'd been awaiting into the front parlour.

Into which she had not wanted to go, not just yet.

Two birds with one stone, Amethyst muttered to herself as she opened the door to the formal gloom of the parlour and walked in.

'My dear, is it true?'

Trust Mrs Podmore to ignore the convention of commencing a visit with polite enquiries after her health, and so on, and launch straight into the matter that really interested her.

'I heard that dreadful Mountsorrel woman has run off and left you. After all you have done for her. The ingrate!'

'How on earth has such a rumour managed to reach your ears?' Amethyst went to the chair opposite Mrs Podmore and reached for the teapot. 'I have only been back five minutes!'

'But she hasn't come back with you, has she? I had it from…the most impeccable source that it was quite another person who alighted from the carriage with you outside your doorstep earlier. A quite inferior-looking person—yes, thank you, I will have one of these cherry slices—who promptly got on the very next stage back to London. You simply must have your cook give me the receipt for my cook. Not that she will make them half so moist, I dare swear. She *will* leave everything baking until it's done to a crisp. But is it true?'

Though Amethyst was sorely tempted to say she could not possibly know if it was true that her cook burned everything to a crisp, she refrained. She knew exactly what Mrs Podmore wanted to find out.

Which was what had happened to Fenella.

'The rumour that Mrs Mountsorrel has run off? Absolutely not.'

'But she is not here, is she?' Mrs Podmore

looked round the room as though she might spy
Fenella lurking in some shadowy corner, the way
she'd always done when one of the doyennes of
Stanton Basset had come calling.

'Indeed not,' replied Amethyst calmly, adding a dash of milk to both their cups.

'Well, where is she, then? Not—' Mrs Podmore sat forward, her eyes brightening '—not
suffered some terrible accident, I hope?'

'Oh, no,' replied Amethyst, dashing Mrs Podmore's hopes. 'In fact, quite the reverse.'

'The reverse?'

Amethyst took a sip of tea, deliberately leaving her visitor trying to work out what could be
the reverse of a terrible accident. Only when Mrs
Podmore's face betrayed a state of complete bewilderment did she relent.

'She has remarried.'

'No!'

'Yes. The Comte de Quatre Terres de...' She
wrinkled her brow in concentration. How irritating. The one time his titles might have come in
useful, she could only recall a small part of one
of them. 'Well, I forget quite where. A French
count, anyway.'

'Well, I never.' Mrs Podmore set her cup down
in its saucer with a snap. 'However did a person

like *her* come to rub shoulders with a French count?'

'Oh, didn't you know?' She widened her eyes in mock surprise. 'Fenella is very well born.' Though she hadn't welcomed Mrs Podmore's visit, now the wretched woman was here, she might as well put her to good use. To set the record straight.

'She made a poor choice of husband the first time round, it is true. A man who left her destitute and estranged from her family. But she is *exactly* the kind of person who should be rubbing shoulders with a French count. Not that we knew he was anything of the sort when we met him. I...'

She'd been about to say she'd hired Monsieur Le Brun as their courier. But once Mrs Podmore knew of it, it would be all over Stanton Basset, and from there the county, and who knew where else, within days. And he hadn't wanted anyone to know about his mission. He'd taken her into his confidence. And she didn't, she realised, want to break faith with him. It would be...well, a perfectly horrid thing to do. He'd probably exaggerated the danger he might be in, should anyone know who he really was, but she couldn't contemplate exposing him to even the possibility of coming to harm. And it wasn't just because she couldn't bear to think of Fenella being widowed a second time. Especially not through something she'd said, or done.

It was for his own sake.

Good heavens. To cover her consternation at discovering she'd somehow started to care about offending a man she'd thought of for weeks as Monsieur le Prune, she took a defensively lady-like sip of tea.

'Well, it makes no difference,' said Mrs Podmore, bristling with annoyance. 'Even if she was high born, it wasn't her place to go taking up with some Frenchman while she was supposed to be working for you. Putting herself forwards, no doubt, with those airs and graces she had.'

Amethyst thanked providence that Mrs Podmore had lost interest in probing any further into the identity of the French count Fenella'd had the temerity to marry. And was revealing, at long last, just what had been at the root of the towns-women's malice. It sounded as though they'd re-sented her for behaving like the lady she truly was. Assumed she'd thought herself too good for the likes of them and decided to take her down a peg or two.

'I have never observed Mrs Mountsorrel *put herself forwards*,' she said icily. 'In fact, I think it was her very reticence that brought out all the protective instincts in…her new husband. And I am pleased for her. She deserves some happiness, don't you think, after all she has been through?'

Mrs Podmore pursed her lips and shifted in her chair. 'What I think,' she said, setting her teacup down with a snap, 'is that you are too liable to get the wool pulled over your eyes by people who are out to take advantage of you, that's what I think. I can't say I'm sorry she's gone. But what I am sorry for is what people will say about you now. Why, you had to come back here all on your own. Which is not the thing, you know, not the thing at all.'

'I hired a person from an agency in London for the journey home—'

'Well, we all know how unsatisfactory she must have been, or you wouldn't have sent her packing the moment you got here.'

'No, that wasn't why—'

'A woman in your position must have a decent female companion, as I am sure I have told you before.'

'Yes, you have,' admitted Amethyst drily. 'Many times.'

'Well, then, you must see that the sooner you engage a proper, unimpeachable chaperon, the better. Oh. I think I may know just the person.'

She got to her feet. 'I must hurry, or I might miss her. I do apologise for making this visit so brief.'

There was no need for an apology. Amethyst couldn't believe how easily she'd got rid of her.

'But I am sure you are tired after your journey.'

Not that it had prevented her from calling in the first place.

'I can call again another time and fill you in with all the latest news of our little town. Not but what you will probably find it all terribly dull after the adventures you must have been having.'

Oh dear. Her lack of interest in whatever gossip Mrs Podmore wanted to share must have shown on her face. She really must take care to guard her expression better.

'No, no, dear, I insist. Though I must say,' she said tartly, 'that travelling doesn't seem to have agreed with you. You look positively wan. What you need now is a good wholesome English meal, followed by a good night's sleep in your own bed. That will soon bring the roses back to your cheeks.'

They were returning already. Mrs Podmore couldn't possibly have meant anything by that comment about sleeping in her own bed. It was only her conscience shrieking that everyone could tell she was a fallen woman now, just by looking at her.

Fortunately Mrs Podmore had already turned her back on Amethyst as she hurried to the door. Keen to get out and spread the news of Fenella's marriage to a French count, no doubt. And if that weren't enough of a coup for her, she'd also got the notion she was going to be able to interfere in some indigent female's life by obliging her to come and work for Amethyst as a companion. If she was in such a hurry to find her, the poor woman must be attempting to escape Stanton Basset at some point today.

She hoped she made it.

Though she wasn't sorry Mrs Podmore would be out and about disseminating the truth about Fenella. There had been enough unpleasant and unfounded gossip about Fenella doing the rounds of Stanton Basset.

At the mention of unfounded gossip her mind flew back, as it did so often since he'd told her, to the scurrilous rumour that Nathan had heard about her. About her having a child out of wedlock.

There had been something niggling at the back of her mind, something about those days, that she hadn't been able to put her finger on, until this moment, when she'd seen how keen

Mrs Podmore was to spread her bit of gossip. Right after she'd kept her own mouth shut about Monsieur Le Brun, out of consideration for his feelings.

The kind of story that Nathan had heard about her was meat and drink to people like Mrs Podmore. If it had reached the ears of someone like that, people would have been twitching their skirts aside as she walked past.

But they hadn't. She'd had no idea what she was supposed to have been guilty of, until just a few days ago.

It meant that Nathan couldn't have repeated the story, not to anyone. Nor could his friend, Fielding.

But Nathan had been furious. He'd wanted to hurt her. He'd told her as much. So, why hadn't he taken the final step and destroyed her completely? He'd had the power to do it. All he would have had to do was repeat what he'd heard and, even though it wasn't true, the damage would have been done. People would always wonder. 'No smoke without fire.' How often had she heard that, in connection to rumours, particularly salacious ones?

What had made him hold back from taking that final step?

One answer came to her mind immediately. It

was the conclusion her aunt would have leapt to. That he wouldn't have wanted anyone to know he'd been deceived by the kind of woman he'd thought she'd been. That it was all a matter of preserving his pride.

But from deep within rose another reason to account for his reticence. A reason that made just as much sense. That he'd done it to shield her from the punishment society would have meted out, had the story been made public. He hadn't wanted to be responsible for blackening her name and ruining her reputation.

'Aunt Georgie, I don't think all men are completely bad,' she said out loud. The room seemed to frown at her. Every item in it was deeply ingrained with memories of her aunt, that was the trouble, and every stick of furniture now reproved her for speaking such heresy.

Though she was trembling, she said it again.

'Men aren't necessarily bad, just because they're men. I think they make mistakes, and get hurt and lash out, just the same as we do. And some of them,' her voice dropped to a whisper, 'some of them...might even be *good*.'

Chapter Fourteen

The sooner she left this place and rejoined Fenella and her family in Southampton, the better.

When he'd come in to collect the tea tray, Adams had interrupted her informing her aunt's chair that she thought Fenella was jolly lucky to have found a man like Monsieur-le-Compte-de-Somewhere-Brown. 'Fenella brought nothing to the marriage but a whole pile of obligations,' she'd been insisting. 'But not only did he not seem to mind, he'd actually fought for her. And Sophie, too. You should have seen his face the first time she called him *Papa*. He loves that little girl. He really does.'

Adams had looked round the room, as though searching for whomever she'd been talking to, though he must have known Mrs Podmore had left, or he wouldn't have come in to clear away.

He'd probably come to the conclusion that she was well on the way to becoming as odd as her aunt had been, walking round the room haranguing the furniture.

No, she sighed, her aunt's house was not a healthy place for her to live. She'd already begun to talk to herself. What next would she do?

Well, it wouldn't come to that. She walked briskly back to her study, drew out a fresh sheet of paper, trimmed her pen and set the process of the move in motion.

There had been many decisions to make. What to sell? What to put away in storage? What to take with her? And how was she going to implement her plan to improve the lot of her workforce from Southampton? Without anyone knowing that she was the one doing it? Practical issues such as these had kept her fully occupied for the next couple of days. During the hours of daylight, at least. But at night, as she had lain in bed, she could not ignore the creeping sense of loneliness and failure that only frenetic activity could keep at bay.

By the end of the week she'd begun to suspect Adams was developing a sort of fatherly concern for her. Or perhaps *fatherly* was not the right word, she grimaced as she tied up the ribbons of her Sunday bonnet. Her father had never shown *concern* when she'd been downcast. He'd always berated her for not displaying proper Christian gratitude, for not always giving thanks in everything. He'd never brought her tea and biscuits at regular intervals, which Adams now did if she lost track of time whilst working her way through the backlog of reports stacked on her desk. Or looked at her with such grave concern when she sat staring into space during meal times, forgetting to keep on raising the fork to her mouth, then nudged a favourite dish towards her, suggesting that cook would be disappointed if she didn't at least try it.

'Adams,' she said as she tugged on her gloves, 'I've come to a decision. I shall be leaving Stanton Basset as soon as I possibly can. But I wondered if you would like to carry on working for me.'

He opened the door for her without betraying any emotion whatever.

'It will be a bigger house, more responsibility, better wages,' she said as she preceded him out of the house.

'And to where, may I ask, are you planning to move?'

Did he have good reason for wanting to stay in the area? She frowned. She had never wondered about his private life before. Or considered he had a right to one. He'd always just been there. A servant. Not a real person.

She'd slipped into the habit of treating him exactly the same as her aunt had always done.

Well, those days were over.

'Somewhere near Southampton. To be close to Fenella.'

'And Miss Sophie,' said Adams, his face softening in what looked like sympathy.

'Yes. Of course, I will understand if you have…ties to this place and do not wish to move away. But I shall be sorry.'

He gave her a nod as he opened the garden gate for her. 'I shall give the matter serious consideration,' was all he would say.

Well, it was a big decision for anyone to make. He'd been here ever since she could remember. And not everyone liked change. Particularly not when they got to his age.

'If you don't come with me and would rather retire,' she said, 'I will make sure you have a decent pension.'

'That is…generous of you,' he acknowledged. 'I had hoped, when your aunt passed, that she might have…' He trailed away. But he had no need to elaborate. Her aunt had not left any of the servants anything.

She shook her head at the slavish way she'd moulded her behaviour to please her aunt. More evidence of her desperate need for approval, she sighed. Well, it had to stop. She wasn't going to live to please anyone else, ever again. She would live by her own beliefs, act according to her own principles and stand on her own two feet.

Her own two feet carried her all the way to church without her mind having to direct their way. They carried her to the pew where she'd always sat without her having to think about that either.

The service commenced. She got to her feet, then dropped to her knees in all the appropriate places, but she was only going through the motions.

Because she couldn't get over the fact that she'd been such a fool. She'd lost Nathan because she'd listened to her aunt's warped views, rather than her own heart.

She'd been happy, in Paris, with him, she sighed. He'd helped her to unfurl, like a tightly defensive blossom in the warmth of spring sunshine. He hadn't tried to dominate her, or change her. He'd just made her feel…first beautiful, then intelligent, and then as though she had an interesting personality. Oh, why hadn't she remembered any of that when he'd said he loved her? Why hadn't she been brave enough to take that leap of faith? Why had she listened to the nasty, suspicious voice in her head telling her he was only interested in her wealth?

She screwed her eyes shut as she repressed a groan. The whole point of travelling to Paris in the first place had been an attempt to…to break free. Hiring Fenella had been her first act of independence and defying her father over the will had been her second.

It was harder to break free from patterns of thought, she realised, than outward behaviour. She could leave Stanton Basset, buy fine clothes and even take a lover. But inside she was still the bewildered child who'd been denied unquestioning love so often that she'd grown the equivalent of a hedge of thorns round her heart.

She sank on to the pew, shutting her hymn book with a chill certainty. She was going to shrivel up and die alone because there would never be, had never been, any other man for her but Nathan.

Even now she knew the very worst of him, it made no difference. As soon as she'd calmed down and had time to reflect, she could see exactly why he'd done every bad thing he'd done. He'd tried, for years, to please his exacting father and then to maintain his honour whilst chained to a woman who despised him. Until he'd got to breaking point and lashed out in rage and pain. Just as she'd done when her own father had demonstrated his lack of faith in her.

But when he'd come to make a clean breast of it, to ask if they could make a fresh start, instead of reaching out to grasp at the chance of happiness, she'd scuttled back behind her hedge of thorns. Which no man could penetrate, without risking getting cut to ribbons.

There wasn't a man alive who could possibly love her enough to do it.

The congregation was stirring, moving towards the door. She could scarcely believe that the service was over without her having taken in one word of it. But everyone else was already streaming out into the churchyard where they would mill about and gossip for at least half an hour.

She fumbled in her reticule for a handkerchief to blow her nose as tears stung her eyes. How on earth was she going to be able to endure the collective inquisition the citizens of Stanton Basset were bound to subject her to, when she was so raw she felt as though someone had been scouring her insides with a scrubbing brush?

The same way she always had, she supposed.

With a series of terse, cutting words that would make them all retreat lest she turn the rapier sharpness of her tongue in their direction.

Oh, God—she *deserved* to end up alone!

'My dear Miss Dalby, do excuse me, but there is someone I would love you to meet.'

All but thick-skinned Mrs Podmore, she sighed. Her unshakeable belief in herself rendered her impervious to even Amethyst's barbs.

She stuffed her handkerchief back in her reticule and prepared herself to meet the poor woman Mrs Podmore had no doubt cajoled and bullied into applying for the post of her companion. She didn't want to frighten the poor creature by unleashing her own pain in a display of venom.

Besides, it was herself she was cross with. If she'd had her wits about her she would have been first out of the door and marched straight down the path for home before anyone could waylay her. But it was too late now. She was well and truly trapped, with only herself to blame.

'I did not have time to tell you our most interesting news,' panted Mrs Podmore, 'when I visited you the other day. But now I should like to introduce you to the newest resident of Stanton Basset.' She stepped aside and waved her hand to summon the person who'd been hovering behind her, rather in the manner of a conjuror producing coins from thin air.

'Allow me to present Mr Brown,' she said, as Nathan stepped forwards.

Nathan? Here in Stanton Basset? Amethyst could not have been more stunned if Mrs Podmore had conjured up a unicorn from behind her velvet-and-bombazine bulk. She was glad she was still seated or her legs might have given way.

'I am pleased to meet you, Miss Dalby,' said Nathan suavely. 'I have heard so much about you.'

'Mr...Brown?' She gazed at him in bewilderment. And excitement that warred with trepidation.

'Mr Brown is an artist,' said Mrs Podmore, completely oblivious, as usual, to the effect she was creating in her current victim's breast. She was far more interested in having just trumped Amethyst's foreign count, who nobody would ever see, with a genuine, visible, novelty. 'He declares he has fallen in love with the charm of the place and intends to make a stay of some months, capturing it all on canvas.'

'An artist,' said Amethyst weakly. So he wasn't trying to conceal everything about himself.

'Oh, you need not be alarmed. Mr Brown is

quite the gentleman. He has taken a lease on old Murdoch's place.'

'Indeed?'

Amethyst's brain finally emerged from the state of shock that seeing Nathan standing in the aisle of St Gregory's had induced, and started coming up with questions. Why had he hired such a massive old mausoleum? How had he been able to afford it? And why was he going by the name of Brown?

And, more importantly, why was he here?

Her heart skipped a beat. Monsieur Le Brun had declared that he would have followed Fenolla to England, to continue courting her. Was this what Nathan was doing?

Or was she clutching at straws?

'How…how long have you been here?' It was the one question she could safely ask. The kind of thing one stranger might say to another upon their first introduction. For if he was going by the name of Brown, and getting Mrs Podmore to introduce him to her, then he clearly didn't want anyone to guess they already knew each other.

'Almost a month, now,' said Nathan.

A month? That meant he must have left Paris almost immediately after she'd turned down his proposal. No wonder he hadn't called on her. He'd been on his way here.

But why? Not that she could ask him that, not here.

Nor could she sit staring at him like this. It wasn't seemly.

'If you will excuse me,' she said, getting to her feet. 'I really must be getting home.'

'Perhaps you will do me the honour of permitting me to call on you some time,' said Nathan. And then, with a swift sideways glance at Mrs Podmore, continued, 'You have a very interesting face. I should like to paint you.'

'And I have told him that if anyone in this town is likely to be able to afford such an extravagance, it is you, Miss Dalby. From what I hear,' said Mrs Podmore with a twitch of her brows.

Her stomach roiled in reaction. The whole town had buzzed with the tale of her father fighting the lawyer over her inheritance. And though nobody knew for sure how much was at stake, they'd definitely overheard him prophesying she'd fritter her entire fortune away within a twelvemonth and have to crawl back to him for forgiveness. Because he'd done so in the voice he normally employed for booming hellfire sermons from the pulpit.

'And I am sure you will agree that we should do what we can to support burgeoning talent, the kind that Mr Brown possesses.' Mrs Podmore leaned forwards and confided, 'He is a most interesting addition to our town, my dear. Quite the gentleman. Much more preferable as a tenant of the Murdoch place than some we might be unfortunate enough to get.'

'Yes, yes, of course,' she said, making for the door as fast as she could.

She didn't feel as if she could breathe properly, even once she'd got outside. She wasn't going to let Mrs Podmore's assumptions spoil whatever chance there might be with Nathan. He couldn't have known about her wealth before he'd come here. He'd come here because he'd meant what he said.

He had.

And anyway, even if he had since found out about her money, hadn't she already decided she didn't care? If Nathan had come here to try to win her, then she wasn't going to let any consideration keep them apart. She'd just spent the most miserable weeks of her life berating herself for not accepting any of his proposals. She most certainly wasn't going to turn down any more.

If he'd really come here to propose again.

Yet why else would he be here, if not to offer for her hand again?

A cold, suspicious voice, that sounded very much like her aunt, whispered, *He could be planning to blackmail you.*

She bowed her head into the sleet, which had started some time during the service, and marched doggedly on, though every breath she took made her chest ache, it had gone so cold.

No—she wasn't going to believe Nathan would do such a thing. Why, he'd had her portrait, which he could have used to attempt to coerce her into marriage, or even blackmail her for money, but he hadn't. He'd just handed it over without making any demands at all.

He'd had the chance to blacken her name ten years ago, too, and hadn't taken it. He was too decent.

Nathan Harcourt? The man whose career was punctuated by scandal and failure?

Yes, him. He was a decent man. Deep down, where it mattered. He'd had good reasons for acting so badly. He'd been devastated by the lies they'd told him. He'd drifted into a career he hadn't wanted and a marriage that had been like a prison. No wonder he'd broken free the only way he could.

You're making excuses for him.

Perhaps she was. And perhaps that made her a foolish, lovestruck woman.

But she didn't care. She was done with assuming the worst of everyone.

She would wait until he'd called, before deciding anything. Hear what he had to say, and then...

Then what?

She didn't know, God help her. She'd just spent the week deciding how she was going to cope without him. Made all sorts of resolutions about striking out in a new direction.

If he really was here to make her another offer, she would gladly toss every single one of her plans out of the window.

And if he wasn't...

If he wasn't, then she'd just have to deal with it.

She barely slept a wink that night.

And it took her an age to dress the following morning. She'd never found her choice of clothing so important before. Pride wouldn't let her wear something that would make her look too eager, just in case he *hadn't* come here to propose again. But she didn't want to dress so soberly that he would take one look at her and think she was going to turn him down, again, either.

In the end, she donned the gown she'd bought for Fenella's wedding. Since he had never seen her in it, it wouldn't have any associations which might put ideas into his head. And it was both suitable for the current weather, being made of fine merino wool, and having long sleeves, yet pretty enough, with its scalloped hem and embroidered detail round the neckline, to make her seem approachable. She hoped.

She had barely nibbled on her toast at the breakfast table, yet she'd managed to bite her nails to the quick by the time Adams came to her study—where she'd been pacing up and down rather than making even a token pretence at shuffling papers round her desk—to inform her that she had a visitor.

'A gentleman,' he said, with a slight inflection on the word which suggested he very much doubted it. 'He claims to have made an appointment. And says his name is Mr Brown.'

How perceptive Adams was. No wonder her aunt had kept him on when she could have saved a fortune by hiring a female as housekeeper to do more or less the same job.

'You are correct upon all counts,' she said, causing one of his eyebrows to quirk, just a fraction. 'He was introduced to me, at church yesterday, as Mr Brown and I did agree to see him.'

The eyebrow rose just a fraction more.

'And, no, I do not think he is a gentleman either.'

His face returned to its proper state of butler-ish blandness.

'Shall I bring refreshments to the morning room? I took the liberty of showing him in there, rather than leaving him cluttering up the hall.'

In spite of her nerves, Amethyst couldn't help smiling at this restrained display of humour.

'Yes, please,' she said. 'Tea would be most welcome.'

Her mouth had gone very dry. And going through all the ceremony of pouring and serving would at least give her something to do if the interview didn't go the way she hoped.

'Tea. Of course, miss. He looks just the sort of man,' said Adams with a perfectly straight face, 'to enjoy drinking tea in the middle of the day.'

And with that last caustic comment upon the character of a man who had come calling upon a single lady when everyone knew she didn't have a chaperon, he bowed himself out of the room.

And then, since there was no mirror in the study she hastily checked her fractured reflection in the multiple panes of the glass-fronted bookshelves, one last time, before going to meet Nathan. Although she'd checked it every few turns of the room, so knew exactly what she looked like. It was just that it was hard to credit she looked so neat and tidy when inside she felt as though she was coming unravelled.

He'd dressed with great care too, she noted the moment she entered the morning room, in immaculate breeches and topcoat, his pristine neckcloth foaming from a damask silk waistcoat. He truly was a sight for sore eyes.

He got to his feet and took a step towards her, then stopped, as though unsure of his welcome.

She smiled, or at least tried to. She was so nervous that it felt a little wobbly and yet tight at the same time.

'Please, won't you sit down?' she said, waving to the seat on the other side of the fireplace as she took her aunt's chair.

Some of the stiffness left his face at her tentative gesture of welcome.

'I wasn't sure if you would even let me in,' he said, resting his arms on the arm of the chair and leaning forwards.

'I shouldn't have done,' she replied. 'It is not the thing to receive a single gentleman when I am without a chaperon. The whole town will be scandalised.'

A frown flickered across his face.

'The last thing I want to do is plunge you into a scandal. That is why I decided it would be better if I got here well before you came back, so it wouldn't look as if there was already anything between us. You made it so obvious that my notoriety would be an issue, here in this little town, that I have done all I can to prevent anyone knowing exactly who, and what, I am.'

Oh. That made perfect sense.

And was incredibly sweet of him.

'That is why you are using an assumed name?'

'Of course. You made it so clear you weren't interested in marrying a man of my notoriety, that I was sure you wouldn't want anyone knowing you'd had a liaison with the notorious Nathan Harcourt. So I took a leaf out of your courier's book. He successfully managed to court your companion under the name of Brown. I hoped it might be as lucky for me.'

'C-courting?' Her breath hitched in her throat. He'd come all this way to court her. In spite of the way they'd parted, her conviction she'd driven him away for good. He must have meant every one of those proposals which she'd discounted, for varying reasons.

'Yes. Courting.' He gave a wry smile. 'And I'd better warn you that I've spent my time in this town learning as much as I could about you— surreptitiously, of course—in the hopes that I might find a chink in your armour.'

'B-but you love Paris. You were so happy there...'

'It would have been a wasteland without you in it. Don't you realise, yet, that I cannot be happy anywhere, unless you are with me?'

He did love her, then. Enough to abandon the work he loved and the home he'd made for himself. Assume a false identity and put up with Mrs Podmore taking him under her wing.

Nobody had ever exerted themselves to such an extent on her account.

'Y-yes. Actually, I think I do,' she admitted shyly. 'Because I have been utterly miserable since our last meeting. I was such an idiot to drive you away.' Tears sprang to her eyes. 'I was so scared I'd driven you away for good.'

He left his chair to kneel at her feet. He seized her hands.

'Does this mean what I hope it means? I've been telling myself that once your temper had cooled and you could think things over rationally, you would be able to forgive me. And give me another chance.'

'I will give you as many chances as you want, so long as you are able to forgive me for being so...' She screwed up her face in disgust as she thought of how narrow-minded and judgemental she'd been. 'For being such a...'

He placed one finger over her lips.

'I've no right to condemn you for anything you've done, or thought. Not with my record.'

He tugged at her hands and drew her to her feet.

'Miss Dalby, once and for all, will you forget all the past mistakes we've both made and marry me?'

'Oh, yes.' She sighed. And then, because her legs went limp, she leaned forwards, rested her head on his chest and said, 'Yes, please.'

'Thank God,' he muttered fervently, putting both arms round her and hugging her tight.

And it felt like coming home. No, better than any home she'd ever known. He was the only person who'd ever accepted her, liked her, loved her, just as she was. Everyone else had tried to change her. Sway her opinions to match their own. But not Nathan.

And then just hugging him wasn't enough. Amethyst raised her face hopefully and he obliged her by meeting her halfway in a kiss. A kiss that went on and on, as though they both needed to drink the other in.

It was only Adams, scuffling against the door as he prepared to bring in the tea tray, that made them break apart, smiling ruefully.

By the time he placed the tray on the table,

they were both seated in the chairs that flanked the fireplace, looking perfectly respectable, if a little flushed and breathless.

Adams glanced from one to the other. His face went more wooden than usual and, without a word, he made a swift exit.

Amethyst's hand was shaking too much to pour the tea.

'Never mind that,' said Nathan with a smile. 'It wasn't to drink tea that I came here today. I had this great long speech planned.'

She darted him a shy smile. 'Should I apologise for stopping you making it?'

He grinned back at her. 'Not in the least. It was just...well, I have a few things I do need to tell you, before I make an honest woman of you. I'd thought I would need to prove to you that I could at least appear respectable if I stood a chance of persuading you that I was husband material, rather than only being good enough for a temporary liaison...'

A pang of guilt shot through her. Had she really made him feel like that? It was so typical of the way she'd been—never giving a thought to what her actions might make other people feel like.

'Which is one reason why I hired the biggest house I could find to rent in this area. Which, coincidentally, happens to be the nearest one to yours. I wanted to demonstrate, you see, that I have the means to support you. I realised, in Paris, that I might have given you the impression that I haven't a feather to fly with—'

'Oh, that doesn't matter one bit, Nathan, you see—'

'Please, hear me out. I need to explain why I was living the way I was when you found me. I was doing it to prove a point. I wanted to demonstrate that I was good enough to make a living from my work alone. And I did. But I have independent means, as well. I can keep you in tolerable comfort, Amy. You don't need to fear that we'll ever have to worry about where the rent will come from.'

'No, we won't. Because I have money, too. Quite a lot of it, actually. Which was one of the reasons I was so suspicious of all the proposals you made to me before. I thought you must have found out about it somehow and was trying to...'

His face froze. 'Yes? Trying to what?'

'I'm so very, very sorry. I know it was nothing of the sort, now. It is just that my aunt, the one who took me in and left me this house, would keep on about how important it was to keep the extent of our fortune a secret, or we'd become targets for fortune hunters. I was convinced that

no man would ever show an interest in me unless it was because he wanted to get his hands
on my money. It became second nature to me
to conceal the fact that I'm a wealthy woman.'

'A wealthy woman.' He frowned. 'Exactly
how large is this fortune?'

She cleared her throat and then, in a matter-
of-fact tone, told him exactly how large, and in
what it consisted, and that moreover she had
plans to expand into France now trading there
was legal again.

By the time she had finished he was looking
at her as though she'd become a total stranger.

'So you are not some simple country girl,
eking out your existence on a modest little wind-
fall from the spinster aunt you cared for in her
last days. And what of Mrs Mountsorrel? Was
she really just a widowed friend with whom you
threw in your lot?' He flung the words at her as
though he was accusing her of something.

Amethyst shook her head. 'I hired her as my
companion so that I could continue living in this
house and run the business interests my aunt had
taught me how to govern. Nathan, why are you
looking at me like that?'

'Can you not imagine?'

She shook her head again, her insides turning

into a cold, solid lump as his gaze turned down-right scornful.

'I thought I knew you. I thought that in spite of the hard veneer you'd acquired, deep down you were still that girl who so enchanted me with her simple, direct approach to life. But you're not her at all, are you?'

'Yes, I am. Just because I'm rich, too—'

He got to his feet, his eyes suddenly blazing with contempt. 'It's not just being rich that is the problem though, is it? You run businesses. You own factories and mills and mines and God knows what else. And you sit here, in this stuffy little town, hidden away like some…spider, spinning a web. Aye, an invisible web, at that. For nobody is supposed to know that it is a woman at the heart of all this enterprise. I never saw it before, but the whole purpose is to make fools of men, isn't it? You delight in making fools of us all. Well, you've certainly made a fool of me.'

'No, I haven't. Truly I haven't. I've explained why I didn't want you to know about it, at first.'

'Not just at first. Even after we'd become lovers. Even when you spurned me, you never admitted the true reason. And it is what you thought, isn't it? That I'm some contemptible fortune hunter. Little things you said to me, your attitude whenever I touched on making our relationship permanent, they should have warned me.'

'Yes, but—'

'Do you think I could want to marry a woman for her money, again? After what I went through last time? Do you know what it does to a man's pride to be labelled a fortune hunter?'

She hadn't. But she was beginning to get an idea.

'The last thing I want is to get leg-shackled to another woman who sees nothing wrong with telling lies to get what she wants. Who has so little integrity she has to buy friends and can only keep them with promise of advancement.'

What?

'Nathan, you don't mean that,' she managed to gasp through the fingers of dread that were squeezing her throat. 'I wasn't lying to you...' His face shuttered.

'Not exactly...'

With a muttered oath he turned and strode for the door.

'You were right all along,' he said coldly, as he set his hand to the door latch. 'We can't go back. We aren't the same people we were when we first met. I...' His face twisted. 'I thought I'd fallen in love with you, all over again, in Paris. I thought you'd got over the pain I put you through and had grown into a strong, admirable woman. A woman I would have been proud to call my wife, and bear my children. I thought…'

He closed his eyes, and shook his head.

'I might have known it was too good to be true. It wasn't real, was it? None of it was real. I've been chasing after a dream. Like some…'

He straightened up and opened his eyes. Eyes which had gone dead and hard.

'Forgive me for taking up your valuable time. I will leave you now. And will not bother you again.'

'Nathan…' She tried to tell him to stop, but her words got tangled up in a sob. She slumped down on to her chair, all strength gone from her legs, as she heard the front door slam behind him.

Oh, why hadn't she said yes, when she had the chance? If she'd said yes to him in Paris, and then explained about her money, he wouldn't have flown into a rage like this, would he?

Would he?

Chapter Fifteen

Shock had taken her legs out from under her. She could no more have run after Nathan and begged him not to go than she could have flown to the moon.

One minute she'd thought all her dreams had come true. Next moment she'd descended into a hellish nightmare. She'd thought Nathan loved her just as she was, but then he'd said he'd never really known her. That he couldn't marry her. That they weren't the same people who'd fallen in love with each other in their youth.

Was he right? Was it too late?

She shut her eyes and bowed her head.

Had they only imagined they'd fallen in love again, in Paris, because they'd both been pretending to be something they were not?

No…no! It was real. She'd had all these long, lonely weeks to ponder it all and she knew it was real. Nathan hadn't had time to think it through, that was all. She dashed a tear from her eye. He'd lashed out—the way she'd done when he'd shocked her with that confession about why they'd broken up the first time.

She leapt to her feet. He'd come after her when she'd lost her temper with him. When her habit of being suspicious had made her afraid to believe in their love. Now it was her turn to go after him and talk some sense into him.

She was halfway across the room to ring for a maid to fetch her coat and bonnet, when she decided she hadn't the patience to wait that long. Far quicker to run upstairs and plunge her arms into her coat herself. Stuff her bonnet on her head as she hurried down the stairs and tie the ribbons as she trotted down the garden path.

She was in such a hurry to catch Nathan and tell him that he was wrong that she didn't see Mrs Podmore coming up the front path until she almost barrelled into her.

'Oh, good. I have just caught you,' said Mrs Podmore, tilting her umbrella to one side to make room for Amethyst. 'I can see you are in a hurry, but this won't take a moment—'

'I'm so sorry, but I haven't time to stop and talk today.'

She tried to step round Mrs Podmore, but the path was narrow, and her visitor determined.

'Wherever you are going, it cannot be so urgent that you have forgotten your umbrella.'

'It is that urgent,' she countered. 'And I hadn't even noticed it was snowing.' Only tiny specks of it, but the first real snow of the winter, nevertheless.

As she looked up in wonder, she had a brilliant idea. She stopped trying to sidestep Mrs Podmore's substantial bulk and looked her straight in the face with what she hoped was a confiding air.

'You see, everything you have ever warned me about has come to pass.'

'Oh?' For once Mrs Podmore didn't seen to know what to say.

'You have been right to warn me, so many times, just how dangerous it is to be without adequate chaperonage.'

'Was I? I mean, of course I was. But—'

'Yes. You see, while Fenella was preoccupied with her own courtship, and there was nobody to make me behave...' she lowered her voice '...I did something quite scandalous.'

Mrs Podmore instinctively leaned closer to hear the whispered confidence, her eyes wide with curiosity.

'I went to Mr Brown's studio, the one he had in Paris, quite alone, to have my portrait painted.'

'No!' Her eyebrows shot up and disappeared into the ruffles under her bonnet.

'Oh, yes. We were alone in his studio for hours at a time. And worse, he persuaded me to pose for him…naked.'

'Naked?' Mrs Podmore screeched the word, her shock temporarily robbing her of discretion. The baker's boy, who'd been walking past, jumped and dropped his tray of rolls, which went tumbling all over the street.

'And, of course, you must know what inevitably followed.'

Mrs Podmore's eyes grew rounder still. Amethyst could see her mind racing.

'I cannot bring myself to say what I fear you are alluding to.'

'Well, I can,' said Amethyst cheerfully. 'We embarked upon a wildly passionate affair.'

'A what?'

The baker's boy's head popped up over the hedge, his eyes wide with glee.

'And now he's pursued me all the way to England. Don't you think that's romantic?' She pressed one hand to her chest. 'I do.' She sighed theatrically. 'And so I've decided to run off with him.'

'Run off with Mr Brown?'

If he'd have her. And if not, she already had

plans to move to Southampton, so nobody would know any different when she disappeared.

'Yes. I enjoyed travelling so much that I can't wait to set off again. We might return to Paris, where we were so happy. Or we might go and see what Italy is like. He's always wanted to go to Italy. And,' she put in before Mrs Podmore could accuse Nathan of latching on to her because of her money, 'I can afford to take him there.'

'No! You must not. Only think what people will say...'

That was exactly what she was doing. Between her and the baker's boy, the news would be all over town within minutes.

'I don't care what anyone says,' she declared. 'I cannot live without him.'

She beamed at Mrs Podmore, who was opening and closing her mouth like a landed trout.

'Good day,' said Amethyst and managed to nip past Mrs Podmore while she was trying to untangle her umbrella from the overhanging branches of her cherry trees. Past the gaping baker's boy, who'd abandoned any pretence at retrieving the spoiled rolls. Up the hill and through the market square she sincerely hoped she'd never have to set eyes on again, before much longer, and along the lane that led to the Murdoch place.

* * *

It wasn't long before she caught sight of Nathan in the lane ahead of her, because he was walking really slowly, his head bowed. Impervious to the snow, which was settling on his shoulders and the crown of his hat.

Hope surged. He couldn't look so sad if he didn't still love her. Didn't regret having left her the way he had.

'I have just one thing to say,' she said as he reached his front door.

He spun round. For a moment she caught a glimpse of the carefree young man who'd argued with her about the Rights of Man over a bottle of beer in a Parisian dance hall. But then his face changed. And the cynical, embittered, disgraced politician stood in his place.

'I have nothing further to say to you, madam,' he said coldly.

'Well, you can just listen then,' she said, pushing past him into the house as an unsuspecting butler opened the door.

'I have had longer to think about…us. Knowing all about the discrepancy in our wealth. And do you know what I have realised?'

'You clearly mean to tell me,' he said wearily. 'You had better come in here.' He pushed open the door to a sparsely furnished parlour and ushered her in.

'Well, let's start with why I've been afraid, for so many years, that no man could ever love me.'

He flinched and walked away from her to stare out of the window.

'Exactly. You hurt me so badly that I lost my ability to trust men. Well, actually, it wasn't all your fault. My father's attitude played a large part in it, too. And then my aunt fostered that suspicion. Because she really, really hated men. She said I'd had a lucky escape anyway, because marriage was nothing but a trap for women. A cage in which some despotic male would lock her. I could understand why she thought like that, but I never wanted to end up like her. She was so…so miserable! She had so much money, but it never did her any good. It didn't make her happy. It didn't compensate for whatever it was that had set her off on her quest for revenge on the entire male sex.

'When she died, I almost slid into the trap of becoming like her. Partly because I had to fight the men around me to hang on to what she'd left me. And I enjoyed winning. I won't deny that I liked it a lot. I liked seeing bullies having to back down, rendering them powerless and sending them away with a flea in their ear.

'But it wasn't enough. It wasn't enough to sit here like—well, you said it—like a spider in my web, holding all the threads together. I didn't want to shrivel up inside, like she had, just because things hadn't turned out the way I wanted.

'Which was why I went to Paris in the first place. I needed to…break out. Find out what I wanted to do with my life. And then I met you.'

She walked across the room to stand behind him. Tentatively she placed one hand on his shoulder.

'I thought you were a penniless artist. And believing that of you was what gave me the courage to take you as a lover. If I'd known you were still comfortably off and only taking a sort of… holiday, I would never have been able to open up to you the way I did. Your privileged background had come between us before. It would have felt like an unbreachable barrier if you'd been swanning about Paris, trading on your right to be treated with the deference due to the son of an English earl. When you started making advances I would have been afraid you were only toying with me, the way I believed you'd toyed with me in the past.'

He made a sort of growling noise and, though he didn't turn round, she could see his cheeks flush. He might accuse her of lying, but he hadn't been completely honest with her either.

'And you wouldn't have pursued me at all, had you known the extent of my wealth, would you?'

'I thought I'd just made that perfectly clear.'

'It wasn't just my wealth that would have kept you away, Nathan. You didn't know I was a virgin, either. You jumped to the conclusion that because I was with a man, I must be his mistress. You most definitely wouldn't have got so jealous of poor Monsieur Le Brun if you'd known I was innocent of everything they told you about me. I suppose you might have still wanted to paint my portrait, perhaps as a memento of the girl you once loved, before I broke your heart and shattered your dreams, but not the rest.'

'I—'

'No, Nathan. Don't you see? If we hadn't both been trying to conceal some aspect of our lives, we would never have got together at all. There were too many obstacles. Too much hurt and suspicion on both sides. The way we got together was the *only* way it could have happened.'

'But—'

'But none of the things that would have kept us apart mattered one jot when we became lovers, Nathan, and don't you dare try to say they did! We were just a man and a woman, rekindling a love we'd both mourned as lost. And it was a deeper, more meaningful love than the naïve, tentative relationship we started the first time round. Because we were both free to spend every moment with each other, untramelled by chaperons, or restrictions imposed by class. You cannot give up on it, just because you've found out I'm wealthy. It's…stupid. And I know exactly how stupid because I did it first. I rebuffed you in just such a welter of suspicion that you are suffering from now. And I've spent the last few weeks working out that I'd been wrong to cast you as the villain of the tragedy I endured as a girl. You were as much a victim as I was.'

'That was then,' he growled. 'This is different,' he said harshly, spinning round so abruptly that it knocked her hand from his shoulder.

'No, it isn't,' she said firmly. 'We fell in love with each other in Paris and that hasn't gone away. It cannot. Ten years and gallons of suspicion weren't able to drown it. The moment we set eyes on each other again, neither of us could rest until we'd come together, in the fullest sense possible.'

'It is no use, though,' he said. 'It cannot work.'

'Of course it can work. It worked in Paris, didn't it? So we can make it work again. If I can forgive you for believing the worst of me, if I can believe that you never proposed to me because you secretly wanted to gain control of my money, if I can stop fearing the loss of my independence, then surely you can see that I am not going to try to control you either? I know I wasn't completely frank with you when we first met in Paris, but surely you can see I'm nothing like Lucasta? I want to marry you because I love you. You, Nathan. The man you are. I don't want you to become something else. I don't want to mould you, or push you, or treat you like a puppet by pulling your strings. I just want to make you happy.'

'And what of all your money? What of that?'

'It doesn't matter.'

'Doesn't matter!' He made an angry, impatient gesture. 'I have my pride, you know. In fact, it's about damn near all I do have left.'

'No, it isn't. You have my heart, too. It's yours whether you want it or not. And there's nothing else of any value at all. Without your love, my life is completely empty. Hollow. Money cannot fulfil me.'

She stepped right up to him and grabbed his lapels. 'I made a mistake leaving you behind in Paris. As soon as I got back here, I saw that without you, I will only ever just…exist. I have been so lonely without you. I need you to be… my companion. My soulmate. Nathan, marry me. Make my life worth living again.'

'I am not the man to make any woman's life worth living,' he said bitterly. 'All my life, people have been telling me that. And I've proved it. My first marriage failed—'

'Because you didn't love each other. You married for all the wrong reasons. Marry for the right ones this time. Because you want a companion and a soulmate. Someone to complete you and make *your* life worth living.'

He took a breath as though about to say something. Closed his mouth. Shook his head. 'It's no use. I was just chasing a dream. Paris was—'

'Paris was a taste of what we could have, if we both trust in the love we found there. When you learned that I hadn't been an unmarried mother, that I hadn't tried to deceive you, I saw the pain etched into your features fade away. And I became a better person when I was with you, too. The anger I'd carried around for so long, like a shield, melted away. I thought that lowering it would make me vulnerable. Instead, it freed me to be myself. And that was the person you loved. The real Amethyst. The one I'd never suspected I could be. It wasn't the girl you knew all those years ago. It was someone I'd become as a result of all I've been through. Just as you'd changed from the boy who swept me off my feet, then broke my heart. You'd grown into a man. A man who'd suffered, and sinned, then finally found a path you could walk with your head held high.

'Money didn't come into it. Reputation didn't matter either. It was who we were when we were together that was important. The fact that we made each other happy.'

'You are right,' he said slowly, 'in that we did make each other happy. But…this is all wrong. A woman doesn't propose to a man.'

'Well, perhaps a woman should, especially if she's been silly enough to turn down a man's proposal so many times it's made him give up hope. Should we both suffer for the rest of our lives because I was too scared to dare believe you really felt something for me? Or because you let my wealth stand between us?'

His hands went to her hips.

'Amy, you are so wealthy you could have any man you wanted. You can't possibly want to throw yourself away on a wretch like me…'

'I don't want any other man. I've never wanted any other man. For some reason, you are the only one who makes me think of kissing and being held, and taking my clothes off and wrapping myself around you.'

'Amy…' He groaned. 'What am I going to do with you?'

'Love me, Nathan. That's all I want from you.'

'I do love you,' he said. 'You're right. It is you…you as you are now that I love, but…'

She didn't let him continue with his protests. She stood on tiptoe, plunged her fingers into his hair and kissed him.

With a groan, he surrendered. He returned

the kiss with interest, holding her so tightly that breathing soon became difficult.

Eventually, she had to tear her lips away, just to breathe.

But when she looked into his face, it was to see doubt and misery lingering beneath the passion.

'Very well,' she said. 'I can see that marriage is too big a step for you to take. So I will just have to be content with living with you, as your mistress.'

'No! I won't demean you by making you sink that low. You've already suffered enough on my account. The last thing I want is to embroil you in a scandal.'

'It might be a bit too late to avoid it,' she admitted. 'On the way here I informed the most determined gossip in the county that I'm going to run away with you. If you don't want to ruin my reputation beyond all hope of redemption, you're going to have to marry me. And if,' she said, lifting her chin defiantly, 'you really can't stomach the prospect of having another wealthy wife, then I can give it all away.'

'What? No—I'd never ask you to do that. It wouldn't be right.'

'I would gladly give it away if it would mean winning you. Nathan, can't you see that it doesn't matter? Any more than your reputation matters?'

'You are really ready to give everything away

and ally yourself to a man whose reputation is just about as sordid as it can be?'

She nodded, her eyes solemn. 'That's why I've just destroyed my own reputation. So that it makes us even.'

He grabbed her shoulders and shook her. 'Amy, telling one woman, in a small market town in the middle of nowhere, that you're going to run off with what she thinks is a penniless artist hardly compares with the stink I created in society.'

'I will put that picture of me naked up for sale in the auction rooms, then,' she declared defiantly. 'In my father's parish.'

He shook his head ruefully. 'Amy, Amy, how can you want to throw everything away like this? On me of all people? I don't know how you can be so sure I won't break faith with you...'

'I know because your whole life went sour when you thought you'd lost me the first time. When you thought I wasn't the girl you'd fallen in love with, but some mirage conjured up from your fevered imagination. I know because I went through exactly the same process. I know because I've never been so happy as I was in Paris, with you. Even though doubt and fear lingered, I had to take what I could have of you. Just as you snatched at what you thought you could have of me. Even when you still believed I was Monsieur

Le Brun's mistress, you came and begged me to leave him and take up with you. You'd been starved of love for so long you were prepared to drink the dregs.

'But, Nathan, you don't have to scrape the dregs of life any longer. We can have the finest vintage. We love each other. What else matters?'

'A great many things,' he said sadly. 'Though you are right about a good deal.' He drew her against his chest, and buried his face in her hair.

'I didn't ever really stop loving you. Even when I thought you the worst kind of woman, when I saw you again, I couldn't prevent myself from wanting you. My body recognised its one true mate.'

She pushed herself away just enough that she could look up into his face.

'It was exactly the same for me. Every time I read some new story about you in the papers, I told myself I was well rid of you. But the moment I saw you again…it was as though there was nobody else in the room. I didn't care what you'd done.'

'I did a great many things of which I'm heartily ashamed now.'

'I know.' Her eyes filled with tears. 'And I also know that if you were as bad as they all say you are, then you wouldn't be ashamed. You wouldn't care.'

'Amy,' he whispered, before lowering his head and kissing her as if she was necessary to his very existence.

She flowed into him, relief rushing through her in a flood.

'They said I was too young to know what I wanted,' he said, breaking off to frame her face with his hands and gaze at her intently. So intently that she knew he was speaking of her.

'Too naïve to know what was good for me. They persuaded me to follow a path that led me to utter misery.'

'I know,' she said. 'They tried to tell me I was too silly to know truth from wishful thinking, too. But we weren't too young. We knew we'd found the road to happiness. And now we've found it again.'

'Then,' he said and swallowed, 'I will take it.' Then uncertainty clouded his features. 'If you're sure?'

'Oh, yes, Nathan, I'm completely sure. And I promise you,' she said earnestly, 'that this time, marriage won't feel like a prison sentence.'

'I'm not the only one who might think of it like a trap, though, am I? You've been so used to running not only your own life, but also that of hundreds of others, through your manufactories, that it's going to be hard for you to give it all up. Especially when I don't really want any of it.'

'Give it all up? I thought you said you didn't want me to give it all away?'

'Yes, but once we marry, it will all belong to me.'

'Yes, but, Nathan, you don't want to change me, any more than I want you to become something you're not, do you?'

'Of course not. I want you to be happy, too.'

'Well, then, if you don't want me to give it all away and you don't want to be chained to a desk yourself, why don't we do something that nobody would expect? Why don't we just snap our fingers at convention?'

He looked at her with a frown for a few seconds, then his expression cleared.

'We can make our marriage anything we want, you're right. We don't need to let society mould us into being anything we don't want to be. Not either of us.' He drew a deep breath. 'If you want to carry on running your business empire, then I won't try to stop you. I don't want to be the one to clip your wings.'

She beamed at him. 'Any more than I would try to stop you painting. Or...or anything you want to do.'

'I should never have walked out on you, earlier. I just...I got so angry when I heard you had so much money. And that you'd concealed so much from me. It all felt...'

'I know,' she said. 'It all got tangled up in memories of your first marriage. Of getting into it before you really knew what Lucasta was like.'

'You are nothing like her,' he said fervently. 'I'm so sorry for implying that you are.'

'I forgive you. You didn't mean it. I've sometimes said things, when I've been angry, that I've regretted later, haven't I? And you didn't listen to the words I said, but judged what was beneath the surface. The emotions that had made me lash out at you. And then you came after me.'

'Just as you came after me.'

'I feel so sorry for Lucasta,' she said, wrinkling her brow. 'Not only because she had you, and didn't appreciate what she had, but also because she had so many frustrated ambitions. If she wanted to have a voice in Parliament, why shouldn't she?'

'Amy,' he gasped. 'That's…revolutionary talk.'

She grinned up at him impishly. 'And even in France, they don't let women into government, do they?'

'Not legally, no, but behind the scenes…'

'Never mind what goes on behind the scenes in France, Nathan. I'm far more concerned with what is going to go on behind closed doors in Stanton Basset.'

As she spoke, she pulled the pin from his neckcloth, then started to work on the complicated knot with determined, if rather unskilled fingers. When he saw she was getting nowhere, he pushed her hands away and loosed it himself.

'Never let it be said that I disappointed a lady,' he said with a lazy smile.

He led her to the rug before the fire, lowered her down on to it and began to undo her gown, with a great deal more expertise than she'd shown with his neckcloth.

'You won't, Nathan. You couldn't.'

He buried his face in her neck, breathing in as though he was intent on inhaling her.

'I will do my utmost not to, my clever darling. My only love.'

And he didn't disappoint her. Right there on the hearthrug.

* * * * *

A sneaky peek at next month...

HISTORICAL

IGNITE YOUR IMAGINATION, STEP INTO THE PAST...

My wish list for next month's titles...

In stores from 7th March 2014:

- ☐ The Fall of a Saint – Christine Merrill
- ☐ At the Highwayman's Pleasure – Sarah Mallory
- ☐ Mishap Marriage – Helen Dickson
- ☐ Secrets at Court – Blythe Gifford
- ☐ The Rebel Captain's Royalist Bride – Anne Herries
- ☐ The Cowboy's Reluctant Bride – Debra Cowan

Available at WHSmith, Tesco, Asda, Eason, Amazon and Apple

Just can't wait?

Visit us Online

You can buy our books online a month before they hit the shops! **www.millsandboon.co.uk**

0214/04

Special Offers

Every month we put together collections and longer reads written by your favourite authors.

Here are some of next month's highlights— and don't miss our fabulous discount online!

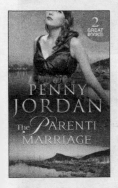

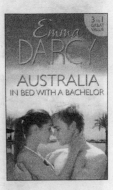

On sale 21st February

On sale 28th February

On sale 21st February

Save 20%
on all Special Releases

Find out more at
www.millsandboon.co.uk/specialreleases

Visit us Online

0314/ST/MB461

The Regency Ballroom Collection

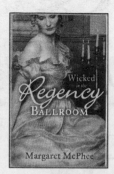

A twelve-book collection led by Louise Allen
and written by the top authors and rising
stars of historical romance!

Classic tales of scandal and seduction in
the Regency ballroom

**Take your place on the ballroom floor now, at:
www.millsandboon.co.uk**

0214/MB458

Join the Mills & Boon Book Club

Want to read more **Historical** books?
We're offering you **2 more** absolutely **FREE!**

We'll also treat you to these fabulous extras:

- **Exclusive offers and much more!**
- **FREE home delivery**
- **FREE books and gifts with our special rewards scheme**

Get your free books now!

visit www.millsandboon.co.uk/bookclub
or call Customer Relations on 020 8288 2888

FREE BOOK OFFER TERMS & CONDITIONS
Accepting your free books places you under no obligation to buy anything and you may cancel at any time. If we do not hear from you we will send you 5 stories a month which you may purchase or return to us—the choice is yours. Offer valid in the UK only and is not available to current Mills & Boon subscribers to this series. We reserve the right to refuse an application and applicants must be aged 18 years or over. Only one application per household. Terms and prices are subject to change without notice. As a result of this application you may receive further offers from other carefully selected companies. If you do not wish to share in this opportunity please write to the Data Manager at PO BOX 676, Richmond, TW9 1WU.

Discover more romance at

www.millsandboon.co.uk

- ❤ WIN great prizes in our exclusive competitions

- ❤ BUY new titles before they hit the shops

- ❤ BROWSE new books and REVIEW your favourites

- ❤ SAVE on new books with the Mills & Boon® Bookclub™

- ❤ DISCOVER new authors

PLUS, to chat about your favourite reads, get the latest news and find special offers:

- 📘 Find us on facebook.com/millsandboon
- 🐦 Follow us on twitter.com/millsandboonuk
- ❤ Sign up to our newsletter at millsandboon.co.uk

WEB_SD